MATHS
IN ACTION

Mathematics in Action Group

Members of the Mathematics in Action Group associated with this book:
D. Brown, J. L. Hodge, R. D. Howat, J. Hunter, E. C. K. Mullan, K. Nisbet, A. G. Robertson

STUDENTS'
BOOK

Nelson Blackie
Wester Cleddens Road
Bishopbriggs
Glasgow
G64 2NZ UK

Thomas Nelson and Sons Ltd
Nelson House Mayfield Road
Walton-on-Thames Surrey
KT12 5PL UK

Thomas Nelson Australia
102 Dodds Street
South Melbourne
Victoria 3205 Australia

Nelson Canada
1120 Birchmount Road
Scarborough Ontario
M1K 5G4 Canada

Cover photograph courtesy of Rolls Royce

© Mathematics in Action Group 1995

First published by Blackie and Son Ltd 1987
New edition published by Thomas Nelson and Sons Ltd 1995
ıⓉⓅ Thomas Nelson is an International Thomson publishing company.
ıⓉⓅ is used under licence.

ISBN 0-17-431432-9
NPN 9 8 7 6 5 4 3

All rights reserved. No paragraph of this publication may be
reproduced, copied or transmitted save with written permission or in
accordance with the provisions of the Copyright, Design and Patents
Act 1988, or under the terms of any licence permitting limited copying
issued by the Copyright Licensing Agency, 90 Tottenham Court Road,
London, W1P 9HE.

Any person who does any unauthorised act in relation to this
publication may be liable to criminal prosecution and civil claims for
damages.

Printed in China.

CONTENTS

INTRODUCTION

Maths in Action—New Edition provides a course in mathematics that covers the Mathematics 5-14 National Guidelines, Standard Grade and Higher Grade in Scotland, the Northern Ireland Curriculum and the National Curriculum in England and Wales.

The new edition builds on experience gained in the classroom with the original series, and particular attention has been paid to providing a differentiated course at every stage. Book 3B provides a course for Standard Grade at Credit/General levels and for NIC/NC at levels 5–8, while Book 3A aims mainly at General/Foundation and levels 4–6. Each chapter starts with a Looking Back exercise, which can be used for revision and to assess readiness for the topic, and ends with a Check-up exercise giving a further element of revision and assessment. Investigative work features prominently in each chapter in the many puzzles, projects, challenges, brainstormers and investigations. Answers to every question (except puzzles, challenges, brainstormers, investigations and 'Topics to Explore') are to be found at the end of this book. The five Review sections are closely based on the Check-ups and Revision exercises in Books 1 and 2, and provide a systematic and thorough revision of earlier work.

Each *Students' Book* is supported by a *Teacher's Resource Book* and, in the first two years, by revised books of *Extra Questions* and *Further Questions*.

The *Teacher's Resource Book* contains Standard Grade, Northern Ireland Curriculum and National Curriculum references for every chapter, photocopiable worksheets, notes and suggestions for further activities, and the answers to the puzzles, challenges, brainstormers, investigations and 'Topics to Explore' in the *Students' Book*. In addition, there are grids which may be photocopied and used to record and assess students' progress.

1 CALCULATIONS AND CALCULATORS

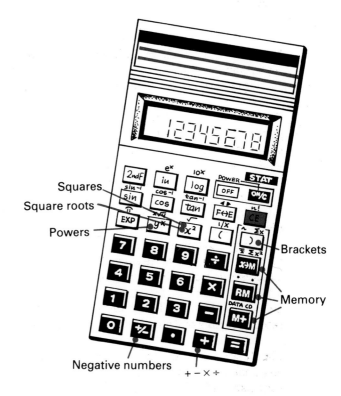

Squares
Square roots
Powers
Brackets
Memory
Negative numbers
$+ - \times \div$

1 Use your calculator for these:

   a $12.8 + 23.5$ **b** $24 - 3.1$ **c** 34×12.5

   d $252 \div 9$ **e** 0.3×370 **f** 17^2

   g $\sqrt{144}$ **h** 0.2×0.3 **i** $100 \div 0.5$

Try $2 + 3 \times 4$ on your calculator.
Does it give 14, or 20?
The correct answer is 14.
Remember the order!

( )
before
$\times \div$
before
$+ -$

Brackets, **O**f; **M**ultiplication, **D**ivision; **A**ddition, **S**ubtraction

2 Calculate:

   a $(12-2)+3$ **b** $(12-2) \times 3$ **c** $(4+8) \div 2$

   d $\frac{1}{2}$ of 36 **e** $3 \times 4 - 5$ **f** $9 - 2 \times 3$

   g $8 \div 4 + 2$ **h** $9 - 6 \div 2$ **i** $10 \div (8-6)$

3 Round:

   a to the nearest whole number

     (i) 3.8 (ii) 7.2 (iii) 12.6

   b to 1 decimal place

     (i) 1.42 (ii) 5.17 (iii) 0.85

   c to 1 significant figure

     (i) 27 (ii) 3.6 (iii) 0.811

When a calculator is turned round 180°, some of
the numbers look like words.

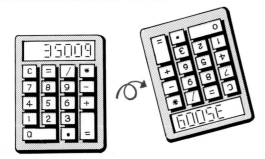

Try to turn 35009 into GOOSE on your own
calculator!

4 a Copy the crossword grid below.

   b Calculate the answers to these clues, then turn
     your calculator round to find the word to enter
     in each space.

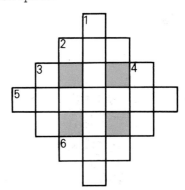

Across

2 $252 \div 9 \times 34 - 14$ (ask for money)

5 $3214 + 1982^2$ (attack a castle)

6 $1 + 7 \times 11 \times 10$ (unwell)

Down

1 $26 \times 268 \times 543 - 1687$ (able to be read)

3 $27 \times \frac{1}{2}$ of $64 + 73$ (you can stand on one)

4 $1000 - 3 \times 2 - 1$ (Humpty Dumpty!)

APPROXIMATION—ROUNDING YOUR ANSWER

(i) Decimal places

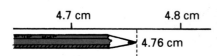

4.7 cm   4.8 cm

4.76 cm

The pencil is 4.76 cm long.
Its length is 4.8 cm, rounded to 1 decimal place,
or correct to 1 decimal place.

Examples
a Rounded to 1 decimal place: $1.83 \rightarrow 1.8$, $24.15 \rightarrow 24.2$, $1.06 \rightarrow 1.1$
b Rounded to 2 decimal places: $2.346\,km \rightarrow 2.35\,km$, $0.123\,kg \rightarrow 0.12\,kg$

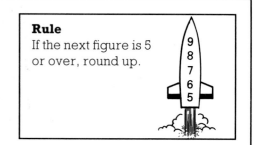

Rule
If the next figure is 5
or over, round up.

9
8
7
6
5

EXERCISE 1

1 Round these lengths to 1 decimal place:

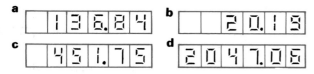

a   2.4 cm   2.5 cm   **b**   8.6 cm   8.7 cm

2.43 cm   8.66 cm

2 Round these mileometer readings to 1 decimal place:

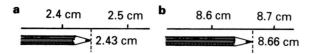

a 136.84   **b** 20.19
c 451.75   **d** 2047.08

3 Round to 1 decimal place:
a 2.19   **b** 6.43   **c** 8.04   **d** 1.85   **e** 0.89

4 Give these correct to 1 decimal place:
a 5.83 seconds   **b** 12.34 metres
c 107.39 litres

5 Round to 2 decimal places:
a 1.234   **b** 5.107   **c** 11.135   **d** 102.201

6 Round to the nearest penny (2 decimal places):
a £1.347   **b** £0.754   **c** £12.109   **d** £101.125

7 Calculate, correct to 1 decimal place:
a $1.97 + 8.79$ **b** $23.44 - 13.86$ **c** $7 \div 6$

8 Calculate, correct to 2 decimal places:
a 0.12×8.69 **b** 5.75^2 **c** $81 \div 3.14$ **d** $\frac{1}{11}$

9 The window cleaners' ladders are 3.78 m and 4.56 m long. Calculate:
a the difference between these lengths
b the total length of the two ladders.

10 Share £400 between seven people, correct to the nearest:
a £1   **b** 10p   **c** 1p

11 a Add the lengths of the four sides of this rectangle to find its perimeter, correct to 1 decimal place.

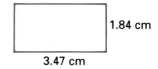

1.84 cm

3.47 cm

b Multiply its length by its breadth to find its area, correct to 1 decimal place.

(ii) Significant figures

To the nearest whole number: 874 bees.
To the nearest 10: 870 bees . . . 2 significant figures.
To the nearest 100: 900 bees . . . 1 significant figure.

Examples
a To 1 significant figure: 18 → 20, 234 → 200, 0.56 → 0.6
b To 2 significant figures: 1351 → 1400, 0.0246 → 0.025

Same rule again:
If the next figure is 5 or over, round up.

EXERCISE 2

1 Round to 1 significant figure:
  a 82 **b** 28 **c** 15 **d** 180 **e** 509

2 Round to 2 significant figures:
  a 363 **b** 118 **c** 3470 **d** 0.135

3 Write these with 1 significant figure:
  a 27 cm **b** 81 hours **c** 5.9 kg **d** 0.018 g

4 Calculate, correct to 2 significant figures:
  a 3.86 + 7.56 **b** 13.01 − 9.75 **c** 2 ÷ 3

5 Using the π key on your calculator, calculate, correct to 2 significant figures:
  a π × 25 **b** π × 8.76 **c** 12.5π

6 Calculate, correct to 2 significant figures:
  a 456 + 123 **b** 456 − 123
  c 456 × 123 **d** 456 ÷ 123

7 Round your answers in question **6** to 1 significant figure.

8 Calculate, correct to 2 significant figures:
  a the perimeter of the rectangle
  b the area of the rectangle

11.7 cm

16.5 cm

CHALLENGE

7 × ☐ = 40—a game for two.
The winner is the person who gets closer to the missing number, in each pair of attempts, using only multiplication. Try it again for 100 instead of 40.

ESTIMATING AND CALCULATING

If you press the wrong key, or press the right key too often, or too lightly, the answer will be wrong!

It's a good idea to check your answer by estimation.

Example
275 + 48

Using 1 significant figure, it's 300 + 50 = 350.

Using my calculator, I get 323.

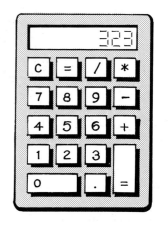

How could you know that the answer would end in 3?

EXERCISE 3A

1 Calculate *mentally*, then check by calculator:
   a 30 + 60   **b** 90 + 80   **c** 70 − 20   **d** 200 − 50

2 (i) Use 1 or 2 significant figures in each number to *estimate* the answer. Write this down.
   (ii) Then use your calculator to *calculate* the answer.
       a 87 + 14   **b** 73 + 48   **c** 124 + 39
       d 136 + 57   **e** 6.9 + 8.3   **f** 15.1 + 13.7
       g 0.88 + 0.23

3 In 8**7** + 6**4**, **7** + **4** = 1**1**, so the answer ends in 1. Check your calculator answer for each part of question **2** in this way.

4 a Which of these is the best estimate for 37 × 23?
       (i) 800   (ii) 8000   (iii) 80 000
   b Which of these could be the correct answer for part **a**?
       (i) 857   (ii) 7091   (iii) 851   (iv) 80 051
   c Check with your calculator.

5 The railway carriages can hold 98 and 87 passengers. Estimate, then calculate, the total:
   a number of passengers
   b length of the two carriages.

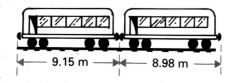

9.15 m   8.98 m

6 Another carriage 9.75 m long, with 125 passengers, is joined to the train. Repeat question **5** for the three carriages.

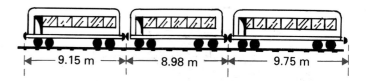

9.15 m   8.98 m   9.75 m

7 Sandra wrote cheques for £25.74, £56.99 and £87.30.
   a Estimate, then calculate, the total of the three cheques.
   b Check the last digit in the total.

8 Estimate, then calculate:
       a 93 − 44   **b** 567 − 193   **c** 184 − 48
       d 296 − 178   **e** 8.7 − 7.8   **f** 19.5 − 8.8
       g 0.62 − 0.25   **h** 321 − 123

EXERCISE 3B

Example
26 × 53

30 × 50 = 1500

By calculator, 1378.

1 Calculate mentally, then check by calculator:
  a 40 × 60 **b** 30 × 200 **c** 400 ÷ 8 **d** 600 ÷ 40

2 Estimate, then calculate, then check the last digit in the answer. For example, in 3**4** × **75**, **4** × **5** = 2**0**, so the answer ends in 0.
  a 34 × 75 **b** 91 × 19 **c** 103 × 64 **d** 25 × 52
  e 6.5 × 8.4 **f** 1.3 × 7.5 **g** 36 × 6.3 **h** 0.81 × 0.37

3 Mr Macallan took a taxi home, 27 miles at 87p per mile. Estimate, then calculate, the amount he had to pay.

4 Estimate, then calculate, correct to 1 decimal place:
  a 564 ÷ 32 **b** 812 ÷ 18 **c** 26.6 ÷ 9.1
  d 61 ÷ 16 **e** 789 ÷ 234 **f** 1047 ÷ 180
  g 0.83 ÷ 0.38

5 Helen's phone call to her cousin in India lasted 17 minutes, and cost £22.78. Estimate, then calculate, the cost per minute.

6 Which of the following cost about £1000? Check with your calculator.

  a
  210 at £4.95

  b
  52 payments of £38

  c
  12 chairs at £90.50 each

INVESTIGATIONS

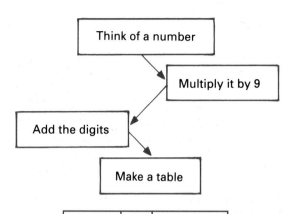

Think of a number → Multiply it by 9 → Add the digits → Make a table

Number	× 9	Add digits
13	117	1 + 1 + 7 = 9

1 Magic 9s
  a *Try this for six different numbers.*
  b *What does the table suggest about numbers that are divisible by 9?*
  c *Try it for two more numbers. Can you say that it will **always** work?*

2 Very odd
  Key the numbers 1 to 9 into your calculator in order, one at a time.
  Use either the [+] *key or the* [X] *key between each number, but check that every answer you get is an **odd** number.*
  For example: **1** [X] **2** [=] *2 won't do*
  1 [+] **2** [=] *3* [+] **3** [=] *6 won't do.*
  Remember to press [=] *each time.*
  a *Explain your method.*
  b *What number is displayed after you key in 9?*

3 Odder still
  a *Calculate:*
    (i) 1 + 3   *(ii) 1 + 3 + 5*
    (iii) 1 + 3 + 5 + 7   *(iv) 1 + 3 + 5 + 7 + 9*
  b *Can you see a pattern in the answers?*
    Try 1 + 3 + 5 + 7 + 9 + 11.
    Can you forecast the sum of the first 20, or 50, or 100 odd numbers?
  c *How many odd numbers are there in;*
    (i) 1 + 3 + 5 + . . . + 31   *(ii) 1 + 3 + 5 + . . . + 999?*
    Can you find a way to calculate this?
    *Forecast the sum of these numbers, and write up your method. Are you sure your method will **always** work?*

EXPLORING YOUR CALCULATOR

EXERCISE 4A

Try these on your calculator. If you cannot get the answer, experiment or ask for help!

Calculation	Possible keying instructions	Answer
a Squares ... 3^2	3 $\boxed{x^2}$	9
b Square roots ... $\sqrt{25}$	$\boxed{\sqrt{}}$ 25 $\boxed{=}$, or 25 $\boxed{2ndF}$ $\boxed{x^2}$	5
c Powers ... 4^3	4 $\boxed{y^x}$ 3 $\boxed{=}$	64

1 Use the $\boxed{x^2}$ key to calculate:

   a 8^2 **b** 13^2 **c** 1.5^2 **d** 234^2 **e** 0.3^2

2 Use the $\boxed{x^2}$ key to help you calculate:

   a $8^2 + 15^2$ **b** $13^2 - 12^2$
   c $1.5^2 + 2.5^2$ **d** $6.6^2 - 4.4^2$

3 Use the $\boxed{\sqrt{}}$ key to calculate:

   a $\sqrt{25}$ **b** $\sqrt{196}$ **c** $\sqrt{1.21}$ **d** $\sqrt{100}$ **e** $\sqrt{0.01}$

4 Calculate (i), then (ii) in each part:

   a (i) $5^2 + 12^2$ (ii) $\sqrt{5^2 + 12^2}$
   b (i) $7^2 + 24^2$ (ii) $\sqrt{7^2 + 24^2}$
   c (i) $6^2 + 8^2$ (ii) $\sqrt{6^2 + 8^2}$
   d (i) $25^2 - 20^2$ (ii) $\sqrt{25^2 - 20^2}$

5 Use the $\boxed{y^x}$ key to calculate:

   a 3^4 **b** 2^5 **c** 4^4 **d** 10^6 **e** 123^2 **f** 0.2^5

6 Use the $\boxed{y^x}$ key to find which number is greater in each pair.

   a 3^5 or 6^3 **b** 2^3 or 3^2 **c** 3^4 or 4^3

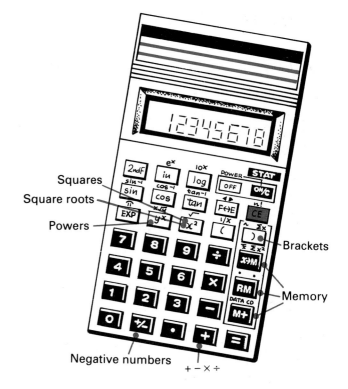

Squares

Square roots

Powers

Brackets

Memory

Negative numbers $+ - \times \div$

7 Use the $\boxed{x^2}$ key to calculate the area of each square.

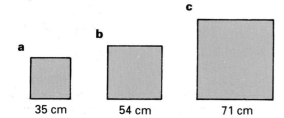

8 Use the $\boxed{y^x}$ key to calculate the volume of each cube.

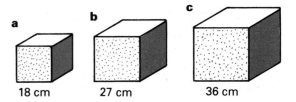

Now try these on your calculator.

Calculation	Possible keying instructions	Answer
d Brackets . . . $5.4 \div (8.7 - 6.9)$	5.4 ÷ (8.7 − 6.9) =	3
e Using memory. Convert 5, 6, 7, 8 and 9 miles to km by multiplying each by 1.609.	1.609 x→M 5 x RM = or RCL	8.045
f Using constant facility for calculations as in **e**.	Then 6 x RM = , etc. Various	9.654, etc.

9 Use brackets to calculate:
  a $36 \div (61 - 43)$ **b** $19 \times (7.3 + 5.7)$
  c $\dfrac{46}{(3.9 + 7.6)}$ **d** $\dfrac{8.3 - 5.8}{(0.19 + 0.06)}$

10 Use brackets to calculate:
  a $\sqrt{(9^2 + 12^2)}$ **b** $\sqrt{(8^2 + 15^2)}$ **c** $\sqrt{(50^2 - 40^2)}$

11 Use the memory, or constant facility, keys to convert these lengths to centimetres, correct to 2 decimal places, by multiplying each by 2.54.
Lengths (inches): 9, 12, 16, 24, 36, 60

12 As in question **11**, convert these sums of money to British currency, to the nearest penny, by dividing each by 1.48.
Money (dollars): 7, 20, 75, 150, 6780

13 Try question **9** again, calculating the part in brackets first, putting it into the memory, then carrying out the multiplication or division.

14 Use the $\boxed{\pi}$ key and the formula $C = \pi D$ to calculate the circumference of each circle, correct to 3 significant figures.

Diameter 2.2 cm   Diameter 1.6 cm   Diameter 1 cm

15 Use the formula $A = \pi r^2$ to calculate the area of each circle in question **14**, correct to 3 significant figures.

EXERCISE 4B

1 Square towels are sold in four sizes, with sides 28 cm, 35 cm, 45 cm and 62 cm long. Calculate:
  a the area of material needed for each size
  b the length of the side of a square towel which has an area of 4900 cm².

2 The town garden is made up of four square lawns. Each lawn is 47 m long.

  a Calculate the area of:
    (i) one lawn   (ii) the four lawns.
  b 1 litre of fertiliser is needed to treat 18 m² of lawn. How many whole litres must be bought to treat the four lawns?

3 This puzzle consists of three pieces of plastic which can be arranged to form a 2 cm by 8 cm rectangle or a 4 cm by 4 cm square.

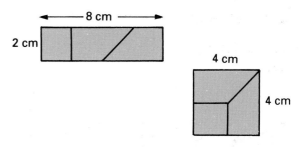

  a Check that the two shapes have the same area.
  b Another set of puzzle pieces can be arranged to form a rectangle 7 cm by 28 cm. Calculate:
    (i) its area
    (ii) the length of side of a square with the same area. (*Hint:* Use the $\boxed{\sqrt{}}$ key.)

4 Calculate:
  (i) the area of each rectangle
  (ii) the length of side, correct to 0.1 cm, of a
    square with the same area.

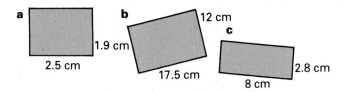

a
2.5 cm
1.9 cm

b
12 cm
17.5 cm

c
2.8 cm
8 cm

5 Calculate, correct to 2 decimal places if
necessary:
  a $17.5 \div (18.4 - 14.9)$ **b** $0.9^2 \times (1.39 + 8.76)$
  c $\dfrac{1.23}{4.56 + 7.89}$ **d** $\dfrac{3057}{4056 - 3965}$

6 Use the memory, or constant facility, to calculate
the heights, correct to 1 decimal place, of these
objects made to a scale of 0.15 for Kim's dolls'
house.

Object	TV	chair	table	chest	sink	stool
Actual (cm)	56	61	102	203	97	32
Scale (cm)						

7 Use the memory, or constant facility, to multiply
each price by 1.175 to find the price the customer
would pay, including VAT, to the nearest penny.

Price on tag	£25	£32	£37	£79	£85	£126
Cost to customer						

8 The diameters of some circular parts of the Lunar
Landing Module are shown. Calculate the
circumference of each part, correct to 2 decimal
places.

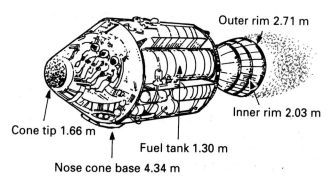

Outer rim 2.71 m

Inner rim 2.03 m

Fuel tank 1.30 m

Cone tip 1.66 m

Nose cone base 4.34 m

A GAME FOR TWO PLAYERS

*The first player sets a target number. The second
player sets the starting number. The players take it
in turn to choose a number to multiply by so that the
target is reached.
The winner is the
first to get within
1 of the target
number.*

Example
Target number 50. Starting number 15.

Player 1   Player 2   Player 1   Player 2   Player 1

$15 \times ③ \rightarrow 45 \times ①.② \rightarrow 54 \times ⓪.⑨ \rightarrow 48.6 \times ①.⑤ \rightarrow 51.03 \times ⓪.⑨⑨$

$\doteqdot 50.52$

*50.52 is within 1 of the target 50, so the first player
wins.*

CHALLENGE

1 *Using only the* ⊠ *key on your calculator, copy
and complete:*
  a *From the diagram,* $x^3 = \ldots$
  b $\left.\begin{array}{l} 2^3 = \ldots \\ 3^3 = \ldots \end{array}\right\}$ *so x is between
    2 and 3,
    nearer . . .*
  $\left.\begin{array}{l} 2.7^3 = \ldots \\ 2.8^3 = \ldots \end{array}\right\}$ *so x is between
    . . . and . . . ,
    nearer . . .*

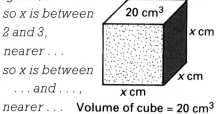

20 cm³
x cm
x cm
x cm
Volume of cube = 20 cm³

  $x = \ldots$, *correct to 1 decimal place.*

2 *Write down an equation for each diagram. Then,
using only the* ⊠ *key on your calculator, find x
correct to 1 decimal place.* **a**, **b** *are rectangles;*
c, **d** *squares;* **e**, **f** *cubes.*

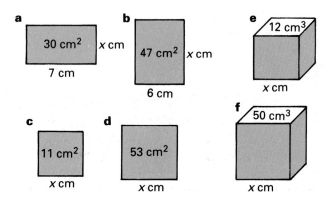

a
30 cm²
x cm
7 cm

b
47 cm²
x cm
6 cm

e
12 cm³
x cm

c
11 cm²
x cm

d
53 cm²
x cm

f
50 cm³
x cm

STANDARD FORM

In America some years ago a swarm of locusts covered an area of 200 000 square miles. There were over 125 000 000 000 000 locusts, with a total weight of 25 000 000 tonnes.

Here is a shorter way to write these numbers:

$200\,000 = 2 \times 10 \times 10 \times 10 \times 10 \times 10 = 2 \times 10^5$

$25\,000\,000 = 2.5 \times 10 \times 10 \times 10 \times 10 \times 10 \times 10 \times 10 = 2.5 \times 10^7$

$125\,000\,000\,000\,000 = 1.25 \times 10^{14}$

Number 1 to 10

Decimal point moves 14 places

1.25×10^{14} is the **standard form**, or **scientific notation**, for 125 000 000 000 000.

Every number can be written in the form $a \times 10^n$, where a is a number between 1 and 10 (including 1), and n is zero or a positive or negative whole number.

EXERCISE 5A

Write all the numbers in questions **1–6** in standard form. For example,
$300 = 3 \times 10^2$ and $3200 = 3.2 \times 10^3$

1 a 400 **b** 4000 **c** 40 000 **d** 400 000

2 a 800 **b** 60 **c** 2000 **d** 500 000

3 a 35 **b** 240 **c** 1200 **d** 78 000

4 a 2340 **b** 305 **c** 93 000 000

5 a A car engine size is 2000 cc.
  b There are 365 days in a year.
  c The school roll is 1563.
  d The Earth's diameter is 12 700 km.

6 a Dinosaurs roamed the Earth 169 000 000 years ago.
  b Light travels at 30 000 000 000 cm/s.
  c The mass of the Earth is 5980 000 000 000 000 000 000 000 kg.
  d The sun is 149 000 000 km away.
  e The most fertile creature is the cabbage aphid. One pest can give rise to 822 million descendants in one year.

On your calculator, key 25 followed by 000 . . . to fill the screen. Now multiply by 10. You should see one of these:

meaning 2.5×10^8 . . . . . 2.5×10^9 . . . . . 2.5×10^{10}

7 Write out these numbers in full.

For example 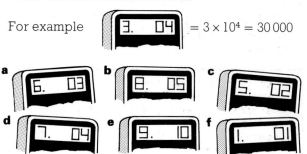 = $3 \times 10^4 = 30\,000$

a 6. 03   **b** 8. 05   **c** 5. 02

d 7. 04   **e** 9. 10   **f** 1. 01

8 Write out these numbers in full.

For example 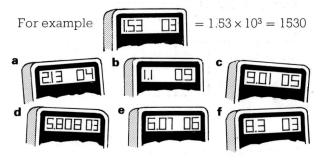 = $1.53 \times 10^3 = 1530$

a 2.13 04   **b** 1.1 09   **c** 9.01 05

d 5.808 03   **e** 6.07 06   **f** 8.3 03

9 18 500 000 people on holiday spent an average of £1800 each.
  a Use your calculator to find the total sum of money the holidaymakers spent.
  b Write out the sum in full.

10 There are 365 days in a year, 24 hours in a day, 60 minutes in an hour and 60 seconds in a minute. Calculate, in standard form, the number of seconds:
  a in 1000 years
  b that you had lived by your last birthday.

EXERCISE 5B

Standard form for very small numbers

Examples

a The eye of a needle is 0.08 cm wide.

$0.08 = 8 \times 10^{-2}$

b Human hair grows at 0.000 0005 cm/s.

$0.000\,0005 = 5 \times 10^{-7}$

Write all the numbers in questions **1–4** in standard form.

For example, $0.0075 = 7.5 \times 10^{-3}$

1 a 0.4   **b** 0.007   **c** 0.0009   **d** 0.02

2 a 0.25   **b** 0.046   **c** 0.1   **d** 0.0037

3 a 0.000 002   **b** 0.000 015   **c** 0.000 0008

4 a The thickness of a sheet of paper is 0.113 mm.
b A film of oil is 0.000 0008 mm thick.
c The mass of an electron is
    0.000 000 000 000 000 000 009 11 kg.

5 Write out these numbers in full.

For example 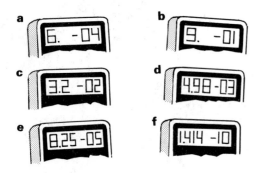 $= 3.5 \times 10^{-4} = 0.000\,35$

BRAINSTORMER

a *Write down the display on your calculator as you divide 3 by:*
  (i) one million
  (ii) one million million
  (iii) one million million million
  (iv) one hundred thousand million million million.
b *Write out number (iv) in full. This is the fraction of a gram that a molecule of water weighs.*

INVESTIGATION

1 *Look for a pattern as you calculate:*

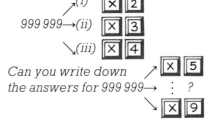

2 a *Look for patterns as you calculate:*
    (i) 11×11 (ii) 111×111 (iii) 1111×1111
b *Can you write down the answers for:*
    (i) $11\,111 \times 11\,111$ (ii) $111\,111 \times 111\,111$?
c *Try the calculations in **b** on your calculator. Compare them with your answers.*

3 a *No hints this time! Calculate:*
    (i) 9×9 (ii) 99×99
    (iii) 999×999 (iv) 9999×9999
b *Can you write down the answers for:*
    (i) $99\,999 \times 99\,999$ (ii) $999\,999 \times 999\,999$?
c *Check your answers to **b** with a calculator.*

CHECK-UP ON CALCULATIONS AND CALCULATORS

1

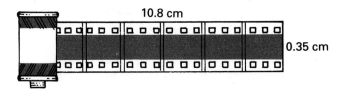

a Add 37 and 64.
b From 91 take away 38.
c Share 145p among 5.
d Subtract 79 from 308.
e Halve 378.

2

Change to minutes:
a   4 hours
b   3 hours 15 minutes.
Change to hours and
decimal fractions of an hour:
c   12 minutes
d   1 hour 45 minutes.

3 Round to 1 decimal place:
  a 3.79 **b** 4.84 **c** 1.05 **d** 12.17

4 Write each of these with 2 significant figures:
  a 139 **b** 4560 **c** 4.81 **d** 1.96

5 Calculate, correct to 2 decimal places:
  a $3.69 + 9.87$ **b** 5.72×0.91 **c** 1.68^2

6 Estimate, then calculate:
  a $234 + 456$ **b** $620 - 149$ **c** 26×47 **d** $441 \div 9$

7 Estimate, then calculate, the area of this strip of film.

10.8 cm

0.35 cm

8 Calculate:
  a 5.8^2 **b** $\sqrt{256}$ **c** 12^4

  d $\sqrt{(9^2 + 40^2)}$ **e** $5.8 \times (8.7 - 4.9)$ **f** $\dfrac{362 - 127}{46.5 + 47.5}$

9 £1 = $1.48. By putting 1.48 into the calculator memory, or using the constant facility, convert these sums of money to dollars.

Pounds (£)	1.00	10	25	270	548	1900
Dollars ($)						

10 A company makes square place mats.
The three sizes shown have sides 30 cm, 25.5 cm and 15.8 cm long.

  a Calculate the area of each mat.
  b The mat for the centre of the table is also square. It has an area of 1500 cm². Calculate the length of its side, correct to 1 decimal place.

11 Play Fair Games make plastic dice which are cubes with sides 12 mm, 15 mm and 25 mm long. Calculate the volume of plastic in each dice.

12 Write in standard form:
  a 1200 **b** 406 000 **c** 0.75 **d** 0.0003

13 Write out these numbers in full:
  a 2.34×10^2 **b** 1.5×10^6 **c** 5.6×10^{-5}

14 Write out the meaning of these calculator displays in standard form, and in full.

a   **b**

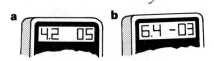

LOOKING BACK

1

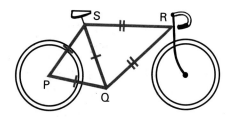

In the gym. Copy the diagrams below, and mark:
  (i) parallel parts with arrows
 (ii) perpendicular parts with right angles
(iii) horizontal parts with the letter H
(iv) vertical parts with the letter V.

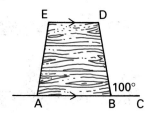

a   **b**   **c**

Parallel bars   Rings   Wall bars

2 a   What is the shape ABDE at the end of this
      vaulting box called?

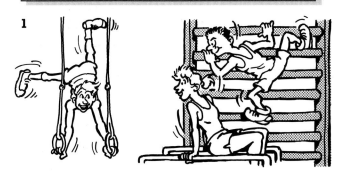

                          100°

b   What size is: (i) $\angle$ ABD   (ii) $\angle$ EDB?
c   What kind of angle is: (i) $\angle$ ABD   (ii) $\angle$ CBD?

3 a   What special type of triangle is:
      (i) PQS   (ii) QRS?

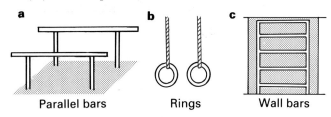

b   What type of quadrilateral is PQRS?
c   Name an angle equal to: (i) $\angle$ RSQ   (ii) $\angle$ RSP.

4 What is the size of each angle
AOB, BOC, . . . at the centre
of the snowflake?

5 All the metal strips are 10 cm long.

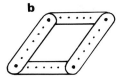

   a   **b**

   (i)   What special name is given to each shape?
  (ii)   Copy each one, and draw its lines of
         symmetry.
(iii)   Mark the centre of symmetry S in each shape.
         Does each shape have quarter-turn
         symmetry, or only half-turn symmetry,
         about S?

6 a   Write down the coordinates of A, B, C and D.
   b   What type of quadrilateral is ABCD?
   c   Write down the coordinates of its centre of
       symmetry.

7 The container on the lorry is a cuboid.
   a   What shape is each side of the container?
   b   How many: (i) edges 3 m long does it have
                  (ii) right angles are at each corner?

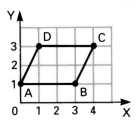

8 Draw a line PQ 6 cm long. Use a protractor to help
you draw:
   a $\angle$ PQR = 75°   **b** $\angle$ QPR = 145°

ANGLES AND TRIANGLES

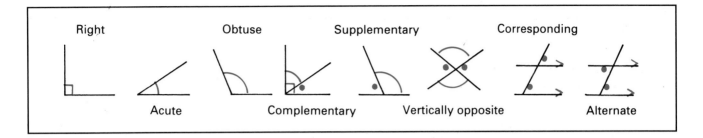

Right	Obtuse	Supplementary	Corresponding
Acute	Complementary	Vertically opposite	Alternate

EXERCISE 1

1 Calculate a, b, c.

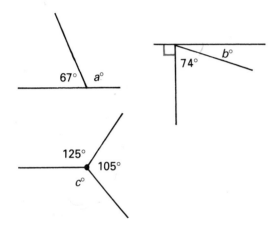

67° a°

74° b°

125°   105° c°

2 Say whether angles a, b, c in question **1** are acute or obtuse.

3 Copy these diagrams, and fill in the sizes of all the angles.

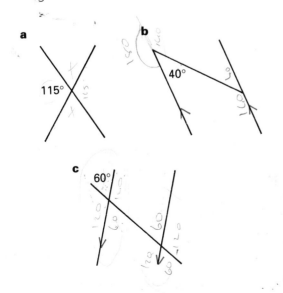

a   115°

b   40°

c   60°

4 Copy the right-hand diagram, and fill in the sizes of all the angles.

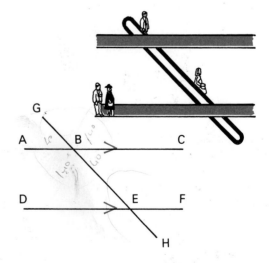

150°

5 On the diagram of the escalator, name the angle which is:
 a vertically opposite ∠ABG
 b alternate to ∠DEB
 c corresponding to ∠GBC.

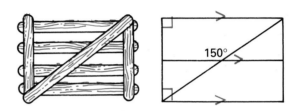

G

A   B   C

D   E   F

H

6 In question **5**, ∠GBC = 135°. Calculate:
 a ∠ABG   **b** ∠ABE   **c** ∠BEF.

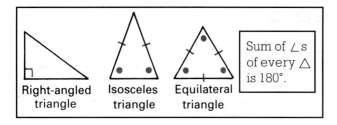

Right-angled triangle   Isosceles triangle   Equilateral triangle

Sum of ∠s of every △ is 180°.

7 Calculate *a*, *b*, *c*, *d*, *e*, *f*.

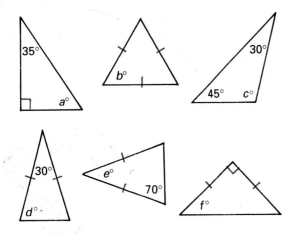

8 Ladder AB leans against a house wall. Copy the diagram and fill in the sizes of the acute and obtuse angles at A and B.

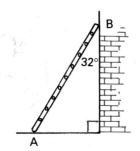

9

a Calculate *p*, *q*, *r*, *s*
b Which of these is a reflex angle?

10 Use a ruler and protractor to make accurate drawings of these triangles.

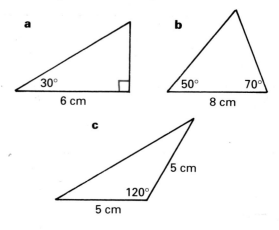

11 Use a protractor to measure the bearing, clockwise from north, of:
a the Rock from the Pier
b the Rock from the Point
c the Lightship from the Rock
d the Point from the Lightship.

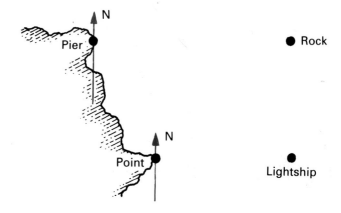

12 Mark point O, and the North line ON. Draw lines from O to show these bearings:
a 030° **b** 090° **c** 135° **d** 180° **e** 230° **f** 300°

13 A ship sails 20 km east, then 20 km north. Draw a diagram, and calculate its bearing from its starting point.

QUADRILATERALS

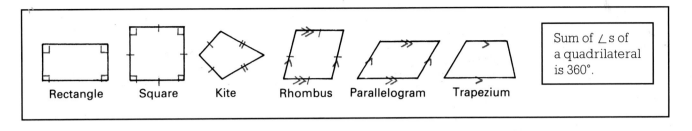

Rectangle	Square	Kite	Rhombus	Parallelogram	Trapezium	Sum of ∠s of a quadrilateral is 360°.

EXERCISE 2

1 Copy these quadrilaterals, and fill in the sizes of all the angles.

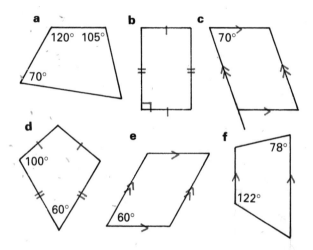

a 120° 105° 70°

b

c 70°

d 100° 60°

e 60°

f 78° 122°

2 Copy these, and fill in the sizes of as many angles as possible.

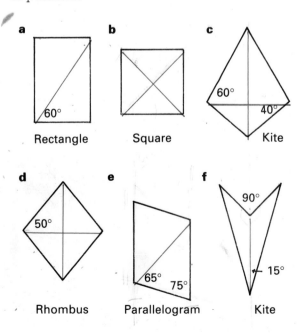

a 60° Rectangle

b Square

c 60° 40° Kite

d 50° Rhombus

e 65° 75° Parallelogram

f 90° 15° Kite

3 Calculate a, b, c.

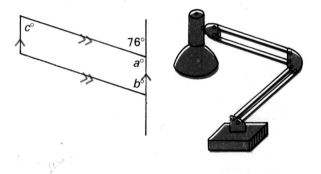

$c°$ 76° $a°$ $b°$

4 Calculate d, e, f.

$f°$ $e°$ 68° $d°$

5 Calculate g, h, i.

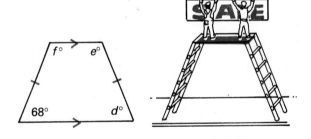

$i°$ 37° $g°$ $h°$

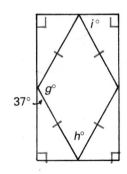

6

Copy this wallpaper border of parallelograms and isosceles triangles, and mark all the angles equal to $a°$, and all those equal to $b°$.

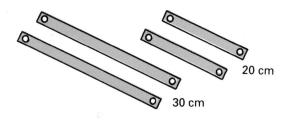

7 These four strips can snap together at the ends.

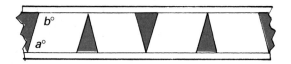

20 cm

30 cm

Draw and name the different kinds of quadrilateral you could make with them.

8 The wooden rods make the square frame stronger.

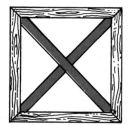

a What can you say about the rods?

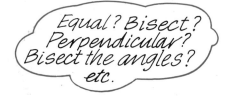

Equal? Bisect? Perpendicular? Bisect the angles? etc.

Repeat part **a** for a frame in the shape of:
b a rectangle **c** a rhombus **d** a kite
e a parallelogram

CHALLENGE

Find some landmarks, such as trees or buildings, near the school or your home, and use a magnetic compass to design a 'treasure trail'. For example, 'Go 30 m on a bearing of 120° from the front gate. What do you find? Then go . . . '

SYMMETRY

CLASS DISCUSSION

1 Which of these shapes have:
(i) one or more axes of reflection   (ii) half-turn symmetry   (iii) quarter-turn symmetry?

2 In rotation, what order of symmetry does each one have (the number of times a tracing fits its outline in one turn about its centre of symmetry)?

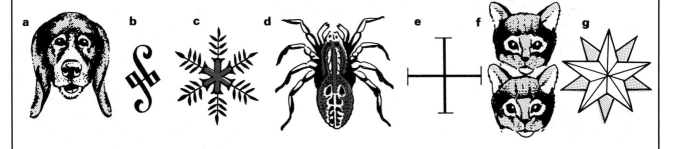

EXERCISE 3

1 AB is the axis of symmetry. Copy this diagram, and fill in the sizes of all the angles at P, Q, R and S.

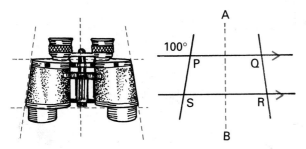

2 The dotted line is the axis of symmetry.

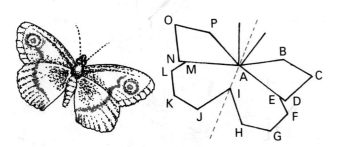

a Name a line equal to:
(i) AP   (ii) ON   (iii) JK.
b Name an angle equal to:
(i) ∠BAD   (ii) ∠IJK   (iii) ∠BCD.
c Name a shape congruent to:
(i) ABCD   (ii) AIJKLM.

3 Trace each shape, and draw its reflection in the dotted line.

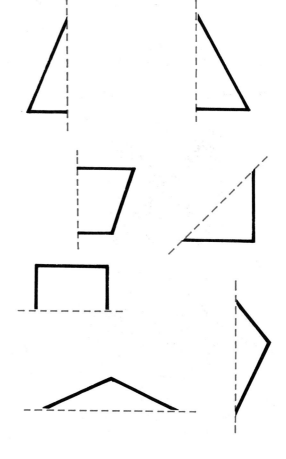

4 Q is the image of P under reflection in the *y*-axis.

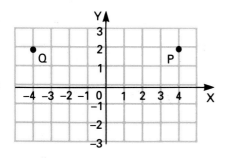

a Write down the coordinates of P and Q.
b R is the image of Q under reflection in the *x*-axis. Write down the coordinates of R.

5 Rectangle PQRS is completed in question **4**. Write down the coordinates of S.

6 Copy the axes in question **4**.
a Plot the point A(−3, 5).
b Plot the images B and D of A in the *y*-axis and the *x*-axis. Write down their coordinates.
c Complete rectangle ABCD. What are the coordinates of C?

7 Copy this shape on squared paper, and complete it so that both dotted lines are axes of symmetry.

8 In how many ways can
a a playing card fit face down on a pack of cards

b a hexagonal socket spanner fit on a hexagonal nut

c an octagonal tin lid fit onto the tin

d a round lid fit on a cylindrical tin?

9 Copy this table and use tracings, if necessary, to help you fill it in.

Name of shape	Number of axes of symmetry	Order of rotational symmetry

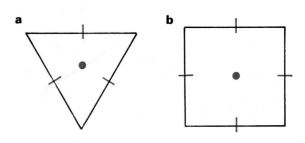

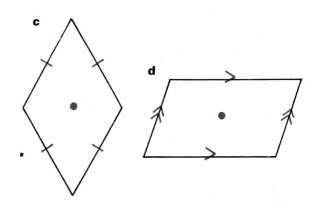

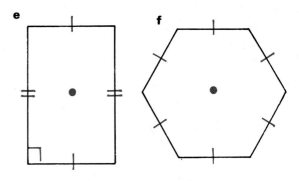

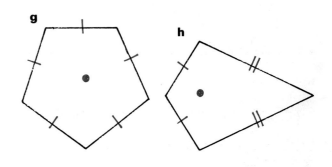

REGULAR POLYGONS

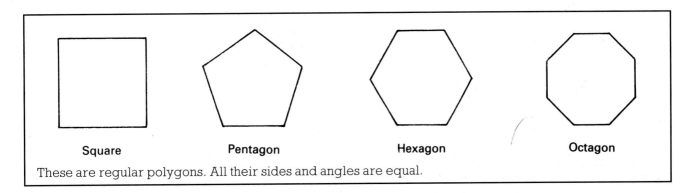

Square   Pentagon   Hexagon   Octagon

These are regular polygons. All their sides and angles are equal.

EXERCISE 4B

1 a Copy, or trace, this regular hexagon, which is made of six equilateral triangles.

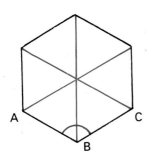

b Fill in the sizes of all the angles.
c What size is each interior angle of a regular hexagon, like ∠ABC?

2 Each triangle in this regular octagon is isosceles.

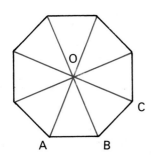

a Calculate the size of each angle at the centre O, like ∠AOB.
b Calculate:
  (i) ∠ABO
  (ii) ∠ABC, an interior angle of the octagon.

3 Sketch a regular decagon (10-sided polygon) and its diagonals.
Repeat all the parts of question **2** for a regular decagon.

4 This is part of a 15-sided regular polygon.

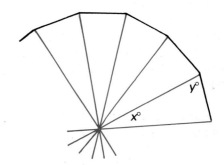

Calculate:
a x **b** y
c the size of an interior angle of the polygon.

5 This tessellation, or tiling, is made from regular hexagons.

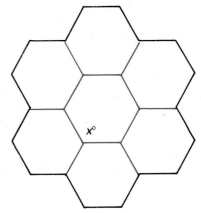

a What size is angle $x°$?
b Explain why you can make a tiling with regular hexagons.

6 Can you find, and sketch, two other tilings made of regular shapes?

7

Hallowe'en masks are printed in large sheets.
a How many sides are in each mask polygon?
b Write down the coordinates of the ears of the masks in:
   (i) the bottom row
   (ii) the left-hand column.

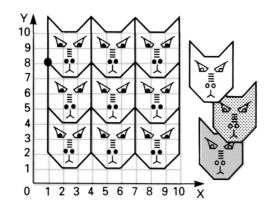

CHALLENGES

1 **a** *Which three regular shapes are used in this pattern?*

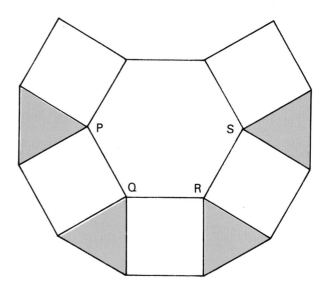

  b *Calculate the size of each angle at P.*
  c *Explain why the three shapes fit together exactly at P, Q, R and S.*

2 *Repeat challenge 1 for this pattern of regular shapes.*

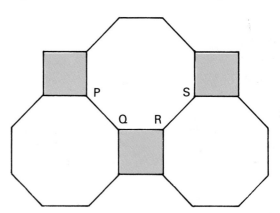

3 *Trace the tilings in 1 and 2, and continue each of them until they cover a page. Colour them to make an interesting pattern.*

COORDINATES

EXERCISE 5A

1 Write down the coordinates of each vertex of this octagon.

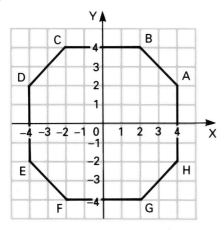

2 a Plot these points on squared paper, then join them up in order:
P(4, 0), Q(2, 3), R(−2, 3), S(−4, 0), T(−2, −3), U(2, −3), P(4, 0)

b What type of polygon have you drawn?

3 Liz puts pins at A, B and C on the pin board.

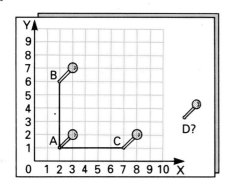

a Where should she put the fourth pin to make a square ABDC?

b What would be the area of the square?

4 George puts an elastic band round pins at P, Q, R and S. Where would he move pin S to make:
a a square PQRS
b a kite PQRS, with PQ = QR?

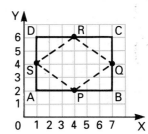

5 a Plot P(1, 2), Q(7, 2), R(4, 5).
b Join the points. What shape have you drawn?
c Calculate the area of the shape.
(Area of triangle = $\frac{1}{2}$ base × height.)

6 a Calculate the area of ABCD.

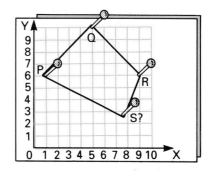

b Write down the coordinates of P, Q, R, S, the midpoints of the sides.
c (i) What type of quadrilateral is PQRS?
(ii) Calculate its area.

7 Each square is 1 cm long.
a Write down:
(i) the coordinates of the centre of the circle
(ii) the lengths of its radius and diameter.
b If A, B, C, D are joined, what shape is made?

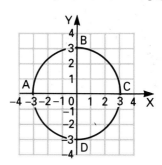

EXERCISE 5B

1 a What shape is ABCD?
b EFGH is a kite. What are the coordinates of G?
c Calculate the area of:
 (i) ABCD
 (ii) EFGH.

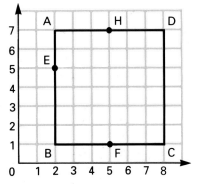

2

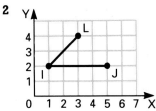

a Write down the coordinates of the vertex K of the parallelogram IJKL.
b Calculate the area of the parallelogram.

3 a Copy this diagram on squared paper.

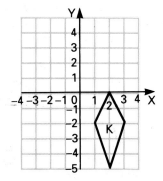

b Draw the reflection of the kite K in the *x*-axis. Write down the coordinates of each vertex.
c Repeat **b** for reflection of the kite K in the *y*-axis.

4 a Place tracing paper over the grid, and mark P on it.

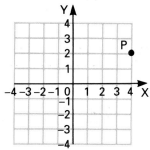

b 'Pin' your pencil at O, and rotate the tracing anti-clockwise through 90°.
c What are the coordinates of P now?
d Repeat **a-c** for a clockwise rotation of:
 (i) 90°   (ii) 180°.

5 Copy this diagram, and draw the image of triangle T after a rotation about O of:
a 90° anti-clockwise
b 90° clockwise
c 180° (does the direction matter?)

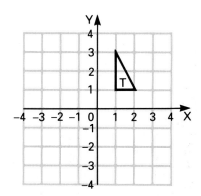

CHALLENGE

Ever-ready Radar Station notes the position of a helicopter at A(3, 140°). The helicopter is circling the station at a distance of 3 km.
a *What is its position if OA turns:*
 (i) 90° clockwise   (ii) 90° anti-clockwise?
b *What is helicopter B's position?*
c *What angle must OB turn through,*
 (i) clockwise   (ii) anti-clockwise, for helicopter B to reach point (4, 250°)?

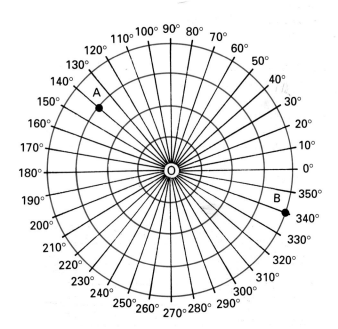

THREE DIMENSIONS

EXERCISE 6A

1 a Write down the mathematical name for each solid.

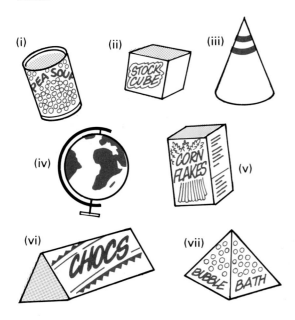

(i)   (ii)   (iii)

(iv)   (v)

(vi)   (vii)

b Can you think of another example of each of these solids in everyday life?

2 Which of the solids in question **1** have at least one face which is:
a circular
b square
c rectangular (but not square)
d triangular?

3 List the number of faces, vertices and edges on each solid in question **1**.

4 For each of the cuboids below, calculate the number of:
(i) small cubes in the top layer
(ii) layers
(iii) small cubes altogether.

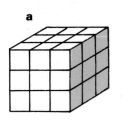
a

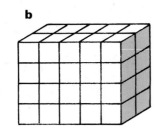
b

5 Calculate the volume of each cuboid below. Remember the formula $V = lbh$.

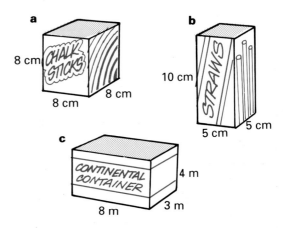

a
8 cm
8 cm
8 cm

b
10 cm
5 cm
5 cm

c
4 m
8 m
3 m

6 These shapes fit through the holes in a shape-sorter toy. In how many ways will each fit:
(i) red face up   (ii) any way possible?

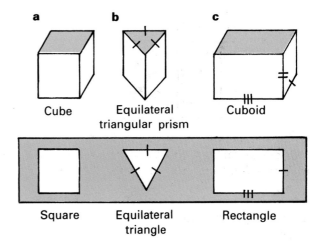

a   **b**   **c**

Cube   Equilateral triangular prism   Cuboid

Square   Equilateral triangle   Rectangle

/ **PRACTICAL PROJECTS**

1 *Many household containers are made from nets drawn on card or plastic. Examine some of these, and draw the nets. What different types of lid are there?*

2 *Use nets of cubes, prisms and pyramids (provided by the teacher) to construct the 'solids'. List the shapes of the faces, and the number of faces, vertices and edges. Find ways of packing a number of each together.*

EXERCISE 6B

1 a Look at this cuboid. Calculate the area of the:
   (i) front face A
   (ii) side B
   (iii) top C.

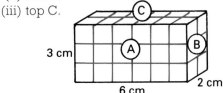

b Add together the area of all six faces to find the total surface area.

2 a Draw a net for this box of cards.
   b Calculate the surface area of the box.

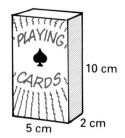

3 Calculate the surface areas of these. Don't include the floor of the hut.

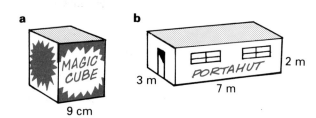

4 Which 3-dimensional shapes would these nets make?

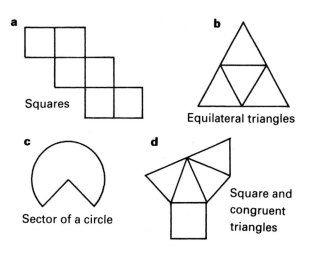

a Squares

b Equilateral triangles

c Sector of a circle

d Square and congruent triangles

5 Make a sketch of the 3-dimensional shapes in question **4**.

6 Melanie knows that a cuboid has three planes of symmetry. (There are three ways in which it can be cut in two so that each half is the mirror image of the other.) The dotted line shows one plane. Make sketches of the other two planes.

CHALLENGES

1 Design a bookcase based on a triangular prism. List details of shapes, sizes, etc.

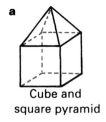

2 Design a box which will hold six matchboxes. Draw its net, list the sizes, then construct the box.

BRAINSTORMERS

1 How many planes of symmetry does each of these solids have?

a Cube and square pyramid

b Octahedron

2 Two cuts of the cake make four pieces of cake. Can you show how three cuts can give more than six pieces of cake?

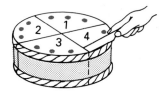

CHECK-UP ON SHAPE AND SPACE

1 Calculate *a*, *b*, *c* and *x*.

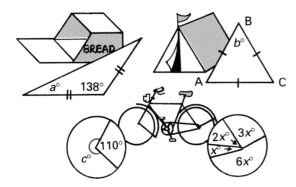
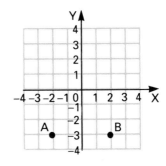
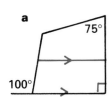
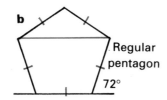

2 Copy the diagrams, and fill in the sizes of all the angles.

a
75°
100°

b
Regular pentagon
72°

3 a What name is given to the pair of angles marked: (i) *x*° (ii) *y*°?

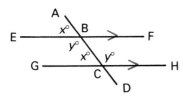

b ∠ABF = 130°. Calculate the size of:
(i) ∠FBC (ii) ∠BCH (iii) ∠EBC.

4 Calculate:
a the bearing of Q from P (*x*°)
b the size of the angle marked *y*°
c the bearing of P from Q.

5 Look at the diagram below. What words or numbers go in the spaces in the sentences that follow?

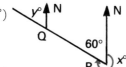

a QRZ is an . . . . triangle.
b PQZWXY is a regular . . . .
c PS and XU are . . . . and . . . .
d *a* = ... **e** *b*+*c* = ...

6 Look again at the diagram in question **5**.
a How many lines of symmetry has
(i) △VWZ (ii) RSTUVZ?
b What is the order of rotational symmetry of PSTUXY about the point Z?

7 a How many lines of symmetry has this star?
b What is its order of rotational symmetry about its centre?

8 a Write down the coordinates of A and B.

b Plot A and B on squared paper, then plot points C(2, 1) and D(−2, 1).
What shape is ABCD?
c Repeat **b** for A, B and the pairs of points:
(i) C(2, 3), D(−2, 3) (ii) C(3, 3), D(−1, 3)
(iii) C(1, 0), D(−1, 0) (iv) C(2, 1), D(−3, 2)
d Calculate the areas of the shapes in **c**(i) and **c**(ii).

9 A cube has edges 5 cm long. Calculate:
a its volume
b its total surface area
c the number of different ways it can fit into a square hole of side 5 cm.

10 Sketch the square floor ABCD. Mark possible positions for the lamp if it has to be placed:
a 2 m from B
b at equal distances from AB and BC
c 2 m from B *and* at equal distances from AB and AC.

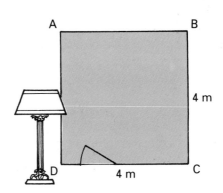
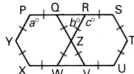

25

REVIEW: NUMBERS 1

NUMBERS

1 Ross James won £10 000 in a golf competition. His expenses were: hotel £342.50, travel £105.40 and caddy's fee £350. How much of his prize money did he have left?

2 Miss Simpson pays her council tax in ten monthly instalments. Calculate each payment if her annual charge is:
a £895   **b** £425.65 (to the nearest penny).

3 This is the price table of spring bulbs at the Glen Garden Centre.

	10	25	50	100
Daffodil	£1.75	£4.00	£7.75	£14.00
Tulip	2.75	6.50	11.75	22.00
Crocus	1.50	3.50	6.00	10.50
Snowdrop	0.90	1.75	3.80	6.50

Calculate the cost of:
a 25 daffodils
b 10 tulips and 10 crocus
c 50 crocus and 25 snowdrops
d 50 daffodils, 50 tulips and 100 snowdrops.

4 Emma is writing a 3000 word essay. So far she has written 1650 words.
a How many words has she still to write?
b She writes 250 words per page. How many pages does her essay take?

5 Write each mileometer reading below to the nearest: (i) 100 km   (ii) 10 km   (iii) km.

a 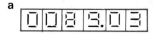   **b**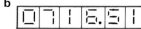

6 What would the readings on the mileometers in question **5** be after a further 354.85 km had been travelled?

7 Write each distance to the nearest 10 km, then to the nearest 100 km.
a 127 km   **b** 841 km   **c** 569 km   **d** 605 km

8 Round each measurement, correct to 1 decimal place.
a 2.16 m   **b** 8.84 cm   **c** 10.05 seconds

9 Round to 2 decimal places:
a 5.163 km   **b** 1.019 litres   **c** 0.305 m

10 Mr Jones, the chemist, weighed out two lots of pills. Calculate:
a the weight of each lot
b the difference between their weights.

11 a Use 1 significant figure in each number to *estimate* the area of each rectangle.

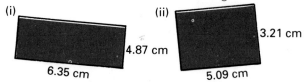

calc **b** Calculate the area of each rectangle, correct to 1 decimal place.

calc **12** Calculate the cost of 1 g or 1 ml of these to decide which is the most economical purchase in each case.

a
350 g . . . 54p
700 g . . . 100p
1 kg . . . 140p

b
75 ml . . . £1.49
85 ml . . . £1.65
110 ml . . . £2.15

calc **13** Use (i) brackets   (ii) the calculator memory, to calculate, correct to 3 significant figures:

a $\dfrac{2403+3527}{97.8+546.2}$ **b** $\dfrac{37.2 \div 5.3}{8.91 \times 0.64}$

14 a *Without using a calculator*, calculate:
(i) $3 \times 4 + 5$ (ii) $3 + 4 \times 5$
(iii) $5 \times 4 - 5$ (iv) $(18-3) \div 5$
(v) $4 \times (8-8)$ (vi) $20 \div (10-6)$
b Check your answers with a calculator.

ORDER
( )
× ÷
+ −

15 Find two more terms for each sequence, and explain the rule you have used.
a 6, 11, 16, 21, . . .   **b** 88, 77, 66, 55, . . .
c 2, 8, 32, 128, . . .   **d** 1, 2, 4, 7, . . .

DECIMALS

1 Which numbers are these arrows pointing to? (Take care with the scales.)

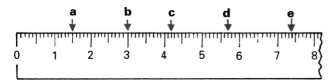

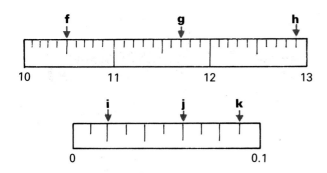

2 Arrange these numbers in order, smallest first:
a 8.7, 7.8, 9.1, 8.1
b 1.23, 0.92, 0.29, 1.08

3 Calculate:
a 8.5 + 7.5, and 8.5 − 7.5
b 8.28 + 6.45, and 8.28 − 6.45

4 Calculate:
a 3.57 + 2.45 − 1.78
b 0.13 + 0.78 − 0.04
c 37.6 − 19.4 + 25.7

5 Ten pencils cost £1.40. At the same rate, calculate the cost of:
a 100 pencils **b** 1000 pencils **c** 1 pencil

6 Calculate the perimeter of this L-shape. The lengths are in centimetres.

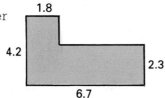

7 Round the lengths of every side in the L-shape in question **6** to the nearest cm.

8 Round to the nearest penny:
a £2.893 **b** £7.068 **c** £5.325 **d** £0.817

9 Multiply each of these numbers by (i) 10 (ii) 100:
a 7.2 **b** 35.1 **c** 9.03 **d** 0.7 **e** 36

10 Divide each number in question **9** by 10.

11 *Estimate*, then calculate:
a 9.7×6 **b** 1.8×7 **c** 18.6×9
d 75.6×2 **e** 0.97×8

12 *Estimate*, then calculate:
a $23.4 \div 3$ **b** $55.8 \div 9$ **c** $22.8 \div 6$
d $72.5 \div 5$ **e** $4.97 \div 7$

13 A unit of electricity costs 5.87 pence.
a *Estimate* the cost of:
(i) 8 units (ii) 32 units (iii) 96 units
b Calculate the actual costs, to the nearest penny.
c How many whole units can be bought for £50?

14 The distance by rail between two towns is 37 km. A day return ticket costs £6.66. Calculate the cost in pence per km.

15 Write in decimal form: **a** $\frac{9}{10}$ **b** $7\frac{7}{10}$ **c** $\frac{23}{100}$ **d** $\frac{3}{100}$

16 To calculate each competitor's final score in a diving contest the three judges' scores are added together, and then multiplied by the 'degree of difficulty' number for the dive.
a Elaine is awarded 5, 5.5 and 5.5 for a dive with a degree of difficulty of 1.4. What is her final score?
b Alan has scores of 6, 6.5 and 5.5 for a dive with a degree of difficulty of 1.8. Find his final score.

17 Lena looks at the exchange rates of £s for American dollars: $1.57 for £1.
a How much does she get for £120, to the nearest cent (hundredth of a dollar)?
b Later she changes $30 back to £s at the same rate. How much does she receive, to the nearest penny?

FRACTIONS, DECIMALS AND PERCENTAGES

1 What fractions, decimal fractions and percentages of these shapes are:
  a rectangles **b** triangles?

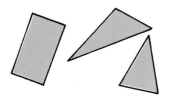

2 Calculate:
  a 25% of £10 **b** 60% of 45 kg **c** 1% of 4 m
  d 40% of £18 **e** 75% of 22 g **f** $33\frac{1}{3}$% of £84

3 A rectangular garden is 43.5 m long and 19.8 m wide. Calculate:
  a its area
  b the length of fence needed to go round the sides.

4 Personal stereos costing £56 are reduced by 10% in a sale. Calculate:
  a the discount
  b the sale price.

5 In a sale a £45 watch is reduced by 15%. How much is:
  a the reduction in price
  b the sale price?

6 The Safe as Houses Building Society offers interest at 4%. Calculate the interest after one year, on:
  a £200 **b** £1500 **c** £85

SAFE AS HOUSES
4% PER ANNUM

7 a Which earns more in a year, £250 at 6% or £280 at 5% per annum?
  b How much more does it earn?

8 Calculate the interest at $2\frac{1}{2}$% per annum on £1200 for:
  a one year **b** six months.

9 Cartons of ice-cream are bought for 65p and sold for 78p. Calculate:
  a the profit on each carton
  b the percentage profit, based on the cost price.

10 A car dealer buys a used car for £2000 and sells it for £2600.
  a Calculate:
    (i) his profit
    (ii) his percentage profit, based on the cost price.
  b What would the selling price be if he wants to make a profit of 35%?

11 Last year, Carr's Garage made a profit of £240 000. The profit came from different activities, as shown in the pie chart.

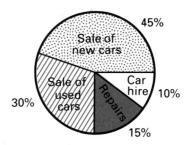

How much profit did each activity make?

12 Copy and complete this table:

Fraction	$\frac{2}{5}$			$\frac{1}{8}$		
Decimal		0.9			0.06	
Percentage			3%			52%

13 What fraction of an hour is 36 minutes:
  a in simplest form
  b as a decimal fraction
  c as a percentage?

14 Calculate the cost of this gas bill.
  Units used: 1486 kW at 1.622p per kW £
  Standing charge: 87 days at 10.4p per day £
  Sub-total: £
  VAT at 17.5%: £
  Total: £

15 Calculate these marks as percentages:
  a 14 out of 25 **b** 12 out of 20
  c 36 out of 40 **d** 62 out of 80

TIME AND TEMPERATURE

1 How many days are there in:
a six weeks **b** December **c** 1999?

2 a April 28th is a Tuesday. What day is May 7th?
b How many days are there from 28th April to 7th May, including both given dates?

3 How many days does the sale last?

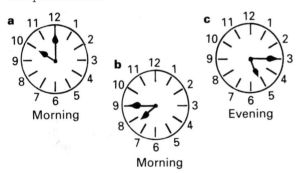

4 How many days are there from 11.5.95 to 12.6.95, including both dates?

5 Write down the time on each clock, using am and pm notation.

6 Write down the times on the clocks in question **5** in 24-hour notation.

7 How many hours are there from:
a 1.30 pm until 10.30 pm **b** 7 pm until 3 am
c 10.45 am until 6.45 pm?

8 *The Music Show:* 7.20 pm–7.50 pm
Races and Racers: 8.30 pm-10.15 pm
Megan wants to record these programmes on a 3-hour tape.
a What 24-hour times should she use?
b How much recording time is left on the tape?

9 Copy and complete the table:

12-hour clock	2 am	9 pm		
24-hour clock			08 00 hours	13 00 hours

10 How long does each journey take?

Depart	09 00	14 45	05 50	23 15
Arrive	10 15	16 15	10 25	06 40

11 What numbers do the arrows point to on these scales?

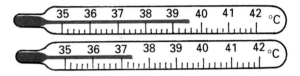

12 Ian's temperature was taken at 1 pm (shown on the first thermometer) and again at 11 pm.

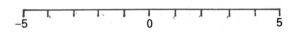

a How many degrees was each temperature above normal (37°C)?
b How many degrees did his temperature fall?

13 One day in July the temperature in Majorca was 31°C, and in Jersey 19°C.
a Which island was warmer? By how many degrees?
b Next day the temperature in Jersey rose by 8°C. What was the new temperature?

14 Copy this number line, and complete it.

15 Write these temperatures in order, coldest first:
5°C, −1°C, −7°C, 0°C, 3°C, −4°C

16 a Which city has:
(i) the highest temperature
(ii) the lowest temperature?

London −3°C, Rome 11°C, Oslo −9°C

b Calculate the difference between the highest and lowest temperatures.

17 Write down the temperature which is midway between:
a 2°C and 12°C **b** 0°C and 5°C
c −4°C and 0°C **d** −6°C and −2°C
e −1°C and 1°C **f** −1°C and 5°C

29

MONEY MATTERS - SAVING AND SPENDING

LOOKING BACK

1 Salim does some money calculations. His results are shown on these displays. Write each one as a sum of money.

a **1.35** b **9.02**

c **1.6** d **12.5**

2 Calculate:
  a the cost of the guitar
  b the amount of each payment.

12 Payments of £7.05

£1500 loan repay in 12 equal instalments

3 $75\% = \frac{75}{100} = 0.75$. Copy and complete this table.

Percentage	25%	50%	123%	8%	8.5%
Decimal					

4 Calculate:
  a the sum of these readings
  b the difference between them.

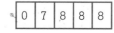

1	0	0	4	7

0	7	8	8	8

5 Calculate:
  a 12% of £50 **b** 5% of 800 km
  c $2\frac{1}{2}$% of £380 **d** 115% of £75

6 Calculate the discount and the sale price of each item.

a **£24** *10% OFF*

b **£32.50** *⅕ OFF*

c **£49.95** *20% OFF*

d **£80** *12.5% DISCOUNT*

7 The price of a Mountain Top bicycle last year was £120. This year the price rose by £5. Find the percentage increase, correct to 1 decimal place.

8 Stevens the Stationers buys pens at £5 for a box of 50, and sells them at 16p each. Calculate:
  a the selling price of 50 pens
  b the percentage profit on a box of pens.

9 Change to percentages:
  a 0.35 **b** 0.6 **c** 0.175 **d** $\frac{1}{10}$ **e** $\frac{1}{8}$

WAGES AND SALARIES

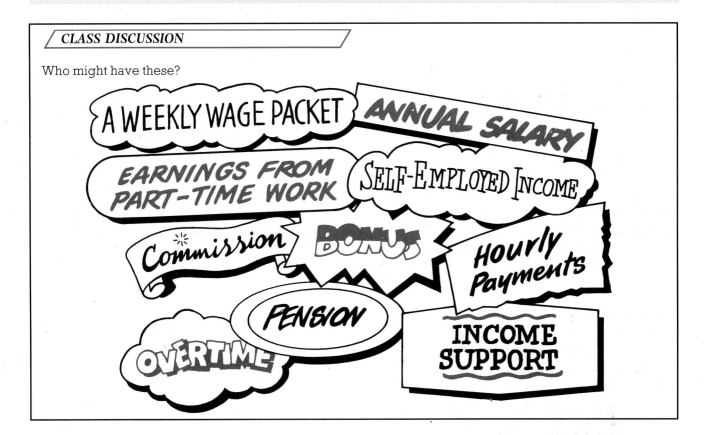

CLASS DISCUSSION

Who might have these?

A WEEKLY WAGE PACKET

ANNUAL SALARY

EARNINGS FROM PART-TIME WORK

SELF-EMPLOYED INCOME

Commission

BONUS

Hourly Payments

PENSION

OVERTIME

INCOME SUPPORT

EXERCISE 1A

1 Shirley got this job.

> WANTED
> **FULL-TIME
> OFFICE ASSISTANT**
> £5.00 PER HOUR

  a How many hours might she expect to work:
    (i) per day (ii) per week?
  b How much would she earn in a week?

2 Leon gets a Saturday job.

> VACANCY
> SHOP ASSISTANT
> SATURDAYS ONLY
> £3.80 PER HOUR

How much will he earn if he works for:
a 4 hours **b** 7 hours?

3

> EXPERIENCED
> WORD-PROCESSOR
> OPERATOR
> SALARY £9600 PER YEAR

Mrs Chan is given the job.
  a Calculate her monthly salary before
    deductions.
  b What could deductions be for?

4 June applied for, and got, this post.

> TRAINEE
> **COMPUTER OPERATOR**
> Starting Salary
> £6360 per annum

  a Calculate her monthly pay.
  b After a year her salary went up by £840.
    Calculate her new:
    (i) annual salary (ii) monthly pay.

5 Mr Slater takes this job.

> ## PART-TIME INSURANCE AGENT
> ### 5pm – 7.30pm – 6 DAYS PER WEEK
> ### * £6.50 per hour + bonus *

a How many hours will he work each week?
b How much will he earn in a week?
c If his weekly bonus is £20, how much would he earn altogether?

Overtime

Higher rates may be paid to employees who work in the evenings or at weekends.

Example

Irene's usual pay is £8 an hour. For overtime she gets:

Evenings—time-and-a-half
$= 1\frac{1}{2} \times$ usual rate $= 1\frac{1}{2} \times £8 = £12$
Weekends—double time
$= 2 \times$ usual rate $= 2 \times £8 = £16$

6 Calculate Irene's pay for:
a 35 hours of weekday work
b 5 hours of evening work
c 3 hours of weekend work.

7 Tom wants to train as an electrician.

> ## ELECTRICIAN'S ASSISTANT
> ### (SUIT SCHOOL LEAVER)
> ### £4.20 PER HOUR + OVERTIME

a If he gets the job, what would his pay be for:
(i) an 8-hour day (ii) a 40-hour week?
b Overtime is paid at time-and-a-half.
What is his overtime pay for:
(i) 1 hour (ii) 4 hours?

8 Jim's pay at the Rainbow Paint Factory is £8.40 an hour. What is he paid for:
a a 37-hour week
b 8 hours of overtime at time-and-a-half?

Commission

Example
Doug is paid 6% commission on all his double glazing sales.
Calculate his commission on sales of £14 000.

Commission = 6% of £14 000.

Remember, $6\% = \frac{6}{100} = 0.06$.

Method 1
6 [%] [×] 14 000 [=]

Method 2
0.06 [×] 14 000 [=]

£840

9 Calculate commissions of:
a 6% of £700 **b** 15% of £18 000 **c** 1% of £100

10 Marie is paid commission of 5% on all carpets she sells.
a How much is she paid for selling a £100 carpet?
b Calculate her commission on sales of:
(i) £200 (ii) £500 (iii) £350 (iv) £689

11 Miss Peach sells cosmetics door-to-door. She doesn't get a basic wage. Instead she is paid 10% commission on her sales. How much would she earn for selling goods priced at:
a £20 **b** £85 **c** £6.20 **d** £101?

12 Guy is a sales assistant in a boutique. As well as a basic wage, he is paid commission of 6% of his sales.

a How much commission will he earn if he sells:
(i) a jacket for £80 (ii) a suit for £120
(iii) a tie for £3?
b Why is commission paid?

EXERCISE 1B

1

Flo runs a flower shop. Her assistant Tracy works 3 hours every afternoon from Monday to Saturday. Flo pays her £3.50 an hour.
  a How much is Tracy paid weekly?
    The daily takings one week are £75, £156, £241, £98, £284 and £277.
  b How much does Flo have left after paying Tracy, and expenses of £537?

2 Mrs Clarke is appointed manager of Eversure Insurance at a salary of £16 000 a year, with annual increases of £500.
  a What is her starting monthly pay?
  b In four years what will be her:
    (i) annual salary   (ii) gross monthly pay?

3 Kevin was a salesman for Sleepsound, and Keith travelled for Soundsleep. In March each of them had sales of £12 000. Who earned more from his pay and commission, and by how much?

4 Each month the workers at Tom's Toy Factory are given a commission of 8% of the profits. Calculate the total commission for the six months from September to February.

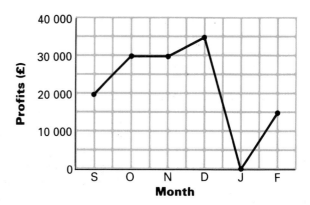

5 Mr Power sells cars. He is paid £110 a week basic, plus 2% of sales. In four weeks he sells seven cars for £7000, £5000, £2400, £1800, £8300, £10 000 and £6500.

  a How much commission does he earn altogether?
  b Would he be better off if he was just paid £350 per week, without any commission for those four weeks?

<hr>

INVESTIGATIONS

Look at advertisements in newspapers.
1 What is the highest annual salary you can find? What is meant by £40k?

2 Find two examples of each of the following ways of being paid:
  a by annual salary   b by weekly wage
  c by commission.

3 Can you find any other 'incentives', or extras?

SAVINGS IN BANKS AND BUILDING SOCIETIES

Billy wants to have his own cheque book. He opens a **current account** in the Moneymaker Bank.

Do you know what each of the terms above means?

EXERCISE 2

1 Billy pays in £50, and gets his own cheque book. Here is the first cheque he wrote.

Date: *23.10.95*	**£ MONEYMAKER BANK** 00-11-22
To: *TopTen*	*pay TopTen &co* Date: *23.10.95*
For: *tapes*	*Twenty-five pounds 10p* £25.10
£ *25.10*	_____ W. O'Reilly
	W.O'Reilly
00001	00001 001122 2020202

   Cheque number   Bank code   Account number

Make a copy of his second cheque:
Number 00002, dated 28.10.95,
payable to 'Hot Hi-fi', for £12.50.

2 Every month a bank statement comes through Billy's letter box. It shows all the money taken out and paid in, and the balance.

MONEYMAKER BANK	William O'Reilly		Account 2020202
Date	Details	Withdrawals	Paid in	Balance
20 Oct	Cash		50.00	50.00
23 Oct	Chq 00001 Top Ten	25.10		24.90
28 Oct	Chq 00002 Hot Hi-fi	12.50		12.40
30 Oct	Chq Regional Council		475.00	487.40
5 Nov	Chq 00003	100.00		

a Explain the entries on:
  (i) 20 Oct (ii) 23 Oct (iii) 30 Oct.
b How much is in his account on:
  (i) 23 Oct (ii) 30 Oct (iii) 5 Nov?

3 Copy these statements, and complete the Balance columns.

a

Out	In	Balance
—	20.00	20.00
8.00	—	
—	10.00	
5.00	—	

b

Out	In	Balance
—	35.00	
17.00	—	
—	5.50	
9.50	—	

4 Billy found that the bank's Savings Account paid interest of 3% p.a. (per annum = yearly) on deposits. Copy and complete:
Interest in one year on £450
at 3% = 3% × £450 = ... (3 $\boxed{\%}$ $\boxed{\times}$ 450 $\boxed{=}$).

5 Calculate the interest Billy would receive in a year on:
a £200 **b** £500 **c** £700 **d** £1250 **e** £50

6 Building Societies also want you to invest money with them, so that they can then lend it to other people to buy houses.

Billy's sister Maeve puts £100 into the Mushroom Building Society. How much interest is she paid after a year?

7 How much interest would Maeve get after a year on savings of:
a £200 **b** £300 **c** £700 **d** £1000?

8 How much interest will the Open Door Building Society pay after one year on deposits of:
a £100 **b** £600 **c** £850 **d** £925?

9 Maeve invests £100 at 8% p.a. Billy invests £110 at 7% p.a. Who gets more interest in a year? How much more?

10 Mrs Wilson, a pensioner, puts her savings of £6600 into the Money Mountain Building Society. After a year she takes out the interest to pay a large bill. How much does she get?

11 Copy and complete:

	Principal	Rate of interest	Interest for 1 year	Interest for 6 months
a	£40	8% p.a.	£3.20	£1.60
b	£230	10% p.a.		
c	£70	6% p.a.		
d	£91.50	4% p.a.		

12 Mrs Dixon invests £960 at 8% p.a. Four months later she takes out the interest to help pay for a new food mixer. How much did she receive?

a Copy and complete:
Interest for 1 year = 8% of £960 = . . .
Interest for 1 month = $\frac{1}{12} \times £ . . . = £ . . .$
Interest for 4 months = $4 \times £ . . . = £ . . .$
b Calculate the interest on:
(i) £180 at 10% p.a. for 6 months
(ii) £240 at 8% p.a. for 3 months
(iii) £1200 at 5% p.a. for 1 month
(iv) £4200 at 7.5% p.a. for 8 months.

BRAINSTORMER

This is part of Billy's bank statement.

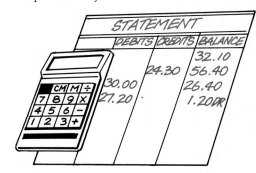

a *Spot the mistake!*
b *If Billy pays in £5 when he finds out he is overdrawn, (DR), what is the balance then?*

INVESTIGATIONS

1 *Banks like to attract young customers. So they have special offers to encourage them to open accounts. Do your local banks have any?*

2 *Investigate the services banks provide for their customers. There are sometimes leaflets on the counter about these.*

3 *Does your school run a bank for pupils? If so, what services does it offer?*

VALUE ADDED TAX (VAT)

CASH PRICE

£90 + VAT

Sheila hands the shop assistant £90, but it isn't enough. She has to add on $17\frac{1}{2}$% VAT.

17.5% of £90 = £15.75

So the guitar costs £90 + £15.75 = £105.75

Teachers, civil servants, police, nurses . . . schools, hospitals. All have to be paid for. So our Government raises money by different taxes. One of these is VAT.

SCHOOL BOOKS, CHILDREN'S CLOTHES, MEDICINES — ZERO RATED

CARS, CYCLES, TV, TOYS, RECORDS, GAS + ELECTRICITY BILLS — VAT IS CHARGED

What is meant by zero-rated? Why are some things zero-rated? What is the present rate of VAT?

VAT RATE = $17\frac{1}{2}$%

SHEILA'S GUITAR IS PRICED AT £90

SHE HAS TO PAY AN EXTRA $17\frac{1}{2}$% OF £90 = £15.75

THE SHOPKEEPER PASSES THIS TO THE GOVERNMENT

a   17.5 % or 0.175 → × Cost → = VAT

b   117.5 % or 1.175 → × Cost → = Cost + VAT

EXERCISE 3

Take $17\frac{1}{2}$% as the rate of VAT (the memory key or constant facility on your calculator can be useful here).

1 Calculate the VAT due on each item:
   a tennis racket, £30   **b** gold chain, £50
   c greenhouse, £750   **d** mountain bike, £160

2 For each toy, calculate:
   (i) the VAT   (ii) the total cost.

a £8   b £20   c £38

3

SCOT TRAVEL
ISLE OF MULL
6 Day Break
£210 including VAT

ISLE OF MULL
SCOTTHOL
6 Day Break
£180 Plus VAT

Alan was in no doubt. It had to be Scotthol; it was cheaper. Teresa wasn't so sure. She did her sums. What did she find?

4 Mrs Hogg buys some spare parts for her car. The prices given are without VAT. Calculate her total bill:

a without VAT **b** including VAT.

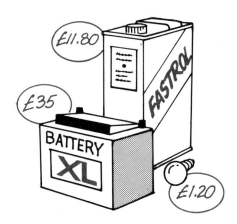

5 This is Mr Hogg's bill at 'The Steak Diner'. Copy and complete it.

THE STEAK DINER

1 SOUP	£1.50
1 STEAK & CHIPS	5.35
1 ICE CREAM	1.80
1 COFFEE	0.95
TOTAL	
+ VAT	
TO PAY	

6 Calculate this plumber's bill.

N. O. LEEK (PLUMBER)

£

3 metres plastic piping at £6.75 per metre

4 hours labour at £15.84 per hour

Subtotal

+VAT at 17½%

TOTAL

7

Calculator in hand, Mrs Singh went round the Cash and Carry. She calculated the total cost of each item by multiplying its price by 1.175. Would she get better overall value at the Cash and Carry or at the Locost Store?

Cash and Carry (VAT to be added)	£15	60p	£1	£2.50	£3.99
Locost Store (including VAT)	£18	65p	£1.15	£3	£4.30

8 In 1993, no VAT was charged on gas and electricity bills. (They were zero-rated.) In 1994, 8% VAT was charged. In 1995, 17.5% was charged. Copy and complete the table for these bills.

1993 (0% VAT)	1994 (8% VAT)	1995 (17.5% VAT)
£130		
£215		

CHALLENGE

A 3-piece suite costs £1280, including VAT. Use a 'trial and improvement' method to find the cost before VAT was added, to the nearest £.
(For example, a guess of £1000 → £1000 × 1.175 = £1175, which is too low.)

£1280 INCLUDING VAT

HOUSEHOLD BILLS

(i) Telephone bills

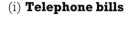

> If your phone wasn't used in a quarter, would you still get a bill?

> The time of day you phone - does it matter?

> How far you're phoning - does it make any difference?

> What about the length of the call?

There is a local rate (L), an *a* rate (up to 56 km) and a *b* rate (over 56 km).
There is a 'cheap' rate and a 'daytime' rate.
If only to help the family finances, have a good look at these tables.

Mon	Tue	Wed	Thu	Fri	Sat	Sun
Cheap rate: 6 pm–8 am					Cheap rate all the time	
Daytime rate: 8 am–6 pm						

Local	1 min	2 min	3 min	4 min	5 min
Cheap	5p	5p	5p	10p	10p
Daytime	5p	10p	15p	15p	20p

EXERCISE 4

1 Are calls at these times charged at cheap rate or daytime rate?
   a Saturday 11 am   **b** Monday 10 am
   c Friday 2 pm   **d** Wednesday 10 pm

2 How much would these local calls cost?
   a 1 minute at cheap rate
   b 2 minutes at daytime rate
   c 4 minutes at cheap rate
   d $3\frac{1}{2}$ minutes at daytime rate

3 What would you be charged for a local call lasting:
   a 5 minutes on Sunday from 3 pm
   b 3 minutes on Friday from 7 pm
   c 2 minutes on Tuesday from 9.30 am
   d $4\frac{1}{2}$ minutes on Thursday from 3.15 pm?

4 Mrs Smith's phone bill is for £84.60, plus VAT at 17.5%. How much does she pay altogether?

5 Look at Mr Gossip's phone bill. Calculate entries A, B and C.

Phone bill	for 000-111-9999
£48.88	Call charges
£20.94	Rental charges from 1 March to 31 May
A	Total
B	VAT at 17.5%
C	**Total amount now due**

6 a Draw up a phone bill like the one in question **5**.
   b Enter call charges of £75.20 and rental charges of £21.85.
   c Complete the calculation for the total amount due.

7 Calculate these telephone bills.

	a	b	c
Calls (£)	36.15	25.50	87.99
Rental (£)	20.94	21.80	21.05
Total (£)			
VAT at 17.5% (£)			
Total to pay (£)			

(ii) **Electricity and gas bills**

Sources of power
In your house, do you use gas, or electricity, or both for the following?

LIGHT HEAT COOKING HOT WATER TV & HI-FI FRIDGE & FREEZER WASHING MACHINE

How do you know how much gas or electricity has been used?
What units are gas and electricity measured in?

EXERCISE 5

1 Look at these meter readings. How many units of gas or electricity have been used in each?

a

METER READING	
Present	Previous
38364	37240

b

METER READING	
Present	Previous
06304	05836

2 Calculate the cost of these units of electricity:
  a 985 units at 7.75p each
  b 1150 units at 7.88p each.

3 Calculate:
  a the cost of 1250 units of electricity at 7.90p each
  b the cost in **a**, plus a standing charge of £6.55
  c the cost in **b**, plus VAT at 17.5%.

4

Mr Watt's electricity bill drops through his letter box. Calculate entries A, B, C, D and E.

SURE SPARK ELECTRICITY			
Meter reading		Charges	Amount (£)
Present	Previous		
18223	17101	A units at 7.55p STANDING CHARGE	B 6.50
		SUB TOTAL VAT AT 17.5%	C D
17 Feb–11 Apr		TOTAL DUE	E

5 Calculate:
  a the cost of 9876 units of gas at 1.525p each
  b the cost in **a**, plus a standing charge of £10.95
  c the cost in **b**, plus VAT at 17.5%.

6 Mrs Spence's gas bill has just come. Calculate entries A, B, C and D. (Entry A is 16 675 units at 1.567p each.)

WONDERFUEL GAS			
Date	Meter reading	Gas supplied	Charges (£)
	Present	Previous	Cubic ft →Units	
9 May	3906	3373	(533) →16675	A *
		STANDING CHARGE		10.94
		SUB TOTAL VAT AT 17.5%		B C
* 1.567p per unit		TOTAL DUE		D

7 Mrs Spence's next gas bill showed that she had used 14 083 units at 1.605p each, and that the standing charge was £11.50. How much had she to pay? Remember to include 17.5% VAT.

8 Here is Mr Watt's next electricity bill. Calculate entries A, B, C, D and E.

Meter reading		Charges	Amount (£)
Present	Previous		
19831	18223	A units at 7.75p STANDING CHARGE	B 6.75
		SUB TOTAL VAT at 17.5%	C D
		TOTAL DUE	E

9 The Jones family use a lot of electricity. Their bill shows 3850 units at 7.45p each, and a standing charge of £6.60. How much do they have to pay, including VAT?

10 Mrs Power has off-peak storage heaters. Here is her bill. Calculate entries A–G.

Meter reading		Charges	Amount (£)
Present	Previous		
01086	00969	Domestic A units at 7.86p	B
00831	00017	Off-peak C units at 3.05p	D
		STANDING CHARGE	7.15
		SUB TOTAL	E
		VAT at 17.5%	F
		TOTAL DUE	G

BRAINSTORMER

Some older gas meters have dials like these.

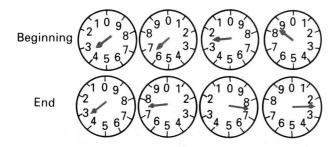

a Write down the reading on each set, and calculate the number of units used.
b Draw the dials when 1034 more units have been used.

INVESTIGATIONS

1 *Ask to see some recent telephone, gas and electricity bills for your own household. Check the calculations.*

2 *One unit of electricity on a bill is 1 kilowatt hour (kW h).*
A typical one-bar electric fire uses 1 kW to run. At 7.5p per kW h it would cost 7.5p to run the fire for one hour.

As 1 kW = 1000 watts, the cost of running a 100 W light-bulb for one hour is 7.5p ÷ 10 = 0.75p. Look at the light-bulbs at home. What are the lowest and highest wattages you can find? How much does it cost to use each of them for one hour?

What would it cost to run:
a *a 7 kW shower for one hour*
b *a 50 W black and white TV set for one hour?*
Look at other electrical appliances at home. Make a list of the number of watts they use, and the cost of running them for one hour.

HIRE PURCHASE (HP)

CLASS DISCUSSION

I'd like to buy it but I'm broke.

Ask what the HP terms are.

£67 HP AVAILABLE

No deposit...

...Just 12 weekly instalments of £6.

a What does HP mean?
b What is meant by:
   (i) deposit   (ii) instalments?
c How much will be paid altogether?
d Is this a good offer? What are the advantages and disadvantages of HP?

EXERCISE 6

1 Colin is very tempted by this HP offer.

FOR SALE £2500
HP TERMS – DEPOSIT £1000
24 MONTHLY INSTALMENTS OF £75

a How much would he have to pay:
   (i) straight away, as a deposit
   (ii) for all 24 instalments
   (iii) in total, by HP?
b How much more is this than the cash price?

In questions **2** to **7**, calculate:
a the hire purchase price
b the difference between the HP and the cash price.

2

CASSETTE PLAYER
CASH £40.00
OR 6 WEEKLY INSTALMENTS OF £7.00

3

RACING CYCLE
CASH PRICE
£117.50
or
12 MONTHLY PAYMENTS OF
£10.40

4

CAMERA
£82 CASH
or £13 DEPOSIT
+ 12 WEEKLY PAYMENTS OF £6

5

CD PLAYER
£25 DOWN
& 24 MONTHLY PAYMENTS OF £6.25.
CASH PRICE £148

6

COMPUTER
CASH £149.99
or £15 DEPOSIT
+ 12 MONTHLY
INSTALMENTS OF £11.75

7

CAR
£4999 CASH
or £999 DEPOSIT
+ 24 MONTHLY
PAYMENTS
OF £199

8

COLOUR TV
£350 CASH
or 10% DEPOSIT
+ 24 MONTHLY
INSTALMENTS
OF £14.80

Calculate:
a the deposit
b the total HP price
c the amount saved by paying cash.

9

EASY BUY
MAIL ORDER
CATALOGUE
KEYBOARD £179
or 20 weeks at £9.20
or 38 weeks at
£5.10

a Calculate the cost of each of the instalment plans.
b How much would you save in each case if you paid the cash price?
c Which method would you choose?

10

EASY BUY
MAIL ORDER CATALOGUE
VIDEO
CASH £579.99

—Easy pay
20 weeks at £29.99
or
38 weeks at £16.49
or
£59.99 deposit +
100 weeks at £5.99

a Calculate the difference between the cash price and the cost by each instalment plan.
b Which do you think is the best value?

PRACTICAL PROJECTS

1 *Select two of the following items, and find an HP plan for each: television set, video, guitar, CD player, motorbike. Use catalogues, or look in shops. Compare the HP cost with the cash price.*

2 *Imagine you are a shopkeeper selling computers at a cash price of £300. Make up an HP plan which includes a deposit and allows payments over 12 months. It has to be attractive to customers, and also cover your costs.*

CHECK-UP ON MONEY MATTERS— SAVING AND SPENDING

1 Gerry applied for this job. What is the monthly salary?

TRAVEL CLERK/ESS
SHOP & OFFICE DUTIES
SOME TRAVEL ABROAD
£9000   Tel: AIR 99

2 Sunil is an apprentice joiner. He is paid £6.70 an hour for a 38-hour working week. Calculate his weekly wage.

3 Ina has a job as a waitress, and receives £204.80 for a 40-hour week. Calculate her hourly rate of pay.

4 Computer operator Tina gets £8.80 an hour, and time-and-a-half for overtime. How much does she receive for:
  a 1 hour of overtime **b** 5 hours of overtime
  c 8 hours of work and 2 hours of overtime?

5 Simon is paid 5% commission on sales of office equipment. What is his commission for sales of:
  a £900 **b** £2300 **c** £75.20?

6 How much interest does the Dawn Building Society pay for a year's deposit of:
  a £500 **b** £1250 **c** £25?

DAWN BUILDING SOCIETY
6% Interest per annum

7 A house repair cost £250 + VAT at 17.5%. Calculate the total cost.

8

METER READING	
Present	Previous
21683	20796

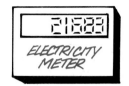

ELECTRICITY METER

Calculate:
  a the number of units used
  b the cost, at 7.75p per unit
  c the cost, when a standing charge of £9.25 is added
  d the final cost when 17.5% VAT is added.

9 Complete the calculation for this phone bill.

Call charges	£45.04
Rental charges	21.10
Sub total	
VAT at 17.5%	————
Total due	════

10

£2400 cash, or a 10% deposit and 24 monthly payments of £95.
  a Which method is dearer, and by how much?
  b How much dearer is it as a percentage of the cash price?

11 Calculate entries A, B, C, D and E in this electricity bill.

SURE SPARK ELECTRICITY			
Meter reading		Charges	Amount (£)
Present	Previous		
27158	26208	A units at 8.10p	B
		STANDING CHARGE	7.20
		SUB TOTAL	C
		VAT AT 17.5%	D
8 Oct–9 Dec		TOTAL DUE	E

4 SCALE DRAWINGS AND SIMILAR SHAPES

1 Write down the ratio of the length of line (i) to line (ii) in each pair.

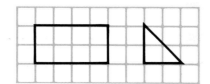

2 On squared paper, draw:
  a a rectangle with sides half as long as the one below
  b a triangle with sides twice as long as the one shown.

3 Calculate:
  a $\frac{1}{2}$ of 20 km   **b** $\frac{1}{10}$ of 70 m   **c** $\frac{1}{100}$ of 250 cm

4 Sue's garden is a rectangular shape, 12 m by 8 m. Use a scale of 1 cm to 2 m to make a scale drawing of its outline.

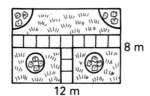

8 m

12 m

5 The scale of a house plan is 1 cm to 1 m. Calculate the actual length and breadth of a room which, on the plan, is:
  a 5 cm by 4 cm   **b** 6 cm by 2.5 cm

6 The 3-figure bearing of east from O is 090°. Write down the 3-figure bearings from O of:
  a south   **b** west
  c north   **d** south-east
  e south-west **f** north-west

7 A trawler sails 15 km north, then 20 km west.
  a Make a scale drawing, using 1 cm to 5 km.
  b How far is the trawler, in a straight line, from its starting point?

8 On the sketch map below,
  a measure the straight-line distances in cm from Oban to:
     (i) Lochgilphead   (ii) Ballachulish
     (iii) Tyndrum
  b calculate the distances in km.
  c find which place lies:
     (i) south of Oban   (ii) east of Oban
     (iii) south-east of Oban.

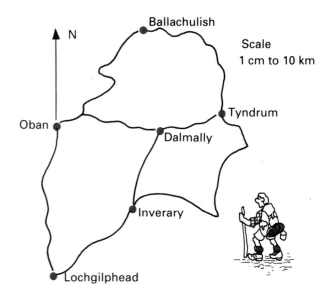

Ballachulish

Scale
1 cm to 10 km

Tyndrum

Oban

Dalmally

Inverary

Lochgilphead

SCALE MODELS AND SCALE DRAWINGS

CLASS DISCUSSION

1 In each diagram you see the real-life picture and its scale picture.

Reduction of the high-jumper

Enlargement of the silicon chip

Reduction of the sailing ship

2 Here are some maps, plans and models where scales are used.

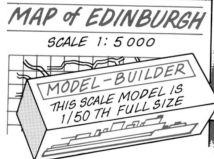

What do the various scales tell you?

EXERCISE 1

1 Measure each line. Then use the scale to calculate the distance it represents.

a |_____| 1 cm to 10 cm

b |_____| 1 cm to 1 m

c |_____| 1:10

d |____| 1:100

2 The side of each small square represents 25 cm.

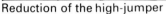

a Calculate the actual length and breadth of:
  (i) the cooker   (ii) the table
  (iii) the whole kitchen.
b How far is it from the table to the cooker?

3 This is a drawing of Sarah's desk, to a scale of 1 cm to 10 cm.

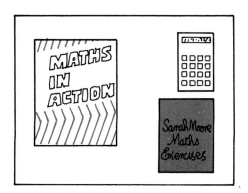

Find the actual length and breadth of her:
a desk **b** Maths book
c exercise book **d** calculator.

4 This model sailing ship was made to a scale of 1 cm to 4 m.

Find the actual:
a length of the ship
b height of each mast.

5 Find the actual height of each of these. The scale is 1 cm to 50 m.

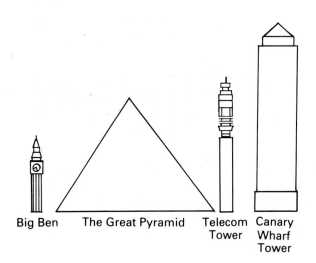

Big Ben   The Great Pyramid   Telecom Tower   Canary Wharf Tower

6 The grid lines are 100 km apart.

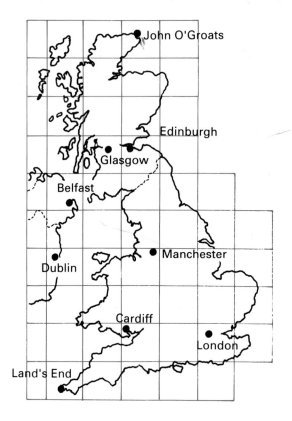

John O'Groats
Edinburgh
Glasgow
Belfast
Dublin
Manchester
Cardiff
London
Land's End

a Measure the grid to find the scale of the map. Copy and complete: 1 cm represents . . . km.
b Find the straight line distance, to the nearest 50 km, from London to each place named.

DUBLIN   EDINBURGH
BELFAST   LONDON
MANCHESTER   LANDS END
CARDIFF

EXERCISE 2

1 Copy and complete this table to find the lengths of lines for the given distances.

Real distance	80 cm	15 km	200 m
Scale	1 cm to 10 cm	1 cm to 5 km	1 cm to 20 m
Length of line			

2 This sketch shows a door with a glass panel. Use a scale of 1 cm to 25 cm to make a scale drawing of the door.

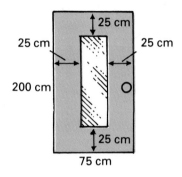

3 Use a scale of 1 cm to 2 m to make scale drawings of the front, back and ends of this sports stand.

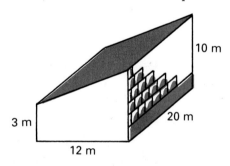

4 A plane flies in a direct line from Glasgow to Edinburgh. The distance is 70 km, and the course bears 080°.
  a Use a scale of 1 cm to 10 km to make a scale drawing.

  b What is the bearing of Glasgow from Edinburgh?

5 Dover is 70 miles from London, on a bearing of 110°. Make a scale drawing, using a scale of 1 cm to 10 miles.

6 *Bluebell* sails 12 km on a bearing of 070°, then 16 km on a bearing of 160°.
  a Make a scale drawing of the journey.
  b How far is *Bluebell* from its starting point?
  c What bearing should it follow to return home?

/ **CHALLENGE** /

List the places visited on this journey, which began at West Kilbride.

Bearing	260°	115°	205°	285°	065°
Distance (km)	19	33	27	52	20

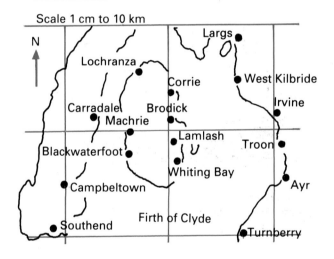

/ **PRACTICAL PROJECTS** /

1 Choose a suitable scale, and make a scale drawing of the view from above (the plan view) of one of these:

2 Find a map of your town, county or country and note its scale. Measure the distance between two places on the map and use the scale to convert this to the actual distance. Repeat this for different pairs of places, and make a table of the distances between them.

ENLARGING AND REDUCING—SCALE FACTORS

1 The scale model of the fighter plane is $\frac{1}{100}$th full size.

$\frac{1}{100}$ is the **scale factor of the reduction**.

2 a The **scale factor of the enlargement** from

(i) to (ii) $= \dfrac{\text{length of (ii)}}{\text{length of (i)}} = \dfrac{4}{2} = \dfrac{2}{1}$ or 2

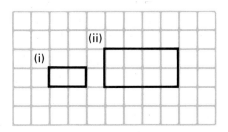

b the scale factor of the reduction from

(ii) to (i) $= \dfrac{2}{4} = \dfrac{1}{2}$

Remember: for an enlargement, scale factor > 1; for a reduction, scale factor < 1.

EXERCISE 3

1 a Copy and complete:

$\dfrac{\text{Length (ii)}}{\text{Length (i)}} = \dfrac{\dots}{\dots} = \dots$

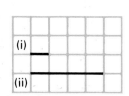

b What is the scale factor of the enlargement from (i) to (ii)?

2 a Copy and complete:

$\dfrac{\text{Length (i)}}{\text{Length (ii)}} = \dfrac{\dots}{\dots} = \dots$

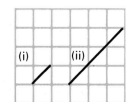

b What is the scale factor of the reduction?

3 What is the scale factor of:
a the enlargement from (i) to (ii)
b the reduction from (ii) to (i)?

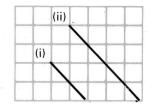

4 On squared paper, enlarge each of the shapes below by a scale factor of 2.

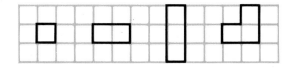

5 On squared paper, enlarge each shape below by a scale factor of 3.

6 On squared paper, reduce the shapes below by multiplying their lengths and breadths by scale factor $\frac{1}{2}$.

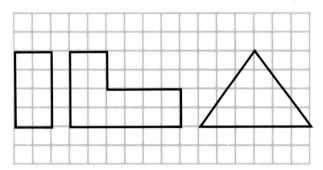

7 On squared paper, reduce or enlarge these shapes, using the scale factors shown.

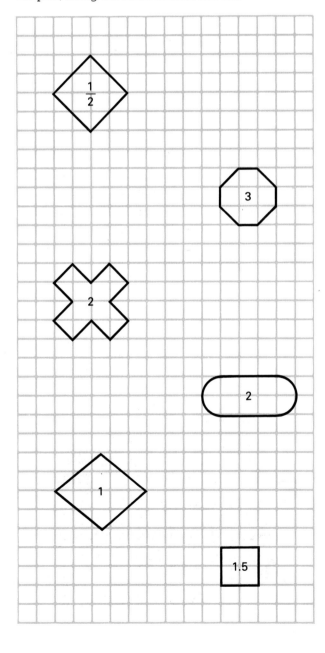

8 a Write down the ratio of the lengths of a pair of corresponding sides of these kites to find the scale factor of:
(i) the enlargement from A to B
(ii) the reduction from B to A.

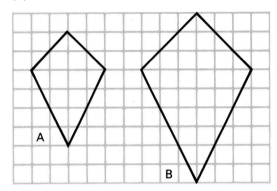

b On squared paper, reduce shape B by multiplying the lengths of its sides by scale factor $\frac{1}{3}$.

CHALLENGE

On squared paper:
a enlarge these letters by scale factor 2

b draw the letters of your first name two squares tall
c enlarge your name by scale factor 2.

CALCULATING LENGTHS USING SCALE FACTORS

Example
A model of this new rocket has to be made to a scale of 1:10.
Calculate the height of the model.

$$\text{Height of model} = \tfrac{1}{10} \times \text{real height}$$
$$= \tfrac{1}{10} \times 25\,\text{m}$$
$$= 2.5\,\text{m}$$

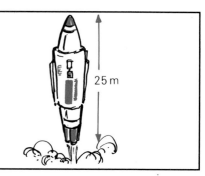

25 m

EXERCISE 4A

1 Fergus has a model of a yacht. The real yacht is 10 times larger (scale factor 10). Calculate:
  a the length of the real yacht
  b the height of the real mast.

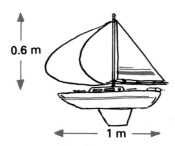

0.6 m

1 m

2 The presenter of a TV quiz is 180 cm tall. The reduction scale factor on the TV screen is $\frac{1}{10}$. What is the presenter's height on the TV screen?

3 Norma's bicycle is half the size of her mother's (scale factor $\frac{1}{2}$).
  a Her mother's bicycle is 80 cm high. How high is Norma's?
  b The diameter of her mother's bicycle wheel is 54 cm. What is the diameter of Norma's?

4 House plans are drawn to a scale of 1:100. The actual house will be 8 m high. Calculate:
  a the actual height, in cm
  b the height on the scale drawing.

5 The model car is 10 cm long. The scale factor for the real car is 40. What is the length of the real car:
  a in cm
  b in metres?

6 The model engine is 20 cm long. The scale factor for the real engine is 50. How long is the real engine:
  a in cm
  b in metres?

7 This elephant is $\frac{1}{50}$ real life size.

  a What is the scale factor of the enlargement to its real size?
  b The elephant in the picture is 6 cm long. Calculate its real length:
    (i) in cm   (ii) in metres.

8 The scale of a map is 1:100 000. A route on the map is 5 cm long. Calculate its actual length in km.

EXERCISE 4B

1 Mike has models for his train set. Their scale is $\frac{1}{100}$th real size.

  a What scale factor would be needed to enlarge them to their real size?

  b Calculate the real size of these models in cm and in metres.

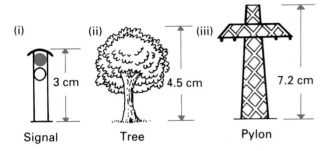

(i) Signal — 3 cm

(ii) Tree — 4.5 cm

(iii) Pylon — 7.2 cm

2 The scale factor for the larger kite is 1.5. Calculate the lengths of its diagonals.

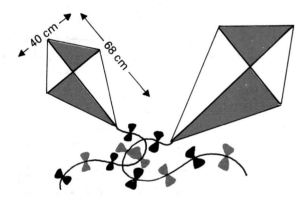

40 cm   68 cm

3 Calculate the lengths of the diagonals of a small kite which has a scale factor of 0.5 to the marked kite in question **2**.

4 The Pop Poster shop sells photographs 10 cm by 8 cm in size, and enlargements 40 cm by 32 cm.

  a What is the scale factor of the enlargement?

  b What are the dimensions of a new poster, with scale factor 10, made from the photograph?

5 A model racing car (scale 1:50) is 8 cm long.

  a Calculate the length of the real car, in metres.

  b The real car is 2 m wide. Calculate the width of the model.

6 Sita is an architect, designing a new block of offices. She begins with a 1:100 scale model.

  a The length and breadth of the model are 120 cm by 40 cm. Calculate the length and breadth of the office block, in metres.

  b The height of the actual block is to be 25 m. Calculate the height of the model, in cm.

INVESTIGATION

Investigate the scales of construction kits of cars, planes, ships, etc., which are sold in toy or model shops. Write a report.

SIMILAR SHAPES

Two objects are **similar** if they have the **same shape**. One is an enlargement of the other.

Illustrations
a The two 5-a-side shields.
b The picture on the slide and the enlarged picture on the screen.

Example
Show that the two dominoes are similar by checking that:
a corresponding angles are equal
b ratios of corresponding sides are equal.

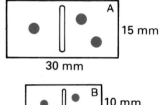

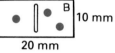

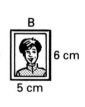

a All the angles are right angles.

b $\dfrac{\text{Length of A}}{\text{Length of B}} = \dfrac{30\,\text{mm}}{20\,\text{mm}} = \frac{3}{2}$ or 1.5

$\dfrac{\text{Breadth of A}}{\text{Breadth of B}} = \dfrac{15\,\text{mm}}{10\,\text{mm}} = \frac{3}{2}$ or 1.5

$\left.\right\}$ equal ratios, scale factor 1.5

So the dominoes are similar.

EXERCISE 5A

1 Which of these dolls does not look similar to the others?

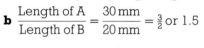

(i)   (ii)   (iii)   (iv)   (v)

2 Jack is having fun in the Hall of Mirrors. Two of his images are similar. Which two?

(i)   (ii)   (iii)   (iv)

3 Newtown High School's photographer offers two sizes of photograph. Are they similar?

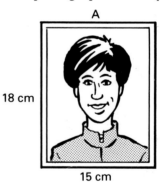

a Check corresponding angles.

b Copy and complete:

(i) $\dfrac{\text{Height of A}}{\text{Height of B}} = \dfrac{\ldots}{\ldots} = \ldots$

(ii) $\dfrac{\text{Width of A}}{\text{Width of B}} = \dfrac{\ldots}{\ldots} = \ldots$

c What is the scale factor of:
(i) the enlargement
(ii) the reduction?

4 Rashid compares the school's 11-a-side and 5-a-side goals. Are they similar?

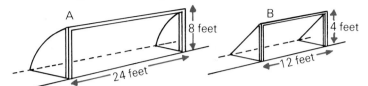

A 8 feet 24 feet

B 4 feet 12 feet

a Check corresponding angles.

b (i) $\dfrac{\text{Height of A}}{\text{Height of B}} = \dfrac{\ldots}{\ldots} = \ldots$

(ii) $\dfrac{\text{Width of A}}{\text{Width of B}} = \dfrac{\ldots}{\ldots} = \ldots$

c What is: (i) the enlargement scale factor
(ii) the reduction scale factor?

5 According to Marie, the school hockey pitch measures 54 yards by 90 yards. A full-size pitch is 60 yards by 100 yards. Are the two pitches similar? Explain your answer.

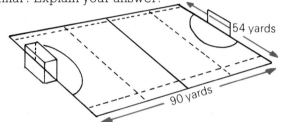

54 yards
90 yards

6 These rugs are similar.
a What is the *enlargement* scale factor?
b Calculate x.

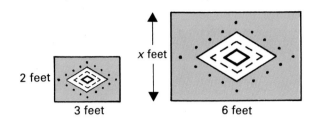

2 feet
3 feet
x feet
6 feet

7 At Tom's school, the indoor and outdoor football pitches are similar.
a What is the *reduction* scale factor?
b Calculate x.

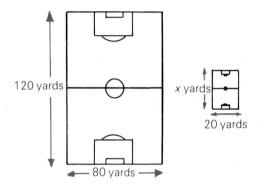

120 yards
80 yards
x yards
20 yards

EXERCISE 5B

1 *Measure* the lengths and breadths of the windows and doors in **a** and **b**, and the fronts of **c** and **d**. Check angles and scale factors (ratios of corresponding sides) to decide which pairs of outlines are similar.

a (i) (ii)

b (i) (ii)

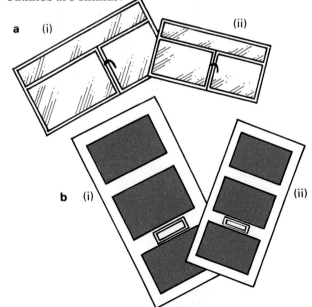

c (i) (ii)

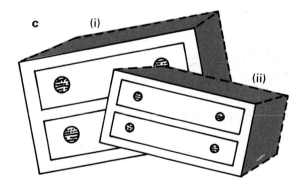

d (i) (ii)

2 a Are the inside and outside of the picture frame similar? Remember to check angles and ratios of sides.

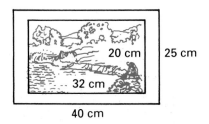

20 cm
25 cm
32 cm
40 cm

b If they are similar, what is the enlargement scale factor?

3 Is the goal area similar to the penalty area of this football pitch? Give a reason for your answer.

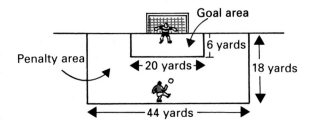

Goal area
6 yards
Penalty area
20 yards
18 yards
44 yards

4

Clear View sell two sizes of similar oval mirrors.

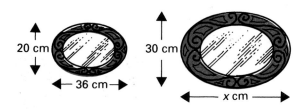

20 cm
36 cm
30 cm
x cm

Calculate:
a the enlargement scale factor **b** x.

5 These table tops are similar. Calculate:
a the reduction scale factor **b** x.

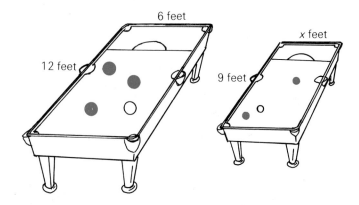

6 feet
x feet
12 feet
9 feet

6 Gill is showing her holiday photographs. Calculate:
a the enlargement scale factor from slide to screen
b the height of the picture on the screen.

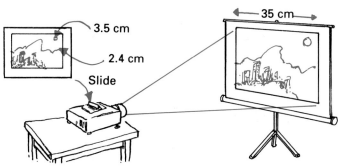

35 cm
3.5 cm
2.4 cm
Slide

7 The flying ducks on Fenella's living-room wall are similar.

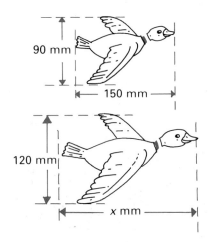

90 mm
150 mm
120 mm
x mm

a Calculate x.
b The larger duck's beak is 36 mm long. Calculate the length of the smaller duck's beak.

INVESTIGATIONS

1 The capital letter Z and the small z are similar to each other on most computers and keyboards. Which other letters are like this?

2 a There are several sets of 'similar' objects hiding in this kitchen. How many can you find? Write them down.

b Can you think of any more sets of similar objects that you might find at home?

PRACTICAL PROJECTS

1 Measure the lengths and breadths of the faces of a videotape case and a music cassette case. Are any of the faces similar?

2 Measure your actual height and your height in a photograph. Calculate the scale factor of the enlargement or reduction. Repeat this for the width of your shoulders. Is the scale factor the same?

BRAINSTORMERS

1

Val makes three hand towels and one bath towel from a strip of material.

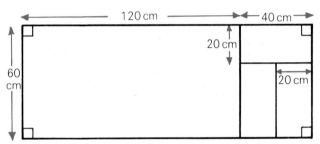

a Are the hand towels congruent (exactly the same shape and size)?
b Is the bath towel similar to a hand towel?

2 Alan calculates these ratios of sides.

$$\frac{\text{Width of } A}{\text{Width of } B} = \frac{48 \, mm}{50 \, mm} = 0.96$$

$$\frac{\text{Height of } A}{\text{Height of } B} = \frac{80 \, mm}{30 \, mm} = 2.67.$$

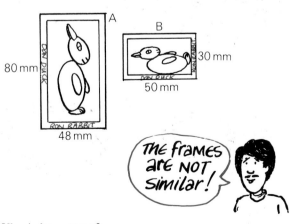

THE frames are NOT similar!

Why is he wrong?

SIMILAR TRIANGLES

In these two triangles:
 (i) corresponding angles are equal
 (ii) ratios of corresponding sides are equal.
So the triangles are similar.

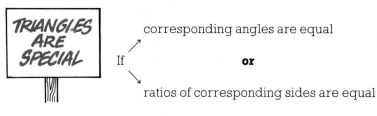

Scale factor: → $\frac{1}{3}$
3 ←

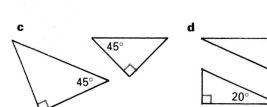

TRIANGLES
ARE
SPECIAL

If   corresponding angles are equal

or

ratios of corresponding sides are equal

the triangles are similar.

Example
a Explain why these triangles are similar.
b Find *x*.

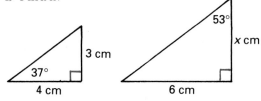

53°

x cm

3 cm

37°

4 cm

6 cm

a The missing angles are 53° and 37°.
   So corresponding angles are equal, and the
   triangles are similar.
b The scale factor is $\frac{6}{4} = \frac{3}{2}$.
   So $x = \frac{3}{2} \times 3 = 4.5$.

EXERCISE 6A

1 List the angles in each triangle. Then say whether
or not the triangles in each pair are similar.

a

40°   40°

b

30°

60°

c

45°

45°

d

70°

20°

e

65°

35°

f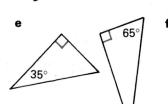

44°

46°

2 The door wedges are similar.
   a What is the enlargement scale factor?
   b Calculate *x*.

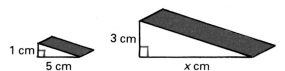

1 cm

5 cm

3 cm

x cm

3 The flag support triangles are similar.
   a What is the reduction scale factor?
   b Calculate *x*.

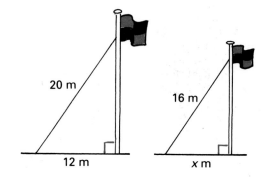

20 m

12 m

16 m

x m

4 Ruth has a 30°, 60°, 90° set-square. Her teacher has a 30°, 60°, 90° blackboard set-square.

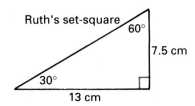

Ruth's set-square

60°
7.5 cm
30°
13 cm

a Why are the two set-squares similar?
b The enlargement scale factor is 4. Calculate the lengths of the sides about the right angle on the blackboard set-square.

5 a Why are these two triangles similar?

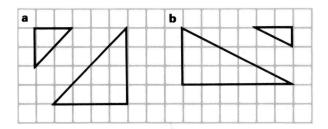

6 cm   2 cm
20°

70°
4 cm

b Calculate: (i) the reduction scale factor
(ii) the enlargement scale factor.

6 Colin is drawing up plans for an escalator. BC = 25 cm.

C
A   B
Scale 1:50

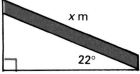

x m
22°

a On his drawing, what is the size of:
(i) ∠B   (ii) ∠C?
b Calculate the length x m of the escalator.

EXERCISE 6B

---

1 In which of these pairs are the triangles similar?

a   **b**

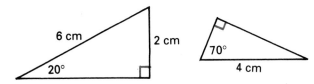

c   **d**

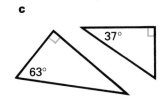

37°

63°

19°

71°

e   **f**

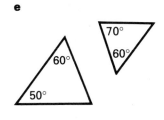

70°
60°
60°
50°

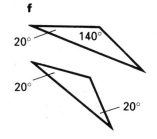

20°   140°

20°

20°

2

DIY Shelf Shop sells two sizes of similar brackets.

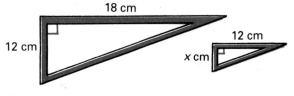

18 cm

12 cm

12 cm
x cm

Calculate:
a the reduction scale factor   **b** x.

3

The corner shelves are equiangular.
(Corresponding angles are equal.)

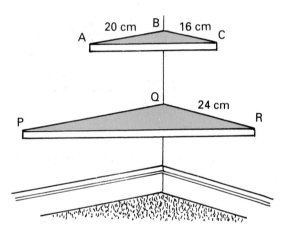

Calculate:
a the enlargement scale factor.
b the length of PQ.

4 The sails are similar, $\angle$ A corresponding to $\angle$ D.

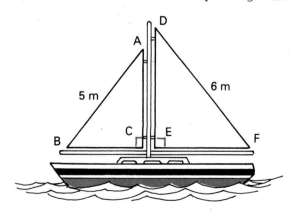

a What is the enlargement scale factor from
△ABC to △DEF?
b If BC = 2.5 m, calculate the length of EF.

5

Select-a-shed sell two different sizes of shed. The
angle of slope of each roof is the same.

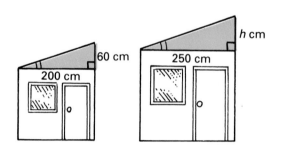

a Why are the shaded parts similar?
b Calculate h.

6 a Why are these triangles similar?

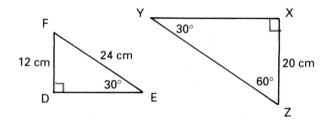

b Which side in △XYZ corresponds to:
(i) DE (ii) EF (iii) DF (opposite equal
angles)?
c What is the enlargement scale factor?
d Calculate the length of YZ.

CHECK-UP ON SCALE DRAWINGS AND SIMILAR SHAPES

1 The lawn in Chris's garden is a 20 m × 12 m rectangle. The circular flower bed in the centre has a radius of 4 m.

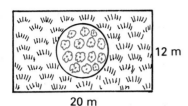

Use a scale of 1 cm to 2 m to make a scale drawing of the lawn and the flower bed.

2 What is the scale factor of:
  a the enlargement from (i) to (ii)
  b the reduction from (ii) to (i)?

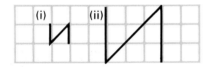

3 On squared paper:
  a enlarge each shape below by scale factor 2
  b reduce each shape by scale factor ½.

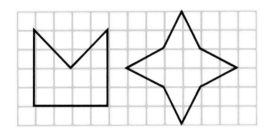

4 The scale factor of this enlargement is 3.

Calculate:
  a the length and breadth of the larger picture
  b the area of each picture.

5 The scale of a builder's plan is 1:1000. Calculate the actual length of a building shown as 5 cm long on the plan. Give your answer in: **a** cm   **b** m.

6 Instaheat make two sizes of radiator. The larger has a scale factor of 2 from the smaller.

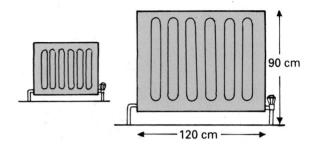

  a What is the reduction scale factor from the larger to the smaller radiator?
  b Calculate the length and breadth of the smaller one.

7 Andrew's model car is made to a scale of 1:50.

  a The model is 7 cm long. Calculate the length of the car, in metres.
  b The actual car is 1.8 m high. Calculate the height of the model, in cm.

8 a Explain why these two triangles are similar.

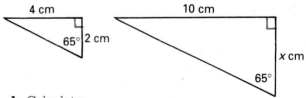

  b Calculate:
    (i) the scale factor of the enlargement   (ii) x.

9 These two goalmouths are similar.

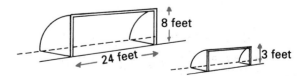

  a What is the reduction scale factor?
  b Calculate:
    (i) the length of the shorter goal line
    (ii) the area of each goalmouth.

REVIEW: LETTERS AND NUMBERS 1

USING LETTERS AND NUMBERS 1

1 There are x £1 coins in each bag. What is the value of x?

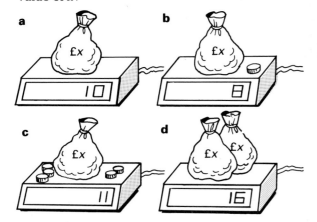

2 Find the value of y in each picture.

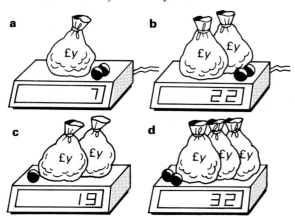

3 Which numbers do these letters stand for?

a $a \rightarrow +5 \rightarrow 8$

b $b \rightarrow -3 \rightarrow 6$

c $c \rightarrow \times 5 \rightarrow 20$

d $d \rightarrow \div 2 \rightarrow 8$

e $e \rightarrow -7 \rightarrow 0$

f $f \rightarrow \times 9 \rightarrow 72$

4 Write in a shorter form:
   a $x+x$ **b** $5y+y$ **c** $3u-2u$
   d $4p-3p$ **e** $x+x-x$ **f** $2x-2x$
   g $5x-x+6$ **h** $y+2+y$ **i** $2t+1-t$
   j $x+y+x$ **k** $x+y-x$ **l** $x+y+x-y$

5 Give the total number of marbles in each set of bags.

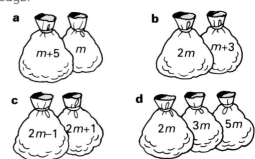

6 a Which numbers do the letters stand for in the sequences in this spreadsheet?
  b What numbers should be in **F1** and **A6**?

	A	**B**	**C**	**D**	**E**
1	2	3	a	5	6
2	4	b	8	10	12
3	6	9	12	c	18
4	d	12	16	20	24
5	10	15	20	25	e

Write these in shorter form:

7 a $m+m+m$ **b** $n+2n+4n$
   c $2x+4x-x$ **d** $y+y-y$
   e $4x+2x+5$ **f** $6+8y+2$
   g $2a+1+2a$ **h** $5+3x+2$

8 a $x+1-x$ **b** $1+y+y$
   c $3z-z+3z$ **d** $t-t+t$
   e $9d-7d-2d$ **f** $5+5x-5-5x$
   g $y+y+z+z$ **h** $m+n-m+n$

9 Each lorry is 6.5 m long, and each car is t m long. What length is this queue of traffic?

10 Simplify:
   a $x+x+x+x$ **b** $4y+3y+2y$
   c $3k+2k+5k$ **d** $m+m-2m$
   e $2p+3-p-3$ **f** $2x+y+x-y$
   g $3c+d+c+d$ **h** $2u-u+2v-v$

USING LETTERS AND NUMBERS 2

1 Find the missing entries in these spreadsheets.

a

	A
1	2
2	4
3	6
12	
13	
n	

b

	A
1	5
2	10
3	15
20	
21	
x	

c

	A
1	2
2	3
3	4
23	
24	
y	

2 a How many hands on:
   (i) 3 clocks
   (ii) 5 clocks
   (iii) c clocks?

b How many points on:
   (i) 1 star
   (ii) 5 stars
   (iii) s stars?

c How many pencils in:
   (i) 5 packets
   (ii) p packets?

d How many grams in:
   (i) 5 weights   (ii) w weights?

e How many wheels on:
   (i) 3 cars   (ii) c cars?

3 Find the value of:
   a $5x$, when $x = 2$ **b** $2y$, when $y = 5$
   c $y+4$, when $y = 3$ **d** $5t+1$, when $t = 2$
   e $10-x$, when $x = 5$ **f** $6+2m$, when $m = 1$
   g $t \times t$, when $t = 10$ **h** $u \times u$, when $u = 1$

4 Copy and complete these tables:

a

x	1	2	3	4
$8x$				

b

y	8	10	12	14
$y-4$				

c

u	1	2	4	6
$u \times u$				

d

v	5	8	11	14
$2v+1$				

5

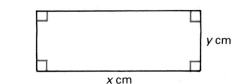

y cm

x cm

a Write down a formula for the perimeter P cm.
b Calculate P when $x = 3$ and $y = 10$.

6

Copy and complete this table for the sequence of triangles of matches.

Number of triangles	1	2	3	4	5		n
Number of matches in perimeter							
Number of matches in shape							

7 a One £1 coin and x 1p coins. How many pence altogether?
   b T triangles and R rectangles, all separate. How many sides altogether?

8 $x = 3$ and $y = 2$. Find the values of:
   a $x+4$ **b** $2x$ **c** $3x+1$ **d** $y-2$
   e $5y$ **f** $3y+4$ **g** $x+y$ **h** xy
   i x^2 **j** y^2 **k** $5xy$ **l** $4x+6y$

USING LETTERS AND NUMBERS 3

1 Write in a shorter form:
  a $4a+2a$ **b** $x+x+x$ **c** $3y-y$
  d $t \times t$ **e** $2 \times n \times n$ **f** $m+m+1$

2 Write down the length of each cane below. Lengths are in centimetres.

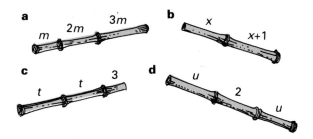

3 Find expressions for the unmarked snakes and ladders.

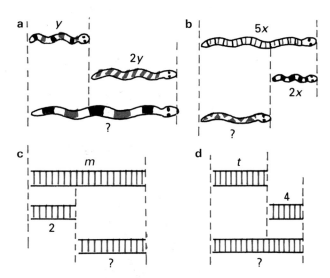

4 Find the output from each machine for each of the two inputs shown.

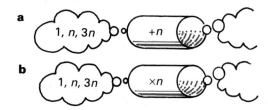

5 $a = 2$, $b = 3$ and $c = 1$. Find the value of:
  a $5a$ **b** $2b+1$ **c** $3b+2c$ **d** a^2+b^2

6 $u = 1$, $v = 3$, $w = 5$. Find the value of:
  a $u+v+w$ **b** uvw **c** u^2 **d** v^2
  e w^2 **f** $4uv$ **g** $2vw$ **h** $2v^2$

7 These shapes are made of squares and rectangles. Find a formula for each perimeter P cm, and each area A cm².

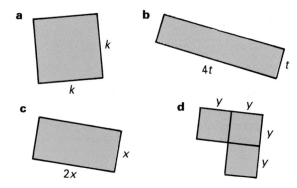

8 Find expressions for the perimeters and areas of these shapes, which are based on rectangles and squares. The lengths are in cm.

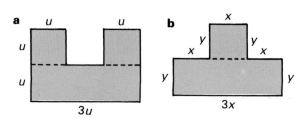

9 Find the areas of these rectangular gardens. Lengths are in metres.

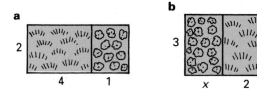

10 Write these without brackets:
  a $2(x+1)$ **b** $3(y+2)$ **c** $4(z+3)$
  d $5(t-1)$ **e** $2(u-2)$ **f** $3(v-4)$
  g $2(5+x)$ **h** $3(1+y)$ **i** $4(4+t)$
  j $6(a+7)$ **k** $8(b-2)$ **l** $9(c-6)$

11 Find a formula for:
  a the length, L cm, of all the edges
  b the area, A cm², of all the faces
  c the volume, V cm³, of the cuboid.

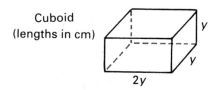

Cuboid (lengths in cm)

POSITIVE AND NEGATIVE NUMBERS

1 Copy and complete these scales:

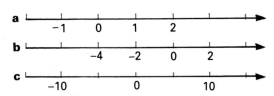

2 Some mid-January night temperatures:
Cardiff $-1°C$; Glasgow $-3°C$; Bristol $-2°C$;
Manchester $-4°C$; Dundee $-6°C$.
a Which place is: (i) warmest (ii) coldest?
b List the temperatures in order, coldest first.

3 a Which number is:
(i) 2 greater than -1
(ii) 2 less than -1?

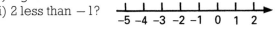

b Which numbers shown on the number line
are: (i) less than -3 (ii) greater than -1?

4 Arrange each set of numbers in order, with the
smallest number first in each.

5 Write down calculations for these walks.

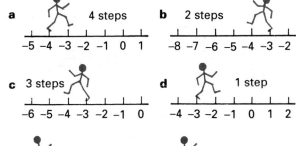

6 Copy and complete:

a $3+1 = \ldots$	**b** $3+1 = \ldots$
$2+1 = \ldots$	$3+0 = \ldots$
$1+1 = \ldots$	$3+(-1) = \ldots$
$0+1 = \ldots$	$3+(-2) = \ldots$
$-1+1 = \ldots$	$3+(-3) = \ldots$
$-2+1 = \ldots$	$3+(-4) = \ldots$
$\ldots\ldots$	$\ldots\ldots$
$-6+1 = \ldots$	$3+(-6) = \ldots$
$-7+1 = \ldots$	$3+(-7) = \ldots$

7 Write down the next four terms in this number
pattern, and calculate the values of all eight
terms: $4+2, 4+1, 4+0, 4+(-1), \ldots$

8 Calculate:

a $2+(-3)$	**b** $3-5$	**c** $-3+7$
d $8+(-6)$	**e** $7+(-8)$	**f** $2-3$
g $-3-7$	**h** $6+(-2)$	**i** $-3+(-3)$
j $-9+8$	**k** $4+(-2)$	**l** $7+(-5)$
m $-3+(-5)$	**n** $-7+(-7)$	**o** $8+(-8)$

9 Which numbers go in the circles?

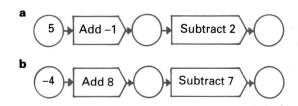

10 Use the 'cover up' method to solve these
equations:

a $x+2 = 1$	**b** $y+5 = 2$	**c** $z-2 = -2$
d $t+1 = 0$	**e** $u-3 = -4$	**f** $3-v = -2$

11 a Copy this diagram on squared paper.

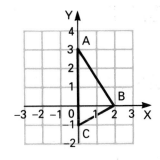

b Complete ABCD so that the y-axis is an axis of
symmetry.
c What shape is ABCD?
d Write down the coordinates of D.

12 $p = -1, q = -2, r = -3$. Calculate the values of:
a $p+q$ **b** $q+r$ **c** $r+p$ **d** $p+q+r$

13 A square tile has vertices at P(1, 1), Q(-1, 1),
R(-1, -1) and S.
a Find the coordinates of S.
b The tile moves parallel to the x-axis, until QR
is on the y-axis. Write down the coordinates of
the new positions of P, Q, R and S.

LOOKING BACK

1 What can you measure with each of these?

2 a How many minutes are there in:
(i) 1 hour   (ii) $\frac{1}{2}$ hour   (iii) $\frac{1}{4}$ hour
(iv) $1\frac{1}{2}$ hours?
 b What fraction of an hour is:
(i) 30 minutes   (ii) 45 minutes
(iii) 10 minutes?

3 a Write down the distance from:
(i) Capital City to Eastport
(ii) Northport to Southport.
 b Which town is farthest from Capital City?

Capital city			
28	North-port		
38	66	South-port	
29	51	42	East-port

4 How much time is there between the times on:
 a watches (i) and (ii)
 b watches (ii) and (iii)
 c watches (i) and (iii)?

(i)   (ii)   (iii)

5 Gregor was training for a cross-country cycling contest. This graph shows his run from home and back again.

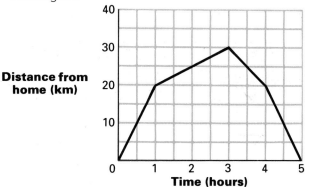

Distance from home (km)

Time (hours)

 a How far from home was he after:
(i) 1 hour   (ii) $4\frac{1}{2}$ hours?
 b (i) When was he farthest from home?
(ii) How far from his home was this?

6 How long did each of these journeys take?

	a	b	c	d
Depart	11.10 am	noon	2.20 pm	4.45 pm
Arrive	11.50 am	1.15 pm	3 pm	5.15 pm

7 Do you know roughly . . .
 a How long a top sprinter takes to run 100 metres?
 b How far a car can travel on a motorway in 1 hour, without exceeding the speed limit?
 c How long a top-class runner takes to run a marathon (26.2 miles)?
 d The speeds, in miles per hour, that Inter-City trains can reach?
 e When you would have to leave home, in order to reach school, 5 km away, by 9 o'clock:
(i) if you were walking
(ii) if you were cycling?

EXERCISE 1A (READING GRAPHS)

1

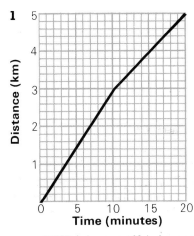

Geoff cycled 5 km to the games field.
a How far had he gone after:
(i) 10 minutes
(ii) 15 minutes?
b How long did he take for:
(i) the whole journey
(ii) the first 3 km
(iii) the last 2 km?

c (i) Which part of his journey was faster?
(ii) Is the slope of the graph steeper here?

2 Time to go home! Sandra lives 8 km from the school.

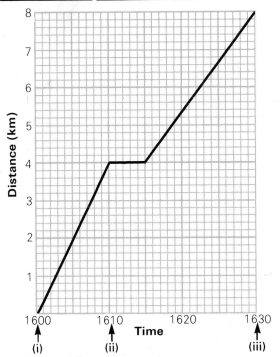

a What time does the bus leave the school?
b What time does Sandra leave the bus?
c What happens between 16 10 and 16 15?
d How far is the bus from the school at 16 10?
e When is the bus 2 km from the school?
f Which part of the journey is fastest?
g Describe the journey like this: 'The bus went quite quickly for 10 minutes, then . . .'

3 Frank and Pete decided to do some training. They ran, and they walked, then they took the bus home.

a Which parts of the graph go with running, walking and travelling by bus?

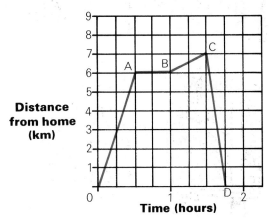

b For how long did they rest?
c During the first $\frac{1}{2}$ hour:
(i) how far did they go
(ii) what was their speed, in km/h?

4 This graph shows Steve's trip to the library and back.

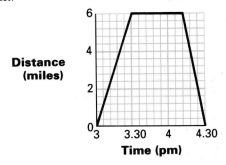

a How far away is the library?
b How long did he take to get there?
c How long did he spend at the library?
d How far did he travel altogether?
e How long was he away from home?
f Which journey was quicker—going to the library, or going home?

EXERCISE 1B (DRAWING GRAPHS)

1

Tony walks 6 km in 70 minutes at a steady pace.
a Copy these axes and scales onto squared paper.

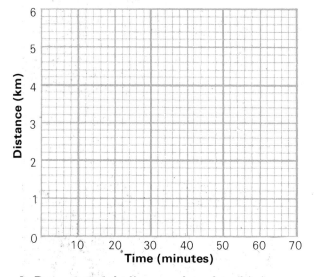

b Draw a straight-line graph to show his journey.
c Use your graph to estimate:
  (i) how far he walks in 40 minutes
  (ii) how long he takes for 4 km.

2 Janet is planning her training runs. In the first 20 minutes she will run 4 km, and in the next 20 minutes she will run 2 km, at steady speeds.
a Use the same axes and scales as in question **1** to draw a graph of her run on another diagram.
b How far does she run altogether?
c How far does she run in the first:
  (i) 10 minutes (ii) 30 minutes?
d Which part of the graph is steeper? What does this tell you about her speeds?

3 William cycles from home to the bicycle shop and back. The 6 km journey to the shop takes 40 minutes. He waits in the shop for 10 minutes, and then returns home in 20 minutes.
a Draw a graph of this information. Use the same scales and axes as in question **1**.
b After what times was he 3 km from home?

PRACTICAL PROJECT

Time yourself or a friend over 100 m when walking, jogging and sprinting. Draw straight-line graphs of all three on the same sheet of squared paper. Explain why the graphs might not give a true picture in each case.

DISTANCE—HOW FAR?

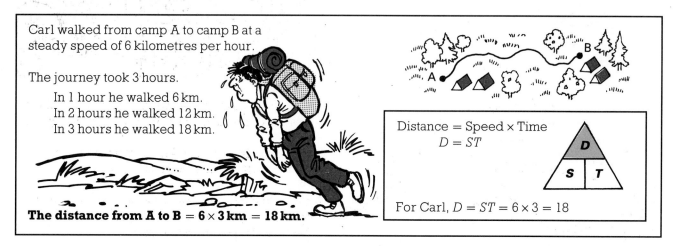

Carl walked from camp A to camp B at a steady speed of 6 kilometres per hour.

The journey took 3 hours.
    In 1 hour he walked 6 km.
    In 2 hours he walked 12 km.
    In 3 hours he walked 18 km.

The distance from A to B = 6×3 **km** = **18 km.**

Distance = Speed × Time
$D = ST$

For Carl, $D = ST = 6 \times 3 = 18$

EXERCISE 2

1 Use the formula $D = ST$ to find the distance you would travel in:
  a 5 hours at 6 km/h   **b** 4 hours at 8 km/h
  c 3 hours at 30 km/h   **d** 7 hours at 10 km/h

2 How far could you travel, in miles:

  a walking,
     at 3 mph
     for 4 hours

  b cycling,
     at 12 mph
     for 2 hours

  c running,
     at 7 mph
     for 3 hours

  d driving,
     at 48 mph
     for 5 hours?

3 Find the length of each journey in km or miles.

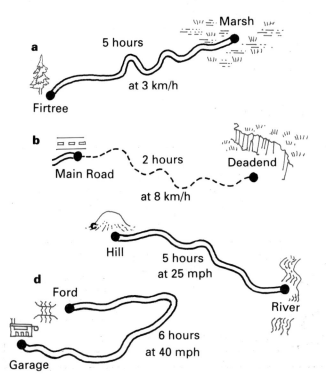

a Marsh — 5 hours — at 3 km/h — Firtree

b Main Road — 2 hours — at 8 km/h — Deadend

Hill — 5 hours at 25 mph — River

d Ford — Garage — 6 hours at 40 mph

4 Calculate the distances travelled on the journeys in this table.

	a	b	c	d
Speed	30 km/h	75 km/h	24 mph	60 mph
Time (h)	5	6	3	9

5

a Ron jogs at 12 km/h. How far in 2 hours?

b The lorry averages 40 mph. How far in 5 hours?

c The racing car can average 245 km/h. How far in 3 hours?

d Marie cycles at 12 m/s. How far in 20 seconds?

6 A bus takes 3 hours, travelling at 30 mph, to reach the bus station. How far has it travelled?

7 Cycling at an average speed of 18 km/h, Khalid reaches home in 5 hours. How far does he cycle?

8 Seiji travels to work in $\frac{1}{2}$ hour, at an average speed of 24 km/h. How far is it to his work?

9 Migrating swallows can keep up an average of 20 mph for 45 hours without stopping for food. How far do they fly in this time?

67

10 How far can Concorde fly in $3\frac{1}{2}$ hours at an average speed of 2300 km/h?

11 Find the length of each bus journey in this table.

	a	b	c
Depart	10.00	14.30	15.00
Arrive	13.00	16.30	16.30
Average speed	25 km/h	38 km/h	36 km/h

12 At an average speed of 55 km/h the *QE2* crossed the Atlantic in 5 days 4 hours. What was the length of the crossing, to the nearest 100 km?

13 a Calculate the distances between the villages.

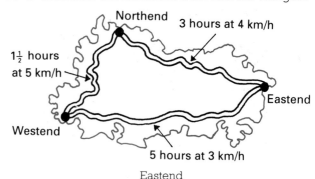

b Copy the table, and fill in the distances.

Eastend	
	Westend
	Northend

AVERAGE SPEED—HOW FAST?

Linda hiked 12 km from camp B to camp C in 4 hours.

12 km in 4 hours,
so 3 km in 1 hour.

Her average speed $= \dfrac{12}{4}$ **km/h = 3 km/h.**

$$\text{Speed} = \frac{\text{Distance}}{\text{Time}}$$

$$S = \frac{D}{T}$$

For Linda, $S = \dfrac{D}{T} = \dfrac{12}{4} = 3$

EXERCISE 3A

1 Use the formula $S = \dfrac{D}{T}$ to calculate the speeds for these journeys:

a 12 km in 3 h

b 40 km in 5 h

c 160 miles in 4 h

d 180 miles in 2 h

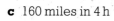

2 Calculate the average speeds for these journeys.

	a	b	c	d	e	f
Distance (km)	20	15	14	5	22	50
Time (h)	4	3	7	5	2	5

3 Calculate the average speed in miles per hour (mph) of a plane flying from:
   a London to Cork, 430 miles in 2 hours
   b Newcastle to Milan, 1000 miles in 4 hours
   c Edinburgh to Hong Kong, 10 000 miles in 20 hours.

4 a Find the average speed of each runner in metres per second (m/s).

100 m in 5 s   180 m in 6 s   200 m in 8 s

b Arrange them in order, with the fastest runner first.

5 Calculate the average speeds for these journeys:

a BY CONCORDE
From London to New York 5520 km in 3 HOURS

b BY MOTORWAY
From Birmingham to Newcastle 332 km in 4 HOURS

6 Calculate the average speeds for these journeys—don't forget the units (km/h, mph, m/s):
a 50 km in 2 hours
b 300 miles in 5 hours
c 100 metres in 10 seconds
d 22 km in 4 hours
e 2800 km in 4 hours
f 48 000 km in 6 hours

7 Whales take 64 days to swim 6000 miles from the Mexican Coast to their feeding grounds in the Bering Sea. Calculate their average speed in miles per day.

EXERCISE 3B

Example
A journey of 80 km takes 1 hour 35 minutes. Calculate the average speed.

35 minutes $= \frac{35}{60} = 0.58$ hour, correct to 2 decimal places.

So 1 hour 35 minutes = 1.58 hour (key 1 $+$ 35 $\div$ 60 $=$).

$S = \frac{D}{T} = \frac{80}{1.58} = 51$ km/h, to the nearest whole number.

1 Write these times in decimal form:
a $1\frac{1}{2}$ hours **b** $2\frac{1}{4}$ hours **c** $\frac{3}{4}$ hour
REMINDER ¼=0.25 ½=0.5 ¾=0.75

2 Using the times in decimal form, calculate each person's speed.

a 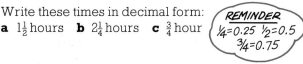 6 km, Hill, Hut
(i) Armando took $1\frac{1}{2}$ h
(ii) Emma took $2\frac{1}{2}$ h
(iii) Kirsty took $1\frac{1}{4}$ h

b Forest 8 km Bridge
(i) Heather took $1\frac{1}{4}$ h
(ii) Claire took $2\frac{1}{2}$ h
(iii) Waheed took $\frac{1}{2}$ h

3 Jane cycled 105 km in 3 hours 30 minutes. What was her average speed?

4 Robin walked $16\frac{1}{2}$ km in 2 hours 45 minutes. Calculate his average speed.

5 Give these in hours in decimal form, correct to 2
decimal places:
a 8 minutes   **b** 44 minutes   **c** 1 hour 19 minutes.

6 Calculate the average speeds for these journeys,
to the nearest km/h:
a 36 km in 1 hour 4 minutes
b 234 km in 2 hours 53 minutes.

7 A bus service runs between East Port and West
Port.
An express bus leaves East Port at 10 00 hours,
and arrives at West Port at 10 30 hours.
A slow bus leaves West Port at 10 00 hours, and
arrives at East Port at 11 00 hours.

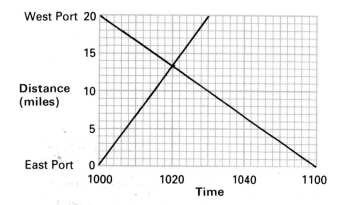

a How far is it from East Port to West Port?
b How long did each bus take to complete the
journey?
c Calculate the average speed of each bus.
d What is the connection between the slope of the
line and the speed of the bus?

8 a Mrs Dean drives from Glasgow to Liverpool in
3 hours 30 minutes. Calculate her average
speed.

Glasgow   Distances in km

343	Liverpool			
341	56	Manchester		
595	264	277	Cardiff	
634	317	296	248	London

b Next morning she continues her journey, and
drives to Cardiff in 2 hours 45 minutes.
Calculate her average speed for this part of the
journey.

9 The radius of the Earth is 6400 km. An aircraft
circles the Earth 50 km above the surface.
Calculate:
a the radius of the aircraft's circular path
b the distance it flies, in one complete circuit, to
the nearest 100 km
c its average speed if it completes a circuit in
18 hours.

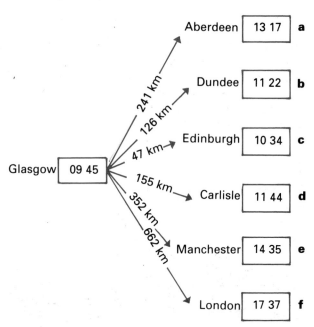

/ **CHALLENGE**

*Calculate the average speeds, to the nearest km/h,
for these journeys.*

Aberdeen | 13 17 | **a**

Dundee | 11 22 | **b**

241 km
126 km
Edinburgh | 10 34 | **c**
47 km

Glasgow | 09 45

155 km
Carlisle | 11 44 | **d**
352 km

Manchester | 14 35 | **e**
662 km

London | 17 37 | **f**

TIME—HOW LONG?

Rory aimed to walk from camp C to camp D at an average speed of 5 km/h.

5 km every hour, so 10 km in 2 hours.

His time for 5 km $= \dfrac{10}{5}$ **h = 2 h.**

NEARLY THERE

$$\text{Time} = \frac{\text{Distance}}{\text{Speed}}$$

$$T = \frac{D}{S}$$

For Rory, $T = \dfrac{D}{S} = \dfrac{10}{5} = 2$

EXERCISE 4

1 Use the formula $T = \dfrac{D}{S}$ to calculate the time for each journey:
  a Mandy cycles 20 km at 10 km/h
  b Ali drives 200 miles at 50 mph
  c Damien walks 16 miles at 4 mph
  d Sue runs 12 km at 8 km/h.

2 Calculate the times for these journeys.

	a	b	c	d
Distance	120 km	36 km	200 miles	1350 miles
Speed	30 km/h	9 km/h	25 mph	450 mph

3 How long would each of these journeys take?
  a walking 14 km at 7 km/h
  b driving 180 miles at 30 mph
  c flying 2000 km at 500 km/h
  d running 400 m at 8 m/s
  e crawling 8 cm at 2 cm/s
  f skiing 500 m at 10 m/s
  g driving at 25 mph for 75 miles
  h walking at 8 km/h for 10 km
  i running at 10 mph for 15 miles
  j rolling at 2 m/s for 7 m

4 When will these buses reach their destinations?

BLUE BUSES
Depart 10am
50 km at an
average speed
of 25 km/h

GREEN LINE
Depart 3.30pm
100 miles at an
average speed
of 40 mph

RED COACHES
Depart 11.15am
150 km at an
average speed
of 50 km/h

5 Use the mileage chart to find how long these journeys would take:
  a Hendon to Airlie at 25 mph
  b Patch to Airlie at 10 mph
  c Hendon to Patch at 20 mph.

Distances in miles

Hendon		
50	Airlie	
60	40	Patch

6 a Find the time taken for each of the four journeys by the tour bus.

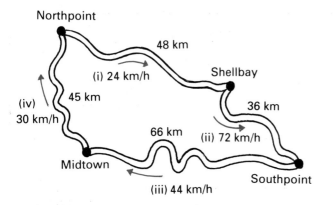

b The bus left Northpoint at 10 15. When did it arrive back?

7 Mr Lindsay, a salesman, leaves Aberdeen at 9 am and drives 780 km to London at an average speed of 60 km/h. This includes time for rests. At what time does he arrive in London?

8 The speed of sound is about 340 m/s. Andrea shouts to Pieter, who is 935 metres away. How long is it before Pieter hears her voice?

9 Light travels at 186 000 miles per second. How long does it take to reach the Earth from the sun, 93 000 000 miles away?

BRAINSTORMER

At 3.26 pm Mr Moss leaves the motorway service station.
The mileometer reads at that time.

Look at the speedometer for his average speed on the motorway.

What time is it when the mileometer reads

4 2 0 1 4 ?

CHALLENGE

Use this table, with the axes and scales shown, to draw a graph of mph against km/h.

km/h	0	40	80	120
mph	0	25	50	75

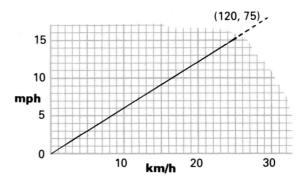

1 Use your graph to change these speed limits in mph to km/h.

2 Use your graph to change these speeds in km/h to mph.

MAKING SURE

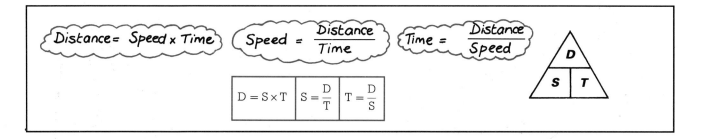

$Distance = Speed \times Time$ $Speed = \dfrac{Distance}{Time}$ $Time = \dfrac{Distance}{Speed}$

$D = S \times T$	$S = \dfrac{D}{T}$	$T = \dfrac{D}{S}$

EXERCISE 5A

1 a Distance 60 km
Time 10 h
Speed?

b Speed 30 km/h
Time 4 h
Distance?

c Distance 100 km
Speed 20 km/h
Time?

d Time 3 h
Distance 63 miles
Speed?

e Speed 30 mph
Distance 120 miles
Time?

f Time $2\frac{1}{2}$ h
Speed 50 mph
Distance?

2 In each of these diagrams, the speed, distance or time is missing. Decide which, then calculate it.

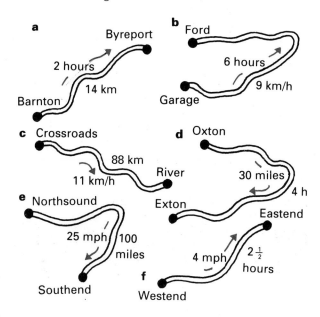

3 The bird called the Manx Shearwater takes 12 days to migrate 3000 miles from Boston, USA to Wales. Calculate its average speed in miles per day.

4 How far does a train go in 3 hours at an average speed of 180 km/h?

5 The balloon floats gently over the Atlantic, carried by air currents at an average speed of 52.5 km/h. The flight takes 148 hours. Calculate the distance the balloon covers.

6 An elephant, a kangaroo and a zebra decide to have a race. The elephant can manage a speed of 40 km/h, the kangaroo 60 km/h and the zebra 50 km/h.
a How far does each one travel in half an hour?
b How long would each animal take to travel 120 km (if they could run that far)?

7 Linda cycled from Newcastle (N), and Paul cycled from Middlesbrough (M).

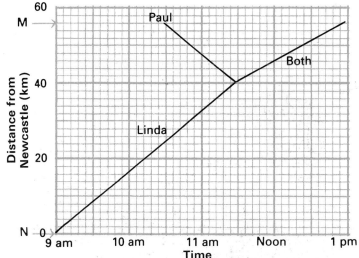

a At what time did they meet?
b How far from Newcastle were they when they met?
c For how long did they cycle together?
d Calculate the average speeds of both whole journeys.

EXERCISE 5B

1 a Distance 150 km
Time 4 h
Speed?

b Distance 4500 km
Speed 600 km/h
Time?

c Speed 52 mph
Time 4 h
Distance?

d Distance 440 m
Time 50 s
Speed?

2 Round the island

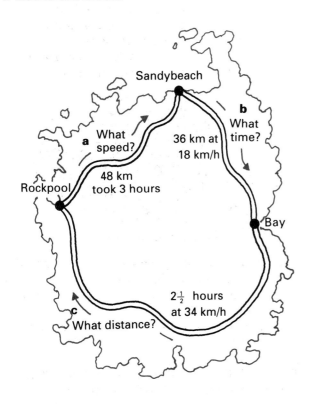

3 There are direct flights between these cities.

Distances in miles

London			
10 68	Stockholm		
17 91	18 20	Athens	
11 83	10 68	21 27	Lisbon

Calculate the average speed for each flight.

	Flight number	Description	Length of flight
a	001	London–Stockholm	4 hours
b	002	Stockholm–Athens	5 hours
c	003	London–Athens	$4\frac{1}{2}$ hours
d	004	Lisbon–Athens	6 hours

4 Which of these cars could be stopped by the police for speeding on the motorway (exceeding 70 mph)?
Car A: 12 miles in 10 minutes.
Car B: 17 miles in 15 minutes.
Car C: 7.5 miles in 6 minutes.

5

$$\underset{06\,34}{\underline{\text{Manchester}}} \longleftarrow 210 \text{ miles} \longrightarrow \underset{09\,04}{\underline{\text{London (Euston)}}}$$

Calculate the average speed of the train.

6 Calculate the average speeds for these journeys, correct to the nearest km/h:
a 1043 km in 3 hours 2 minutes
b 579 km in 1 hour 27 minutes.

7 Copy and complete the table.

	a	b	c	d	e	f
Distance (km)	120	250		1000	65	
Speed (km/h)	8		180		6	346
Time		$2\frac{1}{2}$ h	$1\frac{1}{4}$ h	3 h 20 min		1 h 9 min

CHECK-UP ON GOING PLACES

1 a Calculate the average speed of a journey of 84 km which takes 3 hours.
b How long does it take to travel 240 km at an average speed of 60 km/h?
c How far does a plane fly in 8 hours at 450 km/h?

2 a Amir took 3 hours to walk between Burr and Farr. What was his average speed?

Burr   24 km   Farr

b John walked at 4 km/h. How long did he take?

3 Ricky travelled at 45 km/h. How far is the town from the airport?

Airport   Town
6 hours

4 A lorry leaves the garage to travel to Ayr.
a How far does it travel in 2 hours?
b Calculate its average speed.

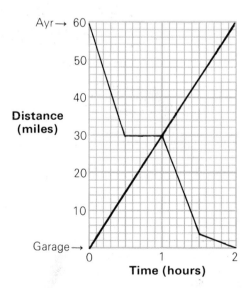

A bus leaves Ayr at the same time as the lorry leaves the garage.
c For how long does the bus stop on its journey?
d How far from Ayr do the bus and lorry pass each other?
e Calculate the average speed of the bus on each of the four parts of its journey.

5 Mr Andrews leaves home at 9 am, and drives 483 miles to London at an average speed of 46 mph. When does he arrive?

6 Miss Brennan flies to Belfast from Leeds, a journey of 370 km, at an average speed of 296 km/h. The plane takes off at 11 30 hours. When does it land at Belfast airport?

7 a How long did the bus take from:
(i) Holeton to Woodend
(ii) Holeton to Treetop?

Number 12 Bus Route

Holeton	09 30
Woodend	10 30
Treetop	12 30

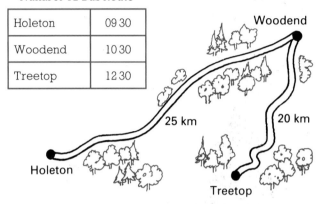

b What was the average speed of the bus from:
(i) Holeton to Woodend
(ii) Woodend to Treetop
(iii) Holeton to Treetop?

8 a Calculate the distance travelled in 2 hours 30 minutes at an average speed of 56 mph.
b At full speed a tortoise can move at 80 centimetres per minute. How long does it take to cross a road 5 metres wide?

c John cycles 15 km in 25 minutes, and then walks 3 km in 50 minutes. Calculate:
(i) the total distance he goes, and the time he takes
(ii) his average speed, in km/h, from start to finish.

9 Depart 15 30; motor 320 km; arrive 18 49. What was the average speed, to the nearest km/h?

6 BRACKETS AND EQUATIONS

LOOKING BACK

1 Write in shorter form:
  a $x+x$ **b** $y+y+y$ **c** $3u+2u$ **d** $4v-v$
  e $y\times y$ **f** $5\times t$ **g** $3\times p\times q$

2 Write down the total number of coins in each picture. The first bag has n coins in it.

a   **b**

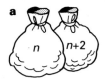

3 Find each OUT entry:

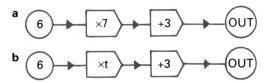

a

b

4 Each bag contains x 1 kg weights, and each ball weighs 1 kg. Find x.

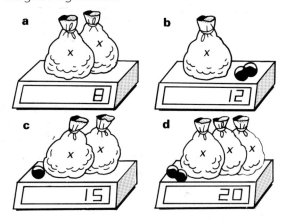

a   **b**

c   **d**

5 Write down, and simplify, expressions for the perimeter of each square and rectangle. Lengths are in cm.

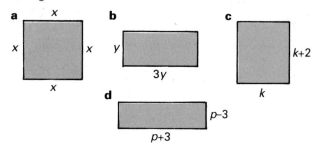

a x

x x

x

b y $3y$

c $k+2$ k

d $p-3$ $p+3$

6 Write down expressions for the areas of the shapes in question **5**.

7 Solve these equations:
  a $2x=8$ **b** $y-4=8$ **c** $t+7=14$
  d $2u-1=9$ **e** $2x+1=x+5$

8 a Five bicycles need 10 wheels. How many wheels are needed for x bicycles?

  b For one photo you need four corner mounts. How many do you need for y photos?

9 Calculate:
  a $5\times(4+2)$
  b $6\times2+4\times3$

Order!
Brackets
$\times\ \div$
$+\ -$

10 Multiply out these brackets:
  a $2(x+3)$ **b** $6(y-1)$ **c** $10(3+z)$

11 Jess thinks of a number, and adds 9. The answer is 23. Find her number by calling it x, making an equation, then solving it.

REMOVING BRACKETS

(i) 3×7, 3 lots of 7, $= 7 + 7 + 7$

(ii) $4a$, 4 lots of a, $= a + a + a + a$

(iii) $2(x + 5)$, 2 lots of $x + 5$, $= x + 5 + x + 5 = 2x + 10$. Shorter, $2(x + 5) = 2x + 10$

(iv) $3(y + 2)$, 3 lots of $y + 2$, $= y + 2 + y + 2 + y + 2 = 3y + 6 \ldots \ldots 3(y + 2) = 3y + 6$

Examples
a $6(x + 3) = 6x + 18$ **b** $2(3y + 1) = 6y + 2$ **c** $u(u + 4) = u^2 + 4u$

EXERCISE 1A

1 Remove the brackets, like this:
$2(x + 3) = x + 3 + x + 3 = 2x + 6$

  a $2(y + 3)$ **b** $3(y + 1)$ **c** $2(t + 5)$
  d $4(n + 2)$ **e** $3(x + 6)$ **f** $5(x + 1)$

2 Multiply out the brackets, like this:
$8(x + 2) = 8x + 16$

  a $3(x + 2)$ **b** $4(y + 1)$ **c** $5(z + 3)$
  d $2(t + 7)$ **e** $6(u + 1)$ **f** $8(x + 4)$
  g $7(v + 3)$ **h** $9(m + 9)$ **i** $7(n + 8)$

3 Remove the brackets. For example,
$5(1 + x) = 5 + 5x$

  a $2(3 + x)$ **b** $6(1 + y)$ **c** $3(2 + z)$
  d $5(5 + t)$ **e** $7(4 + u)$ **f** $8(6 + v)$
  g $4(8 + w)$ **h** $6(6 + m)$ **i** $10(9 + n)$
  j $2(1 + p)$ **k** $9(3 + q)$ **l** $8(2 + k)$

4 Write the OUT entries with and without brackets. For example,

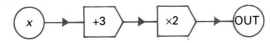

gives $(x + 3) \times 2 = 2(x + 3) = 2x + 6$

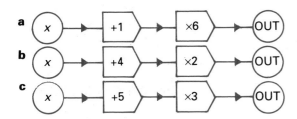

5 Use the given values of x to show that for each value, $2(x + 1) = 2x + 2$.
  a $x = 3$. Calculate: (i) $2(x + 1)$ (ii) $2x + 2$
  b $x = 5$. Calculate: (i) $2(x + 1)$ (ii) $2x + 2$
  c $x = 0$. Calculate: (i) $2(x + 1)$ (ii) $2x + 2$

6 For each diagram, write down the:
  (i) area of the largest rectangle
  (ii) area of each smaller rectangle
  (iii) sum of areas of smaller rectangles.

Check that (i) = (iii). Units are cm.
Write the results like this: $5(6 + 3) = 5 \times 6 + 5 \times 3$

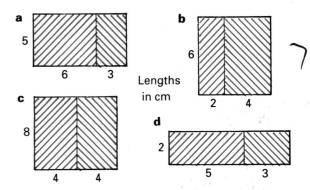

7 Find two ways of writing these areas, as in question **6**.

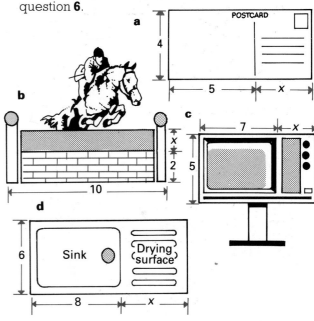

EXERCISE 1B

1 Remove the brackets:
- **a** $5(2x+1)$ **b** $2(3a+1)$ **c** $3(5b+2)$
- **d** $4(2c+3)$ **e** $6(4u+5)$ **f** $8(5v+4)$
- **g** $7(2y+5)$ **h** $6(4z+1)$ **i** $3(3x+4)$
- **j** $5(6+3u)$ **k** $4(5+6v)$ **l** $9(2+3t)$

2 Pair equal calculations. Write each answer as a letter with a number:

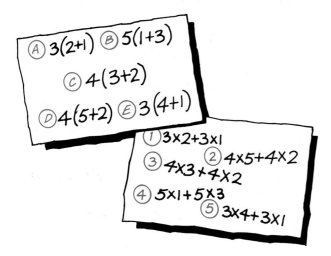

3 Write down two different formulae for the perimeter P cm of each rectangle.

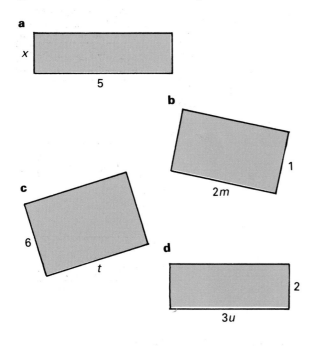

4 Remove these brackets:
- **a** $x(x+2)$ **b** $x(y+3)$ **c** $t(t+1)$
- **d** $a(b+4)$ **e** $b(b+5)$ **f** $c(d+1)$
- **g** $u(u+6)$ **h** $u(v+3)$ **i** $w(w+8)$

5 Write down two different formulae for the area $A\,\mathrm{m}^2$ of each window.

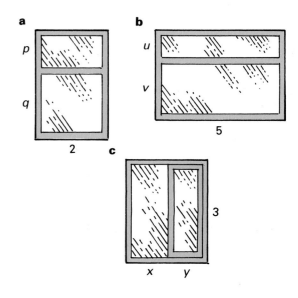

6 Write down two expressions for the area of the largest rectangle in each picture.

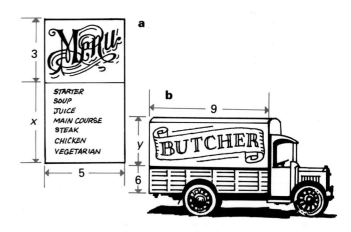

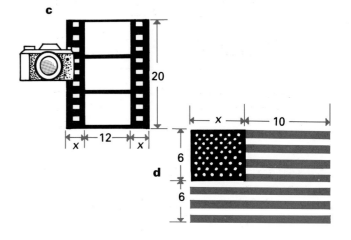

EXERCISE 2A

In the same way as before:

$3(x-2)$, 3 lots of $x-2$, $= x-2+x-2+x-2 = 3x-6$. Shorter, $3(x-2) = 3x-6$

Examples
a $5(n-3) = 5n-15$ **b** $2(4k-5) = 8k-10$

Multiply out the brackets in the balloons.
For example, $6(x-2) = 6x-12$.

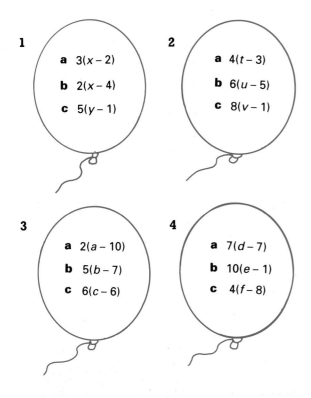

1
a $3(x-2)$
b $2(x-4)$
c $5(y-1)$

2
a $4(t-3)$
b $6(u-5)$
c $8(v-1)$

3
a $2(a-10)$
b $5(b-7)$
c $6(c-6)$

4
a $7(d-7)$
b $10(e-1)$
c $4(f-8)$

5 Write the OUT entries with and without brackets.

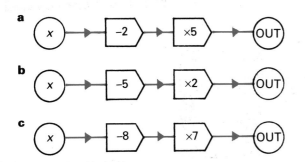

a $x \rightarrow -2 \rightarrow \times 5 \rightarrow$ OUT

b $x \rightarrow -5 \rightarrow \times 2 \rightarrow$ OUT

c $x \rightarrow -8 \rightarrow \times 7 \rightarrow$ OUT

6 Use the given values of x to show that for each one, $3(x-4) = 3x-12$.
a $x = 5$. Calculate: (i) $3(x-4)$ (ii) $3x-12$
b $x = 10$. Calculate: (i) $3(x-4)$ (ii) $3x-12$

7 Remove the brackets. For example,
$6(1-x) = 6-6x$

a $2(5-x)$ **b** $3(4-y)$ **c** $4(6-z)$
d $8(1-a)$ **e** $9(2-b)$ **f** $7(3-c)$
g $6(4-d)$ **h** $5(9-t)$ **i** $10(8-s)$
j $3(7-u)$ **k** $6(8-v)$ **l** $9(1-w)$

8 In each garden, **a**, **b** and **c**, find expressions for the grass area by:
  (i) multiplying its length by its breadth
  (ii) subtracting the flower bed area from the area of the whole garden.

Show that the two expressions are equal by multiplying out the brackets.

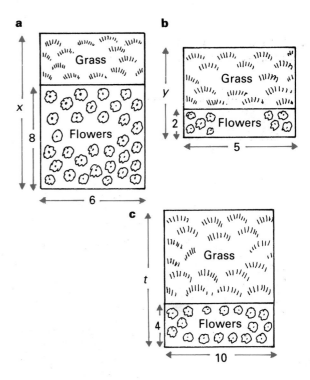

9 Multiply out these brackets:
a $2(a+5)$ **b** $2(a-5)$ **c** $3(2+b)$
d $3(2-b)$ **e** $4(c+1)$ **f** $4(1+c)$
g $4(c-1)$ **h** $4(1-c)$ **i** $5(d+6)$
j $6(e-7)$ **k** $7(7+f)$ **l** $8(g-9)$

REMOVING BRACKETS AND TIDYING UP

EXERCISE 2B

Examples

a $5(x+3)-2x$
   $= 5x+15-2x$
   $= 3x+15$

b $3+2(y-1)$
   $= 3+2y-2$
   $= 1+2y$

c $2(u+3)+3(u-1)$
   $= 2u+6+3u-3$
   $= 5u+3$

In questions **1–4** remove the brackets, then tidy up the answers.

1 a $2(x+3)+4$ **b** $3(x+1)+2$
   c $4(y+2)-3$ **d** $2(y+5)-5$

2 a $2(u+5)+u$ **b** $5(v+1)-v$
   c $6(w+2)+w$ **d** $3(t+3)-t$

3 a $5(y-1)-2y$ **b** $3(x-2)+2x$
   c $7(t+2)+3$ **d** $8(k+1)-2$

4 a $5+2(m+3)$ **b** $8+3(n-2)$
   c $7+4(k-1)$ **d** $10+5(n-2)$

5

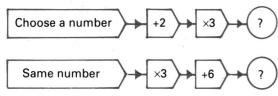

a Do you get the same answer?
b Take x to represent the number, and repeat **a**.
   Explain why the answers are the same.

6 Remove the brackets.
   a $3(2x-1)$ **b** $4(3y-2)$ **c** $5(x-8)$
   d $7(y-1)$ **e** $2(5x-3)$ **f** $2(a+4)$
   g $3(2d+1)$ **h** $5(3c-2)$ **i** $8(2+3k)$
   j $4(u+v)$ **k** $2(a+b)$ **l** $3(x-y)$

7 Remove these brackets, then tidy up.
   a $3(x+1)+2(x-1)$ **b** $5(y+1)+2(y-1)$
   c $2(u-3)+2(u+3)$ **d** $4(v+2)+3(v-1)$
   e $2(y-3)+3(y+2)$ **f** $5(1-a)+5(a+2)$
   g $6(t+4)+4(t-6)$ **h** $8(2-k)+9(3+k)$

8 Find the simplest expression for the perimeter of this window.

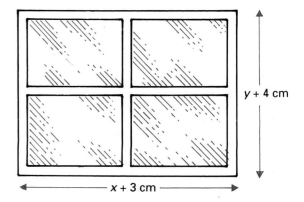

SOLVING EQUATIONS

EXERCISE 3A

Solve these equations.

1 a $x+3=6$ **b** $x-4=8$
   c $y+3=5$ **d** $m+10=11$
   e $k-7=3$ **f** $x-9=4$
   g $t+7=7\frac{1}{2}$

$2x+3=12$
$-3\quad -3$
$2x=9$
$x=4\frac{1}{2}$

2 a $2x=12$ **b** $3y=18$ **c** $7n=49$
   d $5t=50$ **e** $2u=5$ **f** $8v=0$

3 a $2x+1=5$ **b** $2a-1=7$ **c** $3b+8=11$
   d $5y-2=13$ **e** $7m+1=22$ **f** $10x-5=15$
   g $8p-7=33$ **h** $4q+11=51$ **i** $6r-12=3$

> *Example*
> Solve $4(x+1) = 20$ ... Remove brackets
> $\qquad 4x + 4 = 20$ ... Subtract 4 from each side
> $\qquad\quad -4 \quad -4$
> $\qquad\qquad 4x = 16$ ... Divide each side by 4
> $\qquad\qquad\ x = 4$

Solve these equations by multiplying out the brackets first.

4 a $2(x+3) = 8$ **b** $3(x+1) = 12$
   c $3(y-1) = 6$ **d** $4(m-2) = 20$
   e $6(t+3) = 24$ **f** $7(n+2) = 21$

5 a $5(x-1) = 0$ **b** $4(y-3) = 2$
   c $6(p+2) = 12$ **d** $8(k-3) = 40$
   e $7(w+2) = 14$ **f** $9(t+7) = 72$

6 a Explain why the area of this rectangle is $4(x+2)\ \text{cm}^2$.

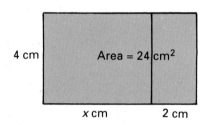

b So $4(x+2) = 24$. Solve this equation.
c What is the length of the rectangle?

7 Make an equation for the area of each rectangle, then solve it, to find the length of the rectangle.

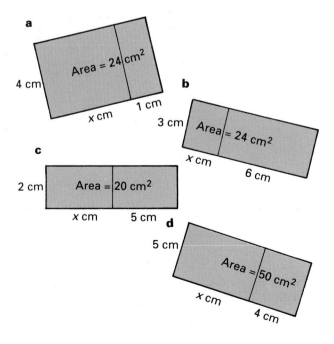

8 Write down an equation with brackets for each part, and solve it.

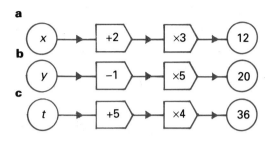

9 Omar bought 5 pencils in a sale, at 3 pence off each. It cost him 15 pence.
Solve $5(x-3) = 15$ to find the original cost of a pencil.

10 Due to inflation, the cost of a stamp was increased by 1p. This meant that the cost for 5 stamps became 95p.
Solve $5(y+1) = 95$ to find the old cost of a stamp.

11 To save money, a company reduced the weight of the contents in a packet by 6 grams. 4 packets now weigh 80 grams.
Solve $4(w-6) = 80$ to find what a packet used to weigh.

EXERCISE 3B

1 Solve these equations:
  a $2(2x+1) = 14$　**b** $3(2y-1) = 15$
  c $4(3u+2) = 32$　**d** $5(4v-3) = 45$

The 'seesaw' is balanced, like this:

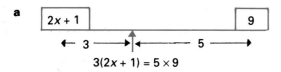

It is balanced because $2 \times 9 = 3 \times 6$.

2 Make an equation for each balance, solve it, and find the weights on the left-hand sides.
The weights are in kg.

a

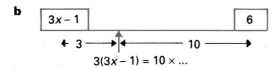

$3(2x + 1) = 5 \times 9$

b

$3x - 1$　　　　6

$3(3x - 1) = 10 \times \ldots$

c

$x+7$　　　　14

d

$y-5$　　　　4

e

$3u + 1$　　　　5

3 Solve these equations:
  a $2(x+3)-4 = 6$　　**b** $6(y-1)+11 = 14$
  c $3(2p+1)+2 = 23$　**d** $5(3t-1)+5 = 15$

4

I've thought of a number, added 7, and then multiplied by 6. The answer is 90. Can you find my number?

Take x for the number, then make an equation and solve it.

5 Make an equation for each picture, and solve it to find the amount of money in each left-hand bag. In **a**, the equation is $6(x+2)+3 = 21$.

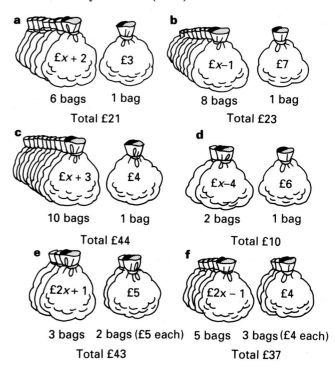

a
£x + 2　　£3
6 bags　　1 bag
Total £21

b
£x−1　　£7
8 bags　　1 bag
Total £23

c
£x + 3　　£4
10 bags　　1 bag
Total £44

d
£x−4　　£6
2 bags　　1 bag
Total £10

e
£2x+1　　£5
3 bags　　2 bags (£5 each)
Total £43

f
£2x − 1　　£4
5 bags　　3 bags (£4 each)
Total £37

6 Make up some problems like the one in question **4**, and solve them.

CHALLENGE

Mr Smart is selling stock from the school shop at bargain prices, but he won't say what the prices of the bars are. His customers have to work them out. He gives them a free bar for the correct answer. Make an equation for each problem, and solve it.

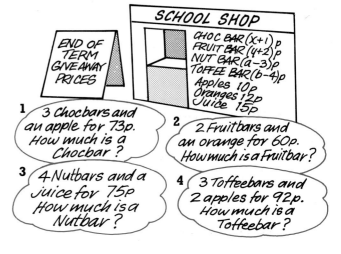

SCHOOL SHOP
CHOC BAR (x+1) p
FRUIT BAR (y+2) p
NUT BAR (a−3) p
TOFFEE BAR (b−4) p
Apples 10p
Oranges 12p
Juice 15p

END OF TERM GIVEAWAY PRICES

1 3 Chocbars and an apple for 73p. How much is a Chocbar?

2 2 Fruitbars and an orange for 60p. How much is a Fruitbar?

3 4 Nutbars and a juice for 75p. How much is a Nutbar?

4 3 Toffeebars and 2 apples for 92p. How much is a Toffeebar?

COMMON FACTORS

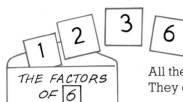

All these cards can go into the envelope, as the numbers are **factors** of 6.
They divide into 6 exactly.

Every factor has a partner, for example 1 and 6, and 2 and 3 in **a** below.

a

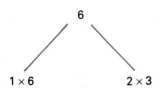

Factors of 6: 1, 2, 3, 6

b

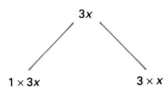

Factors of 3x: 1, 3, x, 3x

EXERCISE 4A

---

1 Copy and complete:

a

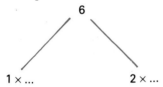

The factors of 6 are 1, 2, . . . , . . .

b

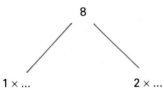

The factors of 8 are . . . , . . . , . . . , . . .

c

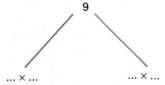

The factors of 9 are . . . , . . . , . . .

d

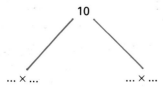

The factors of 10 are . . . , . . . , . . . , . . .

2 Copy and complete:
   a $4 = 2 \times \ldots$ **b** $30 = 6 \times \ldots$ **c** $9 = 1 \times \ldots$
   d $16 = 4 \times \ldots$ **e** $16 = 8 \times \ldots$ **f** $16 = 1 \times \ldots$

3 Copy and complete:

a

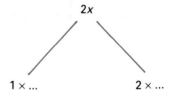

The factors of $2x$ are . . . , . . . , . . . , . . .

b

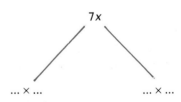

The factors of $7x$ are . . . , . . . , . . . , . . .

c

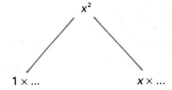

The factors of x^2 are . . . , . . . , . . .

4 Copy and complete:
 a $2d = 2 \times \ldots$ **b** $9y = 3 \times \ldots$ **c** $6t = 3 \times \ldots$
 d $10n = 5 \times \ldots$ **e** $12k = 4 \times \ldots$ **f** $8x = 8 \times \ldots$
 g $u^2 = u \times \ldots$ **h** $v^2 = v \times \ldots$ **i** $w^2 = w \times \ldots$

5 3 is a factor of $12x$. Its partner is $4x$, because $3 \times 4x = 12x$.
  Write down the partners of the given factors.
 a 4 is a factor of 8   **b** 6 is a factor of 30
 c 7 is a factor of 7   **d** 2 is a factor of $6x$
 e 5 is a factor of $10y$ **f** 3 is a factor of $15t$

Example
Find a common factor, and factorise:
 a $6x+9$ **b** y^2-2y

a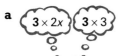
   $6x+9$
   $= 3(2x+3)$
   Common factor 3

b
   y^2-2y
   $= y(y-2)$
   Common factor y

---

6 Copy and complete these. Check by removing brackets.
 a $3x+6 = 3(\ldots\ldots)$ **b** $2x+8 = 2(\ldots\ldots)$
 c $5x-10 = 5(\ldots\ldots)$ **d** $6n+12 = 6(\ldots\ldots)$
 e $8-2m = 2(\ldots\ldots)$ **f** $8k-12 = 4(\ldots\ldots)$
 g $4x+4y = 4(\ldots\ldots)$ **h** $7u-21v = 7(\ldots\ldots)$

7 Factorise:
 a $2x+2$ **b** $2x+6$ **c** $2x+8$
 d $3y+3$ **e** $3y-3$ **f** $3y+6$
 g $2c+4$ **h** $3d-6$ **i** $4e+4$
 j $5x-10$ **k** $7y+7$ **l** $6t-18$

8 Factorise:
 a $5x+5y$ **b** $5x-5y$ **c** $2x+4y$
 d $3u+9v$ **e** $3u-6v$ **f** $3u+12v$
 g $7m+7n$ **h** $7m+14n$ **i** $7m-21n$
 j $2a+2b$ **k** $3c-9d$ **l** $6e-12f$

9 Factorise:
 a $3t+18$ **b** $6u+2$ **c** $2x-20$
 d $9m-15$ **e** $10+2k$ **f** $12-3p$
 g $7a-14b$ **h** $10u+20v$ **i** $15c-18d$
 j $6+6k$ **k** $9-3u$ **l** $8-8v$

EXERCISE 4B

Highest common factor

Examples

a 2 is a **common factor** of 8 and 12, because 2 divides into 8 and 12 exactly.
  4 is also a **common factor** of 8 and 12. Why?
  4 is the **highest common factor** of 8 and 12. Why?

b 2, 3 and 6 are common factors of $30x$ and 12. The highest common factor is 6.

1 Write down the highest common factor of:
 a 6 and 9   **b** 8 and 10   **c** 7 and 14
 d 4 and 8   **e** 8 and 12   **f** 10 and 20
 g 12 and 18   **h** 4 and 12   **i** 16 and 24

2 Factorise these, making sure you have taken out the highest common factor:
 a $4x+4$ **b** $4y+28$ **c** $6z+18$
 d $6u-9$ **e** $9v-9$ **f** $9w-18$
 g $8a+12$ **h** $20b+30$ **i** $12c-18$

3 Factorise:
 a x^2+3x **b** y^2-5y **c** z^2+z
 d s^2-2s **e** u^2+8u **f** t^2-t
 g $2x^2+4x$ **h** $3y^2-6y$ **i** $5z^2+10z$
 j $3p-9p^2$ **k** $4n+12n^2$ **l** $6k-18k^2$

1 Zippo, the magician, can do mathematics 'at a glance'!

$4 \times 91 + 4 \times 9$

$= 400$

$99 \times 7 + 99 \times 3$

$= 990$

$46 \times 17 - 46 \times 7$

$= 460$

How does he do it? Can you calculate $8 \times 91 + 8 \times 9$ *'at a glance'?*

2 Practise on these:
   a $4 \times 8 + 4 \times 2$ **b** $26 \times 7 + 26 \times 3$
   c $42 \times 16 - 42 \times 6$ **d** $36 \times 52 + 36 \times 48$
   e $15 \times 19 - 15 \times 9$ **f** $19 \times 28 + 19 \times 72$

3 Write down the cost of:
   a *12 stamps at 28p each and 12 at 22p*
   b *15 cans of fruit at 64p each and 15 at 36p.*

Is the sum of three consecutive whole numbers always divisible by 3?

*1 **a** Try $1 + 2 + 3$,*
          $2 + 3 + 4$,
          $3 + 4 + 5$,
          $6 + 7 + 8$.
   b *Are you sure that the result is always true?*
   c *Try $n + (n + 1) + (n + 2)$. Can you find a common factor 3? Check for $n = 10$.*

2 Investigate the sum of $4, 5, 6, \ldots$ consecutive whole numbers.
   Try numbers first, then $n, n + 1, n + 2, n + 3, \ldots$ to find common factors.

$5 + 6 + 7 + 8 + 9 +$

CHECK-UP ON BRACKETS AND EQUATIONS

Multiply out the brackets in questions **1** and **2**.

1
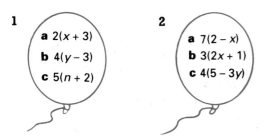
a $2(x+3)$
b $4(y-3)$
c $5(n+2)$

2
a $7(2-x)$
b $3(2x+1)$
c $4(5-3y)$

3 Write down two different expressions for the area of this lock, and show that they are equal.

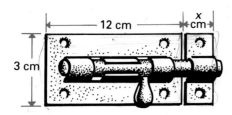

12 cm x cm   3 cm

4 Calculate the values of $6(x+8)$ and $6x+48$ when $x=3$.

5 Remove the brackets, and tidy up.
 a $2(x+3)+4$ **b** $3(y-2)+y$
 c $6+2(u+1)$ **d** $5+3(v-1)$

6 Write the OUT entries with and without brackets.

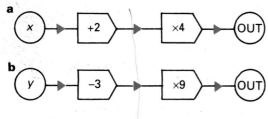

a x → $+2$ → $\times 4$ → OUT

b y → -3 → $\times 9$ → OUT

7 Solve:
 a $x+9=16$ **b** $y-9=0$ **c** $z+3=3$
 d $2d+1=12$ **e** $4e-1=19$ **f** $6t+4=34$

8 Solve these equations by first removing the brackets:
 a $3(x+2)=9$ **b** $2(y-4)=1$
 c $5(w+4)=50$ **d** $4(k-1)=28$

9 Write down an equatio part, and solve it.

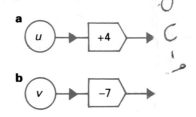

a u → $+4$ →

b v → -7 →

10 a Make an equation, a

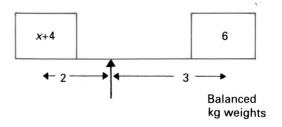

$x+4$ 6

← 2 →   ← 3 →

Balanced kg weights

b Find the weight on the left-hand side.

11 a Make an equation, and solve it.

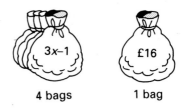

$3x-1$ £16

4 bags   1 bag

Total £48

b Find the amount in each bag on the left-hand side.

12 Find all the factors of:
 a 8   **b** 11   **c** 12

13 Copy and complete:
 a $6x=6\times\ldots$ **b** $6x=2x\times\ldots$
 c $y^2=y\times\ldots$ **d** $3p^2=3p\times\ldots$

14 Factorise:
 a $3x+15$ **b** $2y-14$ **c** $7a-7b$
 d $6m-30n$ **e** x^2-2x **f** y^2-y

REVIEW: STATISTICS AND PROBABILITY

STATISTICS 1

1 The students in Westway High School are asked whether they like Cola, Orange, Tea or Coffee best. Their choices are shown in the pictogram.

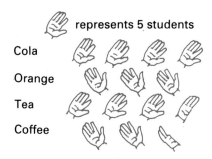

represents 5 students

Cola

Orange

Tea

Coffee

a How many like Orange best?
b Which drink has most votes?
c How many boys and girls took part in the survey?

2 Ben plays a double round of golf. The number of strokes he takes at each hole is shown below.
2, 3, 4, 5, 3, 5, 6, 2, 2, 3, 5, 5, 4, 3, 4, 5, 6, 4,
6, 7, 5, 4, 2, 1, 2, 3, 5, 3, 5, 3, 4, 2, 2, 3, 4, 2

a Draw and complete a table with the headings:
Strokes   Tally   Number of holes
b At how many holes does he take fewer than 4 strokes?

3 The label on a box of Chocos states that there are 25–27 chocolates in each box. The number of chocolates in each of 50 boxes was counted. Here are the results.

Number of chocolates	22	23	24	25	26	27	28
Number of boxes	3	8	4	9	13	10	3

Draw a bar graph of the results.

4 The nurse took Phil's temperature every hour from 8 pm until 3 am.

Time	8	9	10	11	12	1	2	3
Temp. (°F)	101	102	102	101	100	99.5	99	99.5

a Draw a line graph.
b When was Phil's temperature at its lowest?
c Estimate his temperature at:
(i) 11.30 pm   (ii) 4 am.

5 This graph shows the growth of population in the world since 1930. In 1930 the population was 21 hundred million.

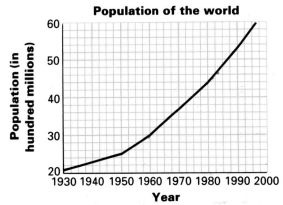

a In which year did the population reach 25 hundred million?
b What was the population in 1960?
c What was the increase from 1960 to 1980?
d Describe the trend in world population.

6 The land use in Peter's garden is shown in this pie chart.

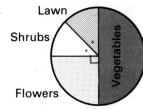

a List the uses of the land in order, greatest first.
b What fraction of the garden is used for:
(i) vegetables
(ii) flowers
(iii) other plants?

7 Margaret took £3.60 to the garden fête.
She spent £1.20 on toys, 60p on sweets, 90p on a book, 50p on the raffle and the rest on the White Elephant stall. Draw a pie chart to show how she spent her money.

8 The English papers have been marked, but the marks are still unsorted. Here they are:
9, 21, 27, 39, 32, 37, 45, 16, 38, 46, 19, 27, 13, 23,
37, 17, 22, 28, 34, 44, 47, 19, 23, 36, 27, 35, 21, 36
a Copy and complete this table.

Mark	1–10	11–20	21–30	31–40	41–50
Number					

b Make a bar graph to illustrate the information in the table.

STATISTICS 2

1 **Westway High School: 14-year-old absentees**

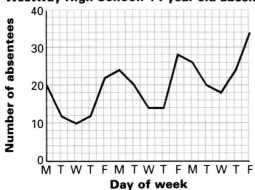

a Calculate the average number of absentees on the Mondays.

b Which weekday had the best attendance?

c Describe two patterns in the graph.

2 Find the mean, median, mode and range for each list below. In each case, say which average best represents the list.

a 28, 28, 29, 30, 30, 30, 31, 35, 164

b 14, 14, 14, 14, 16, 16, 17, 37, 65

c 16, 16, 17, 18, 19, 20, 22, 25, 27

3 Over a fortnight, a country inn recorded the number of guests who stayed each night.

Day (Week 1)	1	2	3	4	5	6	7
Number of guests	16	11	14	17	16	12	12

Day (Week 2)	1	2	3	4	5	6	7
Number of guests	15	16	17	18	14	12	13

Calculate the mean, median, mode and range of the number of guests for:

a (i) Week 1   (ii) Week 2

b the two-week period.

4 a On one diagram draw a line graph of the number of guests each week in question **3**.

b Describe the graphs.

5 Bryan had to log all his phone calls at the office, noting their lengths to the nearest minute.

32, 10, 2, 8, 3, 5, 8, 4, 4, 2,
16, 34, 12, 16, 5, 7, 8, 6, 3, 4,
11, 4, 4, 14, 3, 2, 1, 3, 33, 1

Calculate the mean length of his calls, correct to 1 decimal place.

6 The number of cars passing City High School's gate each minute between 9 and 9.30 am one day is shown below.

10, 24, 24, 18, 24, 31,
35, 30, 24, 21, 28, 30,
37, 9, 28, 34, 16, 13,
19, 26, 17, 21, 23, 19,
29, 27, 27, 31, 35, 15

a Arrange the figures in a frequency table, using the class intervals 1–5, 6–10, . . .

b Use the midpoints of the class intervals to calculate the mean number of cars per minute.

c What is the modal class interval?

7 A sample of students were asked if they had a home computer. The table shows the number who replied 'Yes'.

Age	10	11	12	13	14	15	16	17	18
Frequency	12	15	22	34	40	25	15	12	10

a How many students were in the sample?

b Calculate, to the nearest whole number, the percentage of owners who are:
(i) under 13   (ii) over 14.

c Draw a frequency diagram and a frequency polygon of the data.

8 Flame-light makes candles. The firm wants to find out how long candles of different thicknesses take to burn out. The results are shown in the scatter diagram.

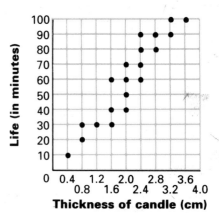

a How many candles were tested?

b Calculate the mean:
(i) thickness   (ii) lifetime of a candle.

c Hold your ruler against the line of best fit to help you estimate the thickness of a candle expected to last 65 minutes.

PROBABILITY 1

1 Choose the best word, or words, to describe the chance of each event below taking place.

Unlikely Impossible Even Chance Likely Certain

a When you add two odd numbers, you will get an even number.
b You can score 1 if you roll two dice.
c You will read this on a school day.
d A month picked at random will contain Friday 13th.
e A person chosen at random will be male.

2 Michael's TV set can receive BBC1, BBC2, ITV and Channel 4. He selects one of these at random. Calculate the probability that:
a he chooses BBC2
b the programme will have advertisements in it.

3 In a recent pet food survey of 600 homes, 360 households had a cat.
Calculate the probability that a home chosen at random from the 600 homes in the survey:
a will have a cat
b will not have a cat.

4 Mary makes a tally table of the ways in which her friends travel to school.
Calculate the probability that one of them chosen at random:
a travels by car
b takes a bus
c doesn't walk.

Mode	Tally
Walk	JHT JHT JHT
Car	JHT JHT III
Bus	JHT JHT IIII
Bike	JHT III

5 Clive uses this spinner to predict the results of football matches for the pools.

Calculate the probability that on the next spin he will get:
a a no-score draw
b a draw
c 1.5 points.

6 A letter is chosen at random from the word SELECTION. Find:
a P(E) **b** P(L) **c** P(vowel)
d P(letter comes after M in the alphabet).

7 At a dance raffle, the organisers sell three books of raffle tickets, red, blue and yellow. Each book is numbered 1 to 100.
What is the probability that when the first ticket is drawn it will be:
a 50 blue
b 50
c red and over 40?

8 A ball is chosen at random from each bag. From which bag are you more likely to choose a white ball? Explain.

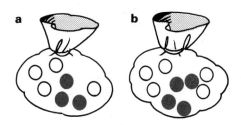

9 How could you estimate the probability that:
a a student chosen at random owns a computer
b January will be the coldest month next year?

PROBABILITY 2

1 This bag contains three white tiles and four black ones.

a One tile is taken out at random. Calculate:
(i) P(W)   (ii) P(B)

b The tile in **a** is found to be black, and is not replaced. A second tile is then taken out at random. What are the values of P(W) and P(B) now?

2

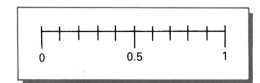

Copy this scale and use arrows to mark the probability that:
a a coin will land tail side up when tossed
b a schoolday chosen at random will be a Wednesday
c you will answer every question in this book correctly
d a month chosen at random will have an 'R' in it
e a dice will show a whole number from 1 to 6, when rolled.

3 There is only a 6% chance of success in a competition. What is the probability of failure:
a as a percentage   **b** as a decimal?

4 A penny is rolled, and lands in one of the squares.

Calculate:
a P(L)   **b** P(£1)   **c** P(10p)   **d** P(win).

5 The Hermes Telephone Company places an advert in the local paper. The newspaper claims that the probability of a reply is 4%.
If 25 000 people buy the paper how many enquiries should the company expect?

6 Local knowledge suggests that the probability of rain on the west coast on any one day in May is 55%. How many days in May would you expect to be:
a wet   **b** dry?

7 This diagram shows the four schools from which Westway High School's first year pupils came.

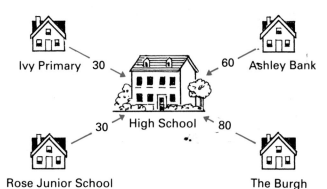

Calculate the probability that a first year pupil chosen at random came from:
a Ashley Bank
b The Burgh
c a school other than The Burgh.

8 Charles wins if he scores 3 or more. What is the probability that he wins with his next turn?

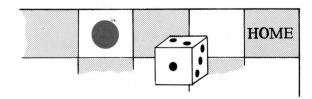

9 A set of 28 dominoes is placed face down, and one is chosen at random. Calculate:
a P(6:3)   **b** P(double)   **c** P(8 dots).

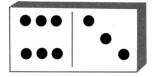

LOOKING BACK

1 Calculate the mean of:
  a 5 cm, 9 cm, 11 cm, 7 cm
  b £12, £16, £14, £15, £13

2 The temperature in Jamal's classroom is noted every hour.

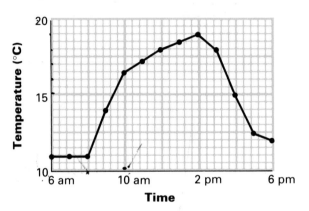

a (i) What was the highest temperature?
   (ii) At what time was this?
b When was the heating switched:
   (i) on (ii) off?
c Between which times was the temperature rising fastest?

3 Katie asks 40 students to choose their favourite type of film.

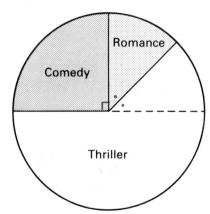

a What fraction of students chose:
   (i) comedy (ii) romance?
b How many students chose each of the three types?

4 Martin kept a note of the time he spent on homework one week.

Day	Sun	Mon	Tue	Wed	Thu	Fri	Sat
Time (min)	130	100	80	80	80	60	65

a (i) Write down the longest and shortest times.
   (ii) Calculate the difference between these (the range).
b What was the most common time (the mode)?
c Calculate:
   (i) the total time he spent on homework
   (ii) the mean time per day.

5 Melanie kept a record of how she spent 24 hours.

Activity	Sleep	School	Homework	Leisure	Other
Time (h)	10	7	2	3	2

a (i) How many degrees in a pie chart would represent 1 hour of the day?
   (ii) Draw a pie chart to illustrate the data.
b Make up a table for 24 hours in your own life, then draw a pie chart.

6 a Show the data in question **5** in a bar graph.
  b Which diagram do you prefer? Why?

FLOWCHARTS

A **flowchart** is a diagram which contains a list of instructions to be carried out in a certain order. It has a title, and then:

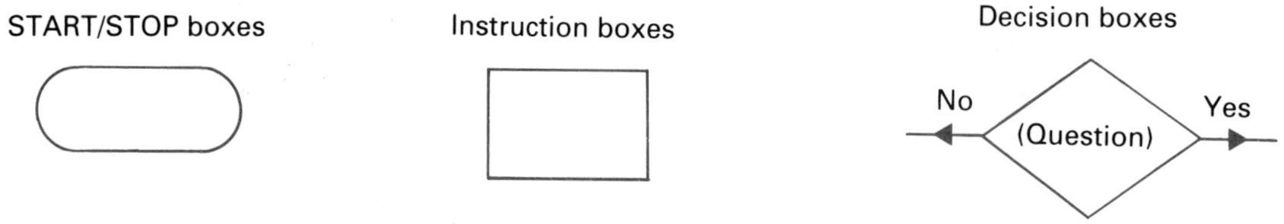
START/STOP boxes
Instruction boxes
Decision boxes
No
(Question)
Yes

Example

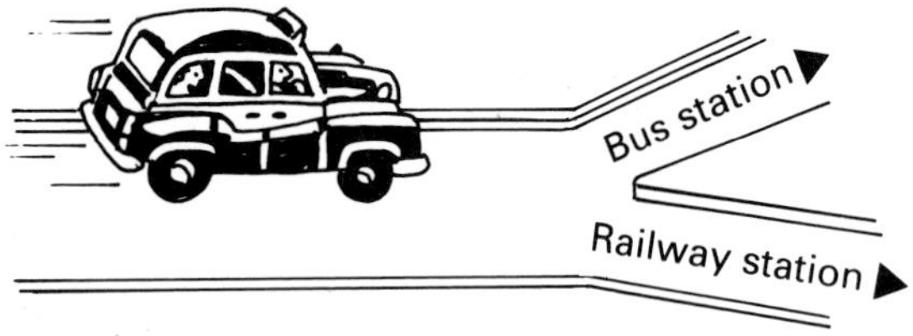
Bus station
Railway station

To take the correct road

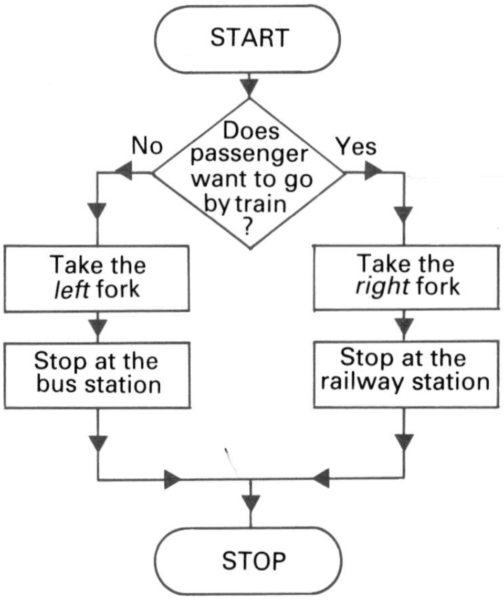
START
Does passenger want to go by train ?
No
Yes
Take the *left* fork
Take the *right* fork
Stop at the bus station
Stop at the railway station
STOP

The passenger in the taxi has a choice. He can take either the bus or the train.

This flowchart describes the taxi driver's actions. Look at the way in which the different boxes are used.

EXERCISE 1A

1 Recipes in older cookery books give oven temperatures in degrees Fahrenheit. Modern cookers use temperatures in degrees Celsius.

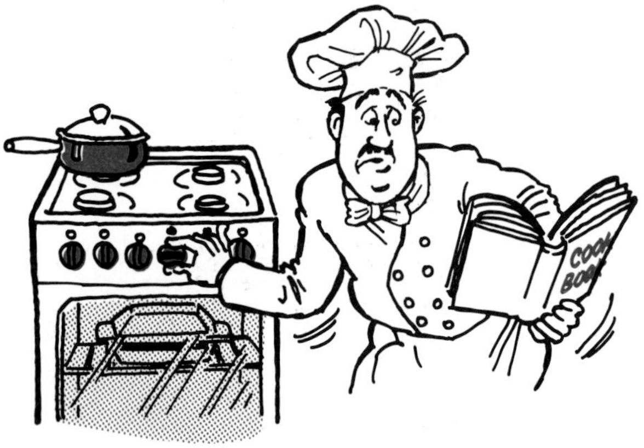
COOK BOOK

Here is a flowchart to convert °F to °C.

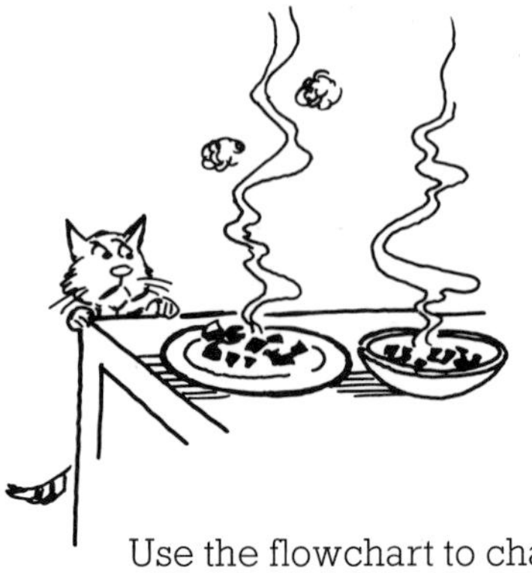

Fahrenheit to Celsius

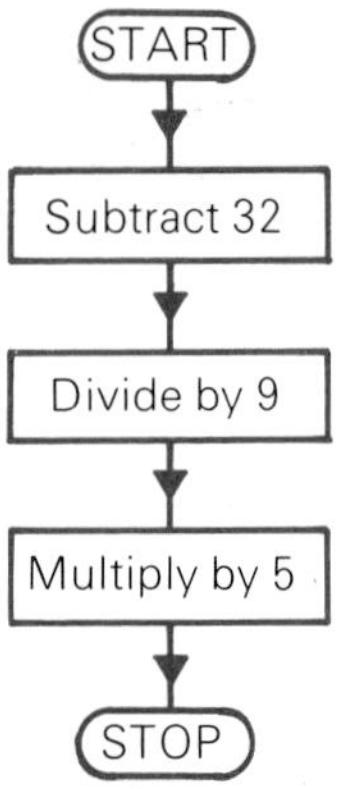
START
Subtract 32
Divide by 9
Multiply by 5
STOP

Use the flowchart to change these temperatures to °C.

a 32°F **b** 77°F **c** 140°F **d** 212°F

2

How deep is the well?

Here is a flowchart for estimating the depth of a well in metres.

How deep are these three wells if you hear the stone hit the bottom after:
a 3 seconds
b 5 seconds
c 8 seconds?

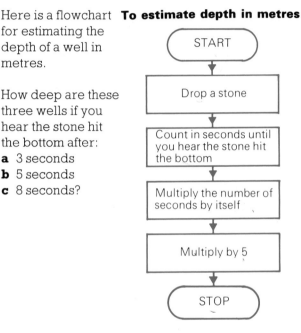

To estimate depth in metres

START

↓

Drop a stone

↓

Count in seconds until you hear the stone hit the bottom

↓

Multiply the number of seconds by itself

↓

Multiply by 5

↓

STOP

3 Some students are helping to plan a weekend trip to the school cottage.

Tom: I'm sure no more than 12 will want to go. A minibus will be big enough.

Ann: What if more than 12 *do* want to go?

Tom: Then we'll need a coach.

Use these boxes to draw a flowchart which describes their plans.

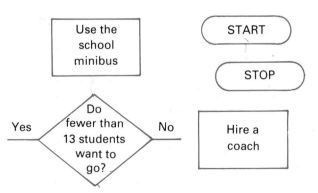

Use the school minibus

START

STOP

Hire a coach

Yes — Do fewer than 13 students want to go? — No

4 You cannot make up your mind whether to watch a western on Channel 4 or a cartoon on Satellite. So you toss a coin. Heads—Channel 4, Tails—Satellite. Arrange the boxes to make a flowchart for this.

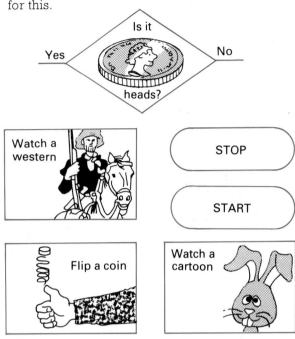

Yes — Is it heads? — No

Watch a western

STOP

START

Flip a coin

Watch a cartoon

5 Jim is delivering a parcel to a block of flats. If the flat is on the first or second floor he will use the stairs. If it is above the second floor he will use the lift. Arrange the boxes in the form of a flowchart.

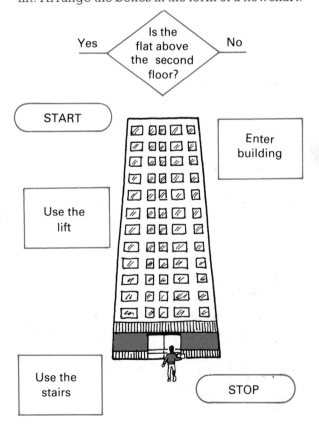

Yes — Is the flat above the second floor? — No

START

Enter building

Use the lift

Use the stairs

STOP

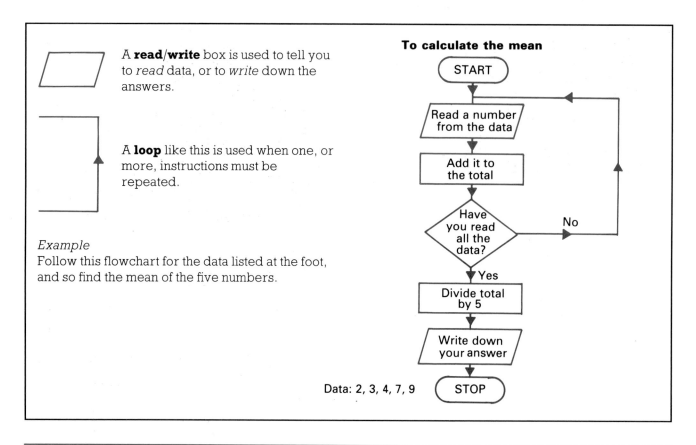

A **read/write** box is used to tell you to *read* data, or to *write* down the answers.

A **loop** like this is used when one, or more, instructions must be repeated.

Example
Follow this flowchart for the data listed at the foot, and so find the mean of the five numbers.

To calculate the mean

START

Read a number from the data

Add it to the total

Have you read all the data?   No

Yes

Divide total by 5

Write down your answer

STOP

Data: 2, 3, 4, 7, 9

EXERCISE 1B

1 A teacher reads out the register to check the students' attendance. Copy the empty flowchart and use the boxes below to fill it in. Give it a title, and draw in all the arrows.

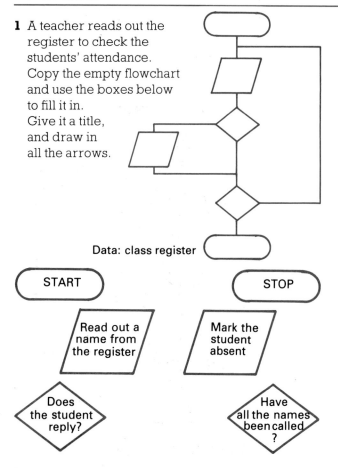

Data: class register

START

STOP

Read out a name from the register

Mark the student absent

Does the student reply?

Have all the names been called?

2 Here is a flowchart without a title.
 a Use the flowchart to process the data.
 b Examine your answers and suggest a title.

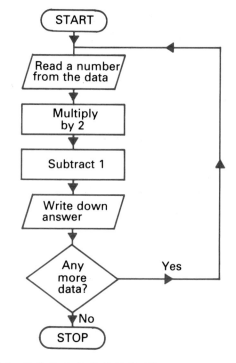

START

Read a number from the data

Multiply by 2

Subtract 1

Write down answer

Any more data?   Yes

No

STOP

Data: 1, 2, 3, 4, 5, 6, 7, 8, 9, 10

3

Copy this empty flowchart, then fill in the boxes to show Iain how to win a prize.

A game at the fair

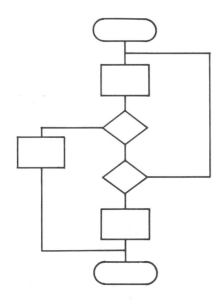

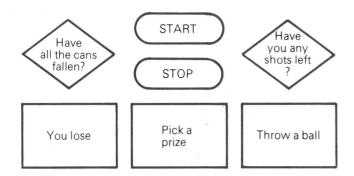

4

To decode a message you need a key.
Here is the key for this code.

SPACE	A	B	C	D	E	F	G	H	I	O	U	P
0	1	2	3	4	5	6	7	8	9	10	11	12

Follow the flowchart to decode this message:

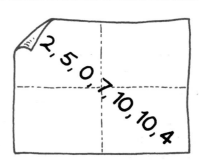

To decode a message

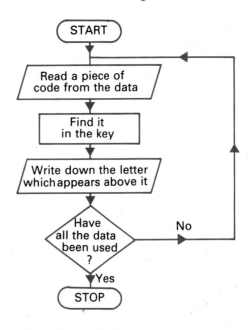

Data: 2, 5, 0, 7, 10, 10, 4

5 Children's coats are sold in 3 sizes:
large, medium and small.

  a Follow the flowchart to find the size and price
    of a coat, if the child's height is:
    (i) 100 cm   (ii) 137 cm   (iii) 155 cm.

  b 'Small' is for heights from 98 cm to 120 cm.
    Describe 'large'.

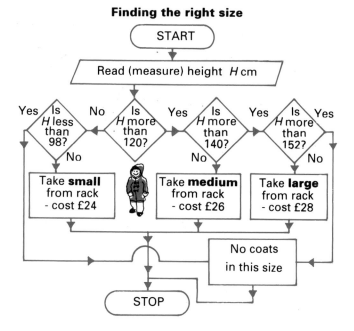

Finding the right size

INTERPRETING GRAPHS

EXERCISE 2

1 a What was the value of bread sales in 1994?

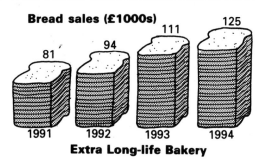

Bread sales (£1000s)

81   94   111   125

1991   1992   1993   1994

Extra Long-life Bakery

  b Calculate the difference in value of the sales in
    1991 and 1993.

2 a Which paper sold most copies, and which sold
    least?

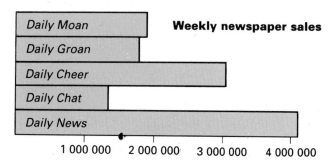

Daily Moan	**Weekly newspaper sales**
Daily Groan	
Daily Cheer	
Daily Chat	
Daily News	

1 000 000   2 000 000   3 000 000   4 000 000

  b Why is it difficult to read the exact sales? Does
    this really matter here?

  c *Estimate* the weekly sales of the *Daily Chat*.

3 a Which of these advertisements do you prefer?
    Why?

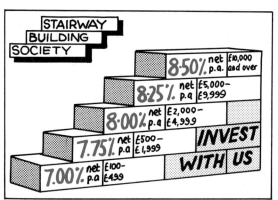

  b Which Building Society gives more interest on:
    (i) £1500   (ii) £7000   (iii) £50 000?

4 a Why is the demand for electricity lowest about 04 00 hours?

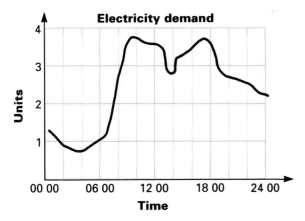

b (i) What are the two peak times?
(ii) Why do you think this is?
c Describe the demand over 24 hours.

5

The graph shows the shortest stopping distances for cars on dry roads.

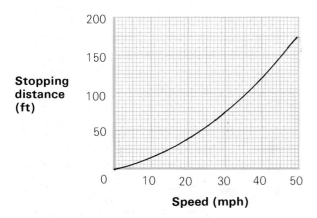

a Why does it start at (0, 0)?
b Estimate the shortest stopping distances for speeds of 15 mph and 31 mph.
c Why does the curve rise from left to right?
d Estimate the speeds for stopping distances of 50 feet and 100 feet.
e Make a table of stopping distances for speeds of 10, 20, . . . , 50 mph.

6 These two graphs show the average heights of girls and boys up to age 18.

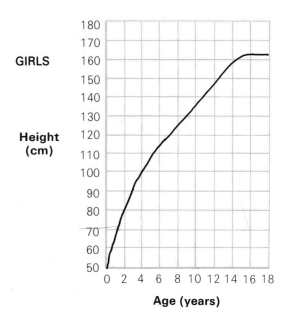

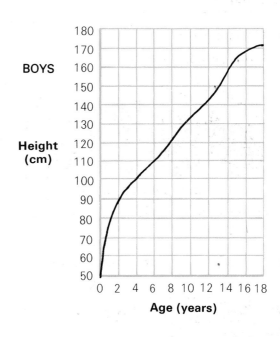

a Estimate the average heights of girls and boys at the age of:
(i) 2   (ii) 4   (iii) 16
b Read off the average ages of girls and boys whose heights are:
(i) 70 cm   (ii) 130 cm   (iii) 160 cm
c At what age do the heights of:
(i) girls   (ii) boys, begin to level off?
d Between what ages are both girls and boys growing fastest?

7 a How many spectators were in the park by:
  (i) 1.30 pm   (ii) 2 pm   (iii) 3 pm?

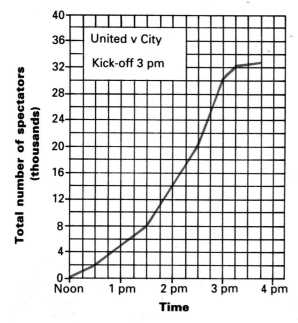

b By what time were 20 000 spectators inside?
c The ground holds 32 000. When should the gates have been shut?
d Sketch the curve, and show what it would look like when the game ends at 4.45 pm.

8 This diagram shows how the cost of producing a CD is made up.

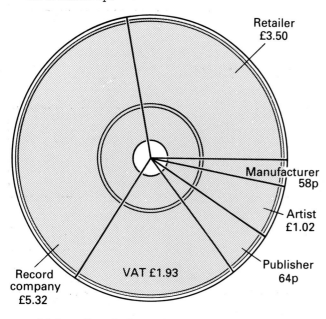

a Make a list of where the money goes, with the largest amount first.
b What is the total cost of the CD?
c What percentage, to the nearest whole number, goes to:
  (i) the record company   (ii) the artist?

9 These pie charts compare the amounts of fuel used in the UK in 1960 and 1992.

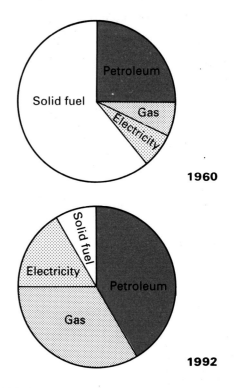

a Which fuels:
  (i) increased their share of the market
  (ii) decreased their share?
b What effect have these changes had on coal mining in the UK over this period?

CHALLENGE

Sketch examples of:

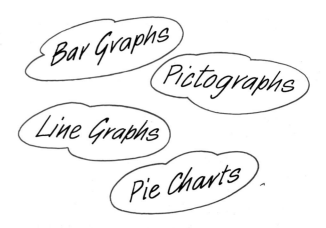

Write down some advantages and disadvantages of each type.

CLASS DISCUSSION/INVESTIGATION

Use these flowcharts to find the range, mode, mean and median of the given data.

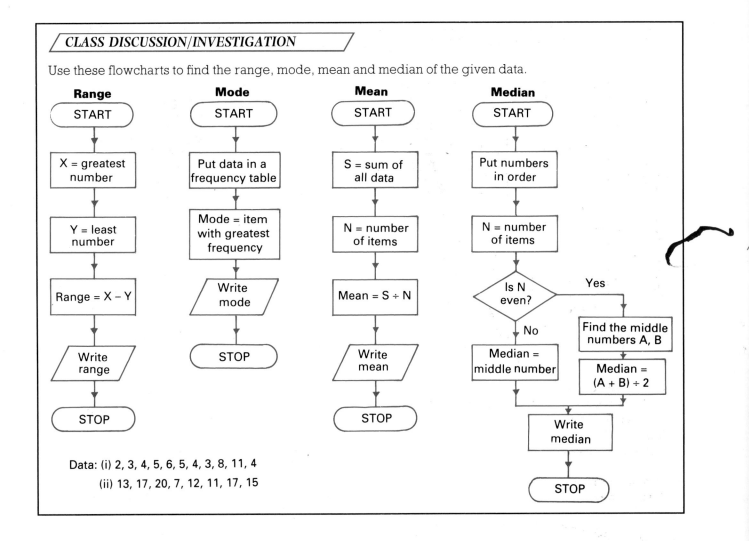

Data: (i) 2, 3, 4, 5, 6, 5, 4, 3, 8, 11, 4

   (ii) 13, 17, 20, 7, 12, 11, 17, 15

USING AVERAGES TO ANALYSE DATA

Reminder
To calculate the mean, mode, median and range of 2, 3, 5, 7, 8, 8, 9, 10:

Mean $= \dfrac{52}{8} = 6.5$ Mode $= 8$ Median $= \dfrac{7+8}{2} = 7.5$ Range $= 10 - 2 = 8$

EXERCISE 3A

1 A test every day for two weeks!
   a Rajiv's marks: 1, 8, 6, 6, 9, 5, 5, 4, 2, 4.
   Calculate the mean and range of his marks.
   b Janice's marks: 5, 5, 4, 4, 7, 7, 5, 3, 4, 6.
   Calculate the mean and range of her marks.
   c Who do you feel did better? Explain.

2 Arrange the data in order, from smallest to largest. Then write down the mode, or modes, for each.
   a Test marks: 15, 16, 17, 16, 11, 14, 17, 18, 15, 16, 13, 18, 16, 15, 17
   b Bus fares (pence): 30, 35, 45, 30, 40, 45, 30, 50, 30, 45, 35, 45
   c Football goals one Saturday: 0, 3, 0, 1, 2, 0, 3, 0, 2, 0, 1, 0, 0, 2, 1, 0, 0, 2

3 Arrange each of the following in order, from smallest to largest, to find the median:
  a 1, 4, 2, 9, 8, 6, 7
  b 4 cm, 12 cm, 2 cm, 3 cm, 1 cm, 6 cm, 2 cm, 3 cm
  c £1.20, £2.70, £1.90, £2.40, £0.80, £4, £2.90
  d 4 g, 8 g, 2 g, 5 g, 5 g, 1 g, 6 g, 2 g.

4 Calculate the mean, modal and median scores for these throws of a dice.

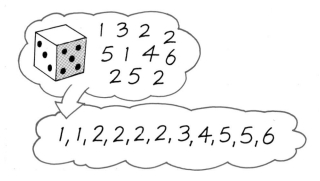

5 Declan was in the final of a high diving contest. The judges' scores for his best dive were:
7.7, 8.8, 8.6, 9.4, 8.5, 8.8, 9, 6.8
  a The lowest and highest scores were ignored. Why do you think this was done?
  b Calculate the mean and range of the remaining scores.

6 The 28 members of class 1Z obtained the following marks (out of 25) in an assessment test:
20   21   16   12   15   21   20
19   16   13   18   19   13   15
17   15   15   14   19   17   22
15   18   20   16   21   22   14
  a Arrange the marks in order, from lowest to highest.
  b Calculate the mean, and write down the median and the mode.
  c What is the range of marks?
  d What would you take as the pass mark?

7 Mr Gordon buys 10 boxes of matches. He finds that they contain 44, 44, 40, 43, 41, 45, 42, 44, 42, 40 matches.

  a Calculate the mean number of matches. Should he complain?
  b What is the mode?
  c Which gives the better picture—mean and range, or mode?

8 The weights, in kilograms, of members of the two tug-of-war teams are shown.

Blue team   **Red team**

65 64 62 62 62 60   47 47 53 55 84 94

  a Calculate the mean, median and modal weight for each team.
  b Who would you expect to win? Why?

9 Two firms manufacture heavy lifting chains. Capital Cranes asks for chains from each to test. The breaking weights of the chains were:
1st firm: 76, 85, 73, 80, 94, 88, 93, 76 tonnes
2nd firm: 120, 42, 120, 38, 140 tonnes
  a Calculate the mean and range, and median, breaking weight for each firm's chains.
  b Which firm would Capital Cranes choose? Why?

PRACTICAL PROJECT

Working on your own, or with a partner, choose a group of pupils and list their ages, weights, heights, or the time they take to travel to school. Calculate the mean, mode and median of the data. Illustrate the data in a statistical diagram.

FREQUENCY TABLES AND AVERAGES

Example
a Make a frequency table for these nine books.
b Calculate the mean, median and modal thickness of the books.

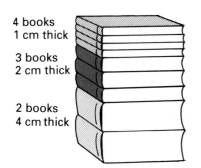

4 books
1 cm thick

3 books
2 cm thick

2 books
4 cm thick

a

Thickness (cm)	Frequency	Thickness × frequency
1	4	4
2	3	6
4	2	8
Total	9	18

b Mean $= \dfrac{18}{9} = 2\,\text{cm}$

Median = 5th book = 2 cm
Mode = 1 cm

EXERCISE 3B

1 At the fair, Anna fires sticker darts at the board.

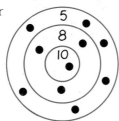

a Copy and complete the table.

Score	Frequency	Score × frequency
5		
8		
10		
Total		

b Calculate her mean, median and modal score.

2 Tony has a go with the darts.

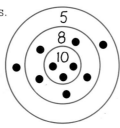

a Make a frequency table like the one in question **1**.
b Calculate his mean, median and modal score.
c Look at the two dartboards. Who got the better score? Do the averages agree with your answer?

3 Ace Bread Slicers claim that their machines cut 24 slices from a loaf.

a Copy and complete the table.

Number of slices	Frequency	Number × frequency
22	3	
23	10	
24	9	
25	6	
26	6	
27	6	
Total		

b Calculate the: (i) mode   (ii) median   (iii) mean number of slices.
c Which average is used in the claim?

4 'I would estimate 60 mm for the average length of these bolts, to the nearest millimetre', said Mr James of the Technical Department. He asked the class to measure the lengths, to check.

a Copy and complete the frequency table.

Length (mm)	Frequency	Length × frequency
58	3	
59	4	
60	2	
61	2	
62	8	
63	1	
Total		

b Calculate the mean, median and modal lengths of bolt.

c Was Mr James' guess a good one?

5 Over a year a building firm placed 50 orders for windows with Windproof Windows, and 50 with Clearglass. This tables shows the time taken for the windows to arrive.

Number of days	2	3	4	5	6	7	8
Windproof	3	4	5	12	15	6	5
Clearglass	0	0	5	25	20	0	0

a For each company, calculate the:
 (i) range   (ii) mode   (iii) median
 (iv) mean of the number of days before the windows arrived.

b Which company would you choose, and why?

6 Jess counted the number of letters in an article in the *Daily Moan*.

a Copy and complete the table.

Number of letters	Mid-value	Frequency	Mid-value × frequency
1–3	2	57	114
4–6		46	
7–9		28	
10–12		6	
13–15		3	
Total			

b Which number of letters, 1–3, 4–6, . . . is most common (the modal class)?

c Calculate the mean word length, correct to 1 decimal place.

7 Dan plotted the positions where his discus landed.

4 m   8 m   12 m   16 m   20 m   24 m

a Copy and complete the table (0–4 includes 0, but not 4).

Distance (m)	Mid-value	Frequency	Mid-value × frequency
0–4	2	1	
4–8	6	2	
8–12			
12–16			
16–20			
20–24			
Total			

b In which zone did most throws land?

c Calculate the mean length of Dan's throw.

PRACTICAL PROJECT

Choose a paragraph in a book or in a newspaper. Make a frequency table for the number of letters in the words. Analyse the data, and write a report.

SCATTER DIAGRAMS

EXERCISE 4A

1 During a two-week school camp, weather readings were taken every day.

These scatter diagrams were drawn.

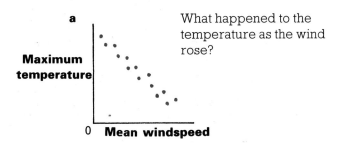

a What happened to the temperature as the wind rose?

b Was the rainfall affected by the wind strength?

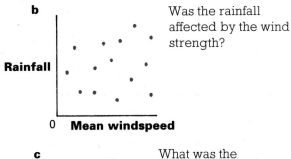

c What was the connection between the temperature and the hours of sunshine?

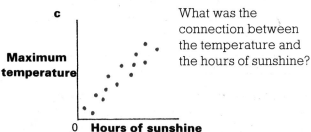

2 Match each scatter diagram with the correct set of axes.

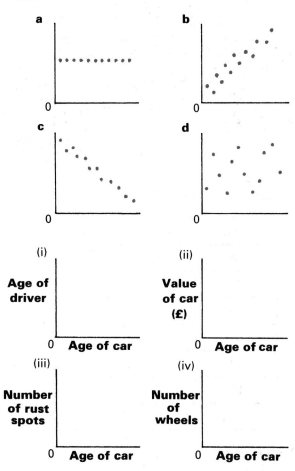

3 Copy these sets of axes, and draw a suitable scatter diagram on each.

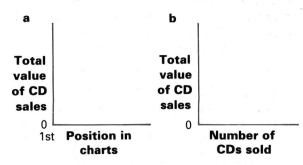

4 Draw scatter diagrams which show the connection, if any, between students' exam marks and:
a their heights   **b** the time spent on revision
c the number of lessons missed through absence.

EXERCISE 4B

1 Marie records the distances and times her friends are from school.

Distance (km)	29	20	4	10	24	15	8	24	12	14
Time (min)	70	50	10	25	60	40	16	55	30	44

The mean distance is 16 km, and the mean time is 40 minutes. She plots the mean point M(16, 40).
a Copy the axes on squared paper, and plot M.

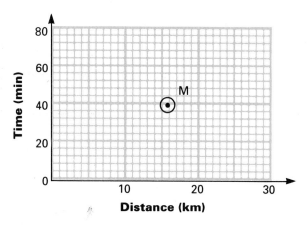

b Draw a scatter diagram, and a line of best fit *through* M.
c Marjorie lives 18 km from school. Estimate her time of travel.

2 Carol and her friends note the number of newspapers they deliver, and the time they take.

Time (min)	50	45	40	40	30	25	20	30	35	28
Newspapers	60	50	45	48	44	36	30	34	43	38

a Calculate: (i) the mean time   (ii) the mean number of newspapers.
b Draw axes on squared paper, and plot the mean point M.

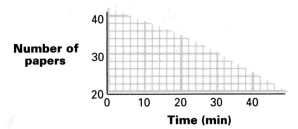

c Draw a scatter diagram, and a line of best fit through M.
d Estimate the time Jason takes to deliver 55 papers.

3 Mal wants to find out if there is any link between a poor defence, in soccer, and the number of points the team has. He chooses ten teams.

Goals against	9	28	19	10	13	20	14	24	16	22
Number of points	25	5	11	24	17	9	16	7	12	6

a Calculate each mean, and plot M on squared paper, as before.
b Draw a scatter diagram, and a line of best fit through M.

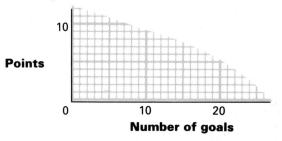

c Describe the link between goals against and points.
d A team has 20 points. Estimate the number of goals scored against it.

INVESTIGATION

Statistics are used in the media (newspapers, TV, magazines, etc.) to advertise and to support arguments and reports. Find examples, and analyse them. Write a report on what you find.

SPREADSHEETS AND QUESTIONNAIRES

NAME	SEX	HAIR	EYES	HEIGHT	WEIGHT	AGE	SHOE SIZE
BARRY	BOY	BLACK	BROWN	175	55	14	9
MARY	GIRL	BROWN	GREY	164	43	13	6
ALEX	BOY	RED	BROWN	160	41	13	5
ZOE	GIRL	BLONDE	BLUE	166	56	14	6
KARL	BOY	BROWN	BROWN	172	58	15	8
VANITA	GIRL	BROWN	GREEN	168	57	14	7
SALMA	GIRL	BLACK	BROWN	163	49	14	5
CHRIS	BOY	RED	GREY	169	47	13	7
TINA	GIRL	BLONDE	BROWN	170	58	15	7
HAYLEY	GIRL	BROWN	BLUE	178	62	16	10
PETER	BOY	BLACK	GREEN	175	56	15	8
DAVID	BOY	BLACK	BLUE	176	58	14	9
LAURA	GIRL	BLONDE	BLUE	165	44	14	6
CAITLIN	GIRL	BROWN	BROWN	161	40	13	5
TONY	BOY	RED	GREY	171	52	14	8

1 a Either design your own questionnaire to collect data about a group of pupils, or use the data in the box above to make a spreadsheet on a computer.

b Use your computer program to:
(i) sort the data with the heights in ascending order
(ii) draw a pie chart of the hair colours
(iii) draw a scatter diagram of shoe sizes and heights
(iv) calculate the mean height and weight.

c Use the computer to search for:
(i) the boy with blue eyes who is over 175 cm tall
(ii) the girl who is 14 years old, with shoe size 7.
Now think up some more questions. (If you are using your own data, make up your own questions.)

2 Design your own questionnaire, collect data and make a spreadsheet for one of these topics:
a shopping survey; travel to school; school meals.

A DAY TRIP

The pupils in Mrs Adams' class are planning a day trip. There are five suggestions for the outing, and the pupils list their preferences in order, 1 to 5.

1 Two groups of four friends have exactly the same preferences. What are their initials?

2 a Make a tally chart for each suggestion, like the one that has been started here for the seaside.

Preference	Tally	Frequency
1	JHT JHT I	11
2		
3		
4		
5		

b Which destination has been given most:
(i) first choices
(ii) last choices?

3 Try to use your statistics to reach an agreement for going to each place.

4 Mrs Adams has to decide on the destination. How can she make the fairest choice?

5 In the end she decides that the form will split up and go to two different places.
a Is it possible for all the pupils to have:
(i) their first choice
(ii) their first or second choice?
b Which two places does she choose? List the initials of the pupils going to each one.

PUPIL	SEASIDE	LONDON	ZOO	CONCERT	FUNFAIR
J.A.	1	4	2	5	3
W.A.	5	1	3	4	2
R.B.	1	2	5	3	4
T.C.	3	5	2	1	4
S.E.	5	1	3	4	2
J.F.	1	5	2	3	4
T.F.	5	4	2	1	3
I.H.	2	1	5	3	4
J.M.	1	2	5	4	3
P.M.	4	1	5	3	2
R.M.	1	4	2	5	3
S.N.	5	2	3	1	4
A.P.	5	1	4	3	2
J.R.	4	2	5	1	3
T.R.	1	5	2	3	4
W.R.	5	1	3	4	2
K.S.	1	5	2	4	3
N.S.	4	2	5	1	3
C.T.	5	1	3	4	2
G.T.	1	2	5	3	4
S.T.	1	5	2	3	4
A.W.	5	4	2	1	3
K.W.	5	4	2	1	3
P.Y.	1	5	2	3	4
R.Y.	1	5	2	4	3
T.Y.	5	2	3	1	4

CHECK-UP ON HANDLING DATA

1 Use the flowchart to calculate the total bill for the given data.

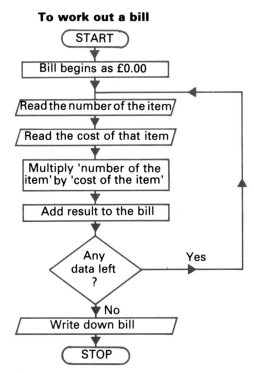

To work out a bill

START
↓
Bill begins as £0.00
↓
Read the number of the item
↓
Read the cost of that item
↓
Multiply 'number of the item' by 'cost of the item'
↓
Add result to the bill
↓
Any data left ? — Yes
↓ No
Write down bill
↓
STOP

Data: 3, £2.99, 5, £6.50, 6, £1.95, 4, £12.30

2

Annual sales of a large department store

Key: ▨ ladies' clothes ▨ men's clothes

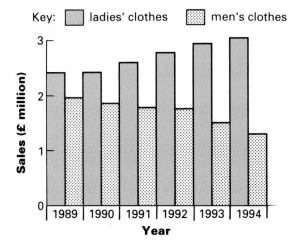

a Did the store sell more men's or ladies' clothes over the six-year period?
b In which year were the sales of men's clothes about half that of ladies'?
c Describe the trend of the sales of each type of clothes.
d Roughly, what was the total amount in sales of men's clothes?

3 Gemma grew sunflowers for a competition.

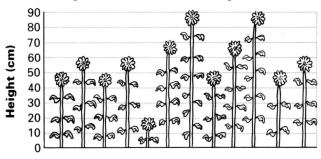

Calculate the:
a range **b** mode **c** median **d** mean height of the sunflowers.

4

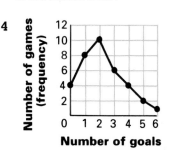

a Copy and complete the frequency table.
b Calculate the mean number of goals, correct to 1 decimal place.
c Write down the median and modal number of goals.

Goals scored	Frequency	Goals × frequency
0	4	
1		

5 a Copy and complete this table:

Number of press-ups	Mid-value	Frequency	Mid-value × frequency
11–15	13	5	
16–20		8	
21–25		13	
26–30		6	
	Total		

b Calculate the mean number, to the nearest whole number.
c Which is the modal class?

6 Copy the axes and draw scatter diagrams to illustrate any connections you think exist between the items shown.

PYTHAGORAS

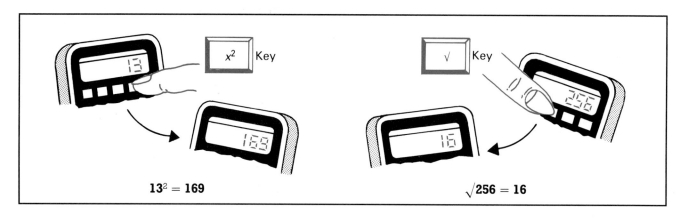

$13^2 = 169$ $\sqrt{256} = 16$

LOOKING BACK

1 Use the $\boxed{x^2}$ key on your calculator to calculate:

a 7^2 **b** 19^2 **c** 1.8^2 **d** 0.9^2 **e** 0.3^2

2 Calculate the area of each square:

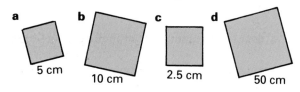

a 5 cm **b** 10 cm **c** 2.5 cm **d** 50 cm

3 Use the $\boxed{\sqrt{}}$ key on your calculator to find:

a $\sqrt{9}$ **b** $\sqrt{36}$ **c** $\sqrt{1.96}$ **d** $\sqrt{0.36}$ **e** $\sqrt{289}$

4 Calculate the length of side of each square.

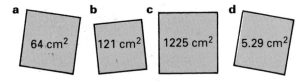

a 64 cm² **b** 121 cm² **c** 1225 cm² **d** 5.29 cm²

5 This grid has centimetre squares. Write down:
a the coordinates of A, B, C and D
b the lengths of AB and BC
c the area of square ABCD.

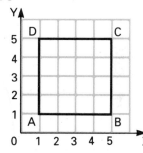

6 Repeat question **5** for this diagram.

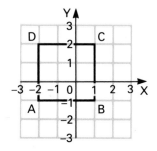

7 How many slabs are there in these square paved areas?

a 6 slabs **b** 15 slabs

8 How many square slabs with 1 metre sides are along each edge of these square patios?

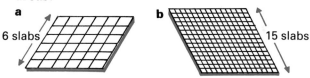

a 16 m² **b** 144 m²

9 Calculate:
a $4^2 + 5^2$ **b** $2.5^2 + 1.5^2$ **c** $17^2 - 16^2$

10 Calculate, correct to 1 decimal place:
a $\sqrt{12}$ **b** $\sqrt{8.4}$ **c** $\sqrt{0.37}$ **d** $\sqrt{124.6}$

11 Sketch these shapes, and mark all the right angles.

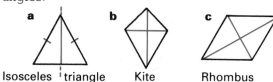

a Isosceles triangle **b** Kite **c** Rhombus

CLASS DISCUSSION/EXERCISE 1

1 a *Estimate* the lengths x m and x cm in these diagrams.
  b What other method could you use to find the lengths?

(i)

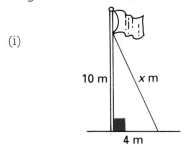

(ii)

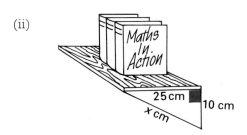

(iii)

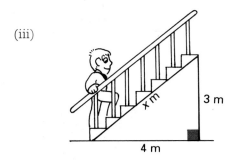

2 Make a table, and start to fill it in by counting the small squares in the diagram below.

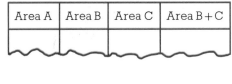

Area A	Area B	Area C	Area B + C

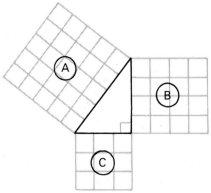

3 Add more entries to the table by counting squares to find the areas of the squares on the sides of these right-angled triangles. Remember to count half-squares.

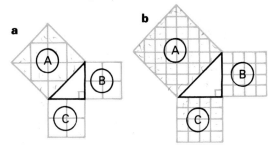

4 a Enter these areas in the table also.
  b Can you see the connection between area A and area B + C every time?

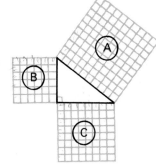

In fact it is always true that:
in a right-angled triangle, the square on the hypotenuse (the side opposite the right angle) is equal to the sum of the squares on the other two sides.

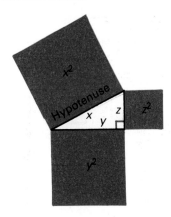

This is called the **Theorem of Pythagoras.**
Pythagoras was a Greek mathematician who lived in Sicily in the sixth century BC.
He gave a proof of the result $x^2 = y^2 + z^2$.

Pythagoras' Theorem connects the *areas* of squares on the sides of right-angled triangles. Using your calculator, you can then calculate the *lengths* of the sides.

109

5 Calculate the lengths of the sides of these squares (**e** and **f** correct to 1 decimal place).

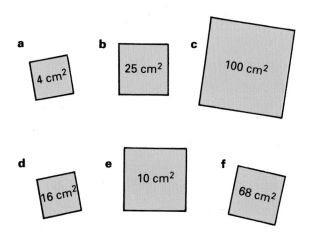

a 4 cm²

b 25 cm²

c 100 cm²

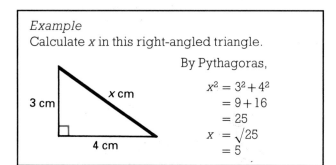

d 16 cm²

e 10 cm²

f 68 cm²

Example

Calculate x in this right-angled triangle.

By Pythagoras,

$$x^2 = 3^2 + 4^2$$
$$= 9 + 16$$
$$= 25$$
$$x = \sqrt{25}$$
$$= 5$$

3 cm x cm   4 cm

---

6 Calculate x in each triangle. The heavy side is the hypotenuse, the side opposite the right angle.

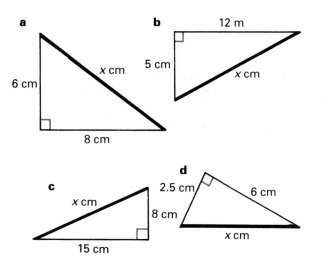

a 6 cm x cm   8 cm

b 12 m   5 cm x cm

c x cm   8 cm   15 cm

d 2.5 cm   6 cm   8 cm x cm

7 Go back to the diagrams in question **1**.
Calculate x in each one to find the lengths, correct to 1 decimal place, of the wire, bracket and staircase.

PRACTICAL PROJECTS

1 *Make accurate drawings or tracings of these two Pythagoras diagrams.*
Cut the shaded squares into the pieces shown, and try to fit them together to cover the square on the hypotenuse of the right-angled triangle.

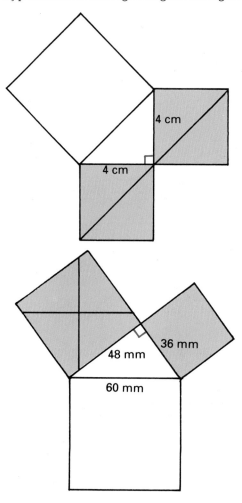

4 cm   4 cm

36 mm   48 mm   60 mm

2 a *Draw this right-angled triangle on squared paper.*

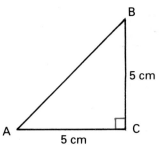

B   5 cm   A   C   5 cm

b *Measure AB, correct to 0.1 cm. Check by calculation.*

3 *Repeat **2** for a right-angled △ABC with AC = 4 cm and BC = 3 cm.*

EXERCISE 2A

Note: Throughout these exercises, units of length are only marked in practical situations.

1 Calculate x in each right-angled triangle. For example, in **a**, $x^2 = 9^2 + 12^2$, etc.

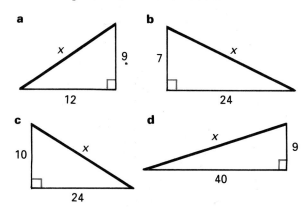

a

x

9

12

b

7

x

24

c

10

x

24

d

x

40

9

2 Calculate y in each triangle.

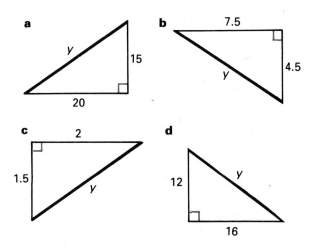

a

y

15

20

b

7.5

y

4.5

c

2

1.5

y

d

12

y

16

3 Calculate a, b, c, d, correct to 1 decimal place.

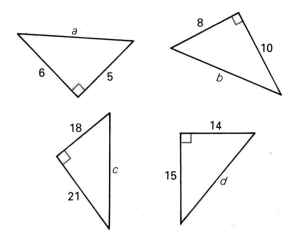

a

6

5

8

10

b

18

21

c

14

15

d

4 Calculate the length of the hypotenuse in each triangle.

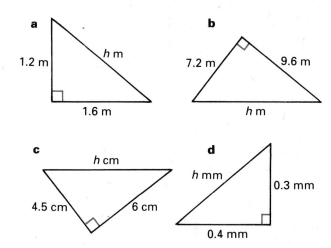

a

1.2 m

h m

1.6 m

b

7.2 m

9.6 m

h m

c

h cm

4.5 cm

6 cm

d

h mm

0.3 mm

0.4 mm

5 Calculate the length of the ladder.

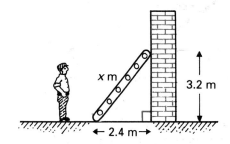

x m

3.2 m

← 2.4 m →

6 Calculate the length of the ramp.

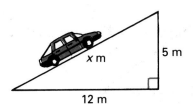

x m

5 m

12 m

7 Calculate the length of the wire.

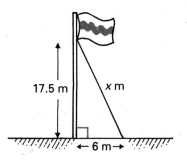

17.5 m

x m

← 6 m →

8 Calculate the distance (x m) Ewan runs along the ground to the foot of the steps for another turn on the slide.

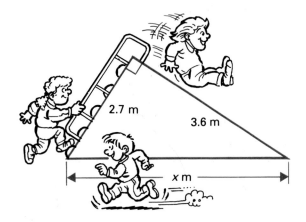

2.7 m

3.6 m

x m

9 How long is the sloping edge of the bracket?

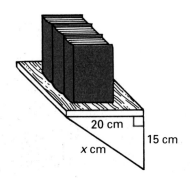

20 cm

15 cm

x cm

10 Calculate the length of Channel Street.

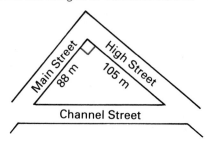

Main Street
88 m

High Street
105 m

Channel Street

11 Calculate the distance x metres.

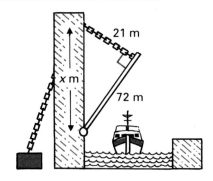

21 m

x m

72 m

PRACTICAL PROJECT

a *Measure the length and breadth of:*
(i) this book   (ii) your desk or table.
b *Calculate the length of a diagonal of each one, then check by measurement.*

EXERCISE 2B

First find the right-angled triangle

1 Name all the right-angled triangles you can see in these diagrams.

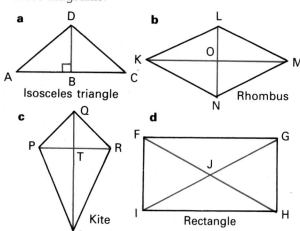

a   D

A   B   C

Isosceles triangle

b   L

K   O   M

N   Rhombus

c   Q

P   T   R

Kite

S

d   F   G

J

I   H

Rectangle

2 Calculate a, b, c, d, e (e correct to 1 decimal place).

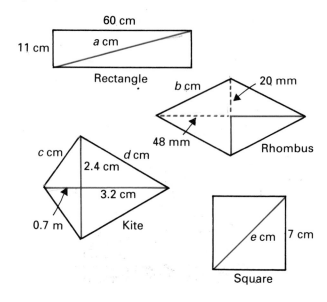

60 cm

11 cm a cm

Rectangle

b cm   20 mm

48 mm   Rhombus

c cm   2.4 cm d cm

3.2 cm

0.7 m   Kite

e cm   7 cm

Square

3 The gate is rectangular. Calculate the length of the diagonal bar.

1 m

2.4 m

4 Calculate the length of a diagonal of the square record cover, correct to 1 decimal place.

COLLECTION of KOOL KATZ

12 inches

5 Calculate the length of the sloping edge of the roof.

x m

2.4 m

7 m

6 The car jack is rhombus shaped. Calculate:

a *x*
b the perimeter of the jack.

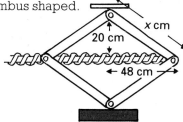

x cm

20 cm

48 cm

7 Calculate the length of each edge of the kite-shaped earring.

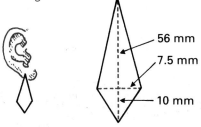

56 mm

7.5 mm

10 mm

8 Calculate the lengths of the edges of the sails on this model yacht.

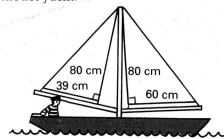

80 cm 80 cm

39 cm 60 cm

PUZZLE

How many right-angled triangles can you find in this square? Name them all.

D   C

O

A   B

CHALLENGE

It is not always easy to measure the diagonal (corner to corner) distance in a room because of desks or furniture. Find a way to calculate it, and try out your method in the classroom or in a room at home—but first estimate the distance.

INVESTIGATION

a *Use Pythagoras' Theorem to calculate the length of the hypotenuse of this triangle.*

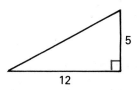

5

12

b *Copy this table of 'Pythagorean triples', and fill in the gap in the second row.*

3	4	5
5	12	
7	24	25
9	40	41

c *Use the sequences of numbers in the columns to guess three more numbers in each column.*

d *Check that in rows 5, 6 and 7 the sum of the squares of the first two numbers is equal to the square of the third one.*

CALCULATING DISTANCE USING COORDINATES

Brian is hiking from Amber to Bolt. You can see both places on the map. Each square on the grid is 1 km long. How far does he have to hike?

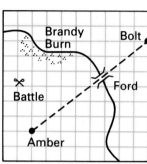

Step 1
Sketch a right-angled triangle.

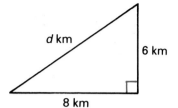

Step 2
By Pythagoras' Theorem,
$$d^2 = 8^2 + 6^2$$
$$= 64 + 36$$
$$= 100$$
$$d = 10$$

The distance from Amber to Bolt is 10 km.

EXERCISE 3

Where lengths are not exact, give them correct to 1 decimal place.

1 (i) Sketch each triangle, and mark the lengths of the two shorter sides in each.
   (ii) Calculate the length of the hypotenuse of each triangle.

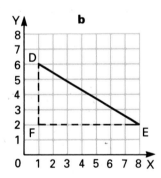

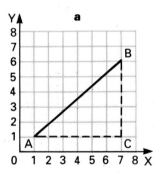

2 The classroom ceiling is covered with tiles of side 1 metre. Sketch a triangle with hypotenuse AB, and calculate AB.

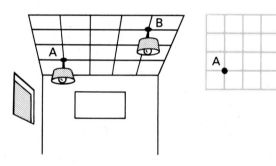

3 Two plants grow on a patio made of square slabs of side 1 metre. Sketch a triangle with hypotenuse QR, and calculate QR.

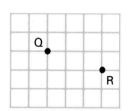

4

Angus is a shot-putter. The points where the shots land are plotted on this 1 m grid. Calculate the lengths of his throws, from 0.

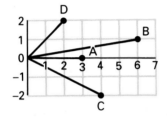

5

Fred is taking part in a cross-country run. He can take the long road by the path, or cut across The Moss. The Moss, however, is tough going and he decides he won't go this way unless it saves him at least 4 km.

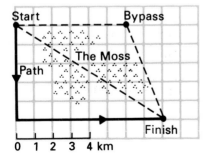

a Should he cross The Moss?
b He could also use the bypass. How much shorter than the path is this route?

6 a Plot the points P(1, 1), Q(2, 5) and R(6, 4).
  b Calculate PQ and QR.
  c What kind of triangle is PQR?

7 (i) Plot each set of points, and join them up.
  (ii) Calculate the length of the hypotenuse of each
     triangle.
  a A(1, 1), B(5, 4), C(5, 1)
  b D(6, 2), E(9, 8), F(9, 2)
  c G(2, 4), H(6, 8), K(2, 8)

8

The only way to get from A to B in this mountainous country is to go by the pass CD. The dotted line AB shows the route of a proposed tunnel. The side of each square is 1 km long.

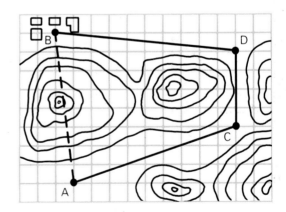

Calculate:
a the length of the tunnel route, AB
b the length of the road route A → C → D → B
c the saving in distance by the tunnel.

CALCULATING THE LENGTH OF A SHORTER SIDE IN A RIGHT-ANGLED TRIANGLE

Example
A ladder 6.5 m long is set up 2.5 m from a wall.
How far up the wall will the ladder reach?

By Pythagoras,
$$x^2 + 2.5^2 = 6.5^2$$
$$x^2 + 6.25 = 42.25$$
$$\underline{-6.25 \quad\quad -6.25}$$
$$x^2 = 36$$
$$x = 6$$
The ladder will reach 6 m up the wall.

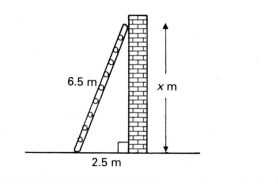
6.5 m   x m
2.5 m

EXERCISE 4A

1 Use Pythagoras' Theorem to calculate *x*.

a
17
x
15

b
29
x
21
6

c
37
x
35

d
6.8
x

2 Calculate *a*, *b*, *c*, *d*, correct to 1 decimal place.

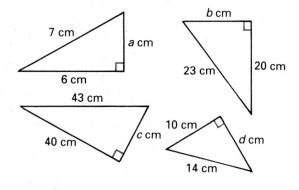
7 cm
a cm
6 cm
b cm
23 cm
20 cm
43 cm
40 cm
c cm
10 cm
d cm
14 cm

3

a
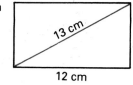
13 cm
12 cm

Calculate the height of the rectangle.

b
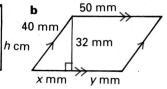
50 mm
40 mm
h cm
32 mm
x mm   y mm

In the parallelogram, calculate: (i) *x*   (ii) *y*.

4 Calculate the length of the vertical cable.

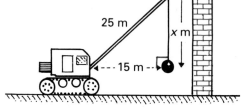
25 m
x m
15 m

5 Calculate the height of the back of the bookcase.

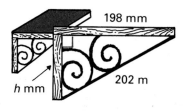
198 mm
202 m
h mm

6 Calculate the distance *d* m between the struts on the clothes dryer.

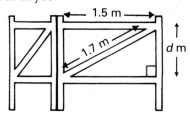
1.5 m
1.7 m
d m

7 Calculate:
a AB
b DC

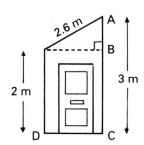
2.6 m
A
B
3 m
2 m
D   C

EXERCISE 4B

1

Pauline is making a kite. Help her, by calculating x and y.

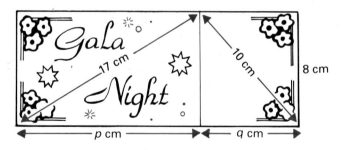

2 On this invitation card, calculate:
a p **b** q **c** the width of the card.

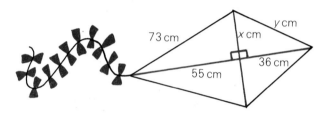

3 The length of the diagonal of the picture is 30 cm. Calculate x.

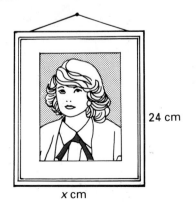

4 Two planes are flying over a church, one above the other. A radar station 8 km from the church plots the planes at distances of 9 and 10 km.

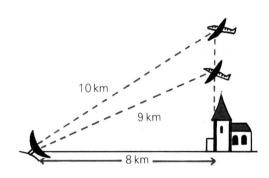

Calculate, to the nearest *metre*:
a the height of each plane above the ground
b the height of one plane above the other.

5 Calculate:
a x
b y
c the height of the block of flats.

USING PYTHAGORAS' THEOREM IN ISOSCELES TRIANGLES

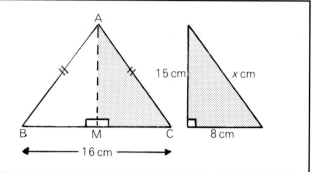

△ABC is isosceles.
AM is the axis of symmetry, so the angles at M are right angles, and BM = MC = ½BC = 8 cm.
Using Pythagoras' Theorem,
$x^2 = 8^2 + 15^2$ or $x^2 = 8^2 + 15^2$
$= 64 + 225$ $\quad x = 17$, using a calculator
$= 289$
$x = \sqrt{289} = 17$

So AC is 17 cm long.

EXERCISE 5

1 △DEF is isosceles.
  a Write down the length of ME.
  b Calculate DE.

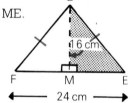

2 The front of the tent is an isosceles triangle.
  a Write down the length of BC.
  b Calculate AB.

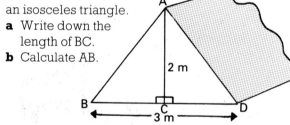

3

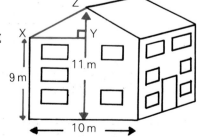

Calculate the length of the supporting strut PQ of the swing, correct to 3 significant figures.

4 a Write down the lengths of:
  (i) XY (ii) YZ

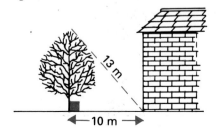

  b Calculate the length of the sloping edge XZ of the roof, correct to 3 significant figures.

5 Copy the isosceles △ABC.
  a Draw a line CM from C to AB, meeting AB at M, and making two right-angled triangles AMC and BMC.
  b Calculate:
    (i) the height of △ABC
    (ii) the area of △ABC.

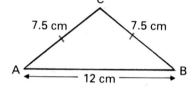

6 Each face of the pyramid is an isosceles triangle. The entrance is at the centre B of the base.
  a Sketch △TAC, with TA = TC.
  b Draw TB, and calculate its length.

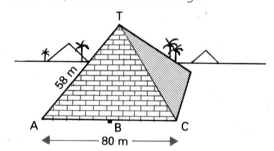

BRAINSTORMER

  a *If the tree is blown down will it hit the house?*
  b *How high can the tree be before there is a risk of it hitting the house?*

YOUR CHOICE—SELECT A STRATEGY

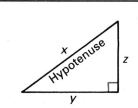

By Pythagoras: Also:
$$x^2 = y^2 + z^2 \qquad y^2 = x^2 - z^2$$
$$z^2 = x^2 - y^2$$

Make right-angled triangles if necessary.

EXERCISE 6A

1 Calculate a, b, c, d.

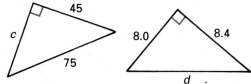

2 Calculate e, f, g, h.

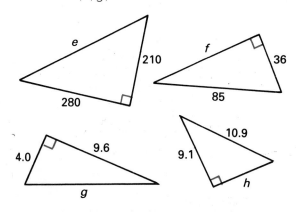

3 How far from the tree is the wire fixed to the ground?

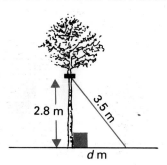

4 Calculate the length of the sloping edge of the roof of Fido's kennel.

5 Calculate the height of the van.

6 Calculate the height of the frame, in millimetres.

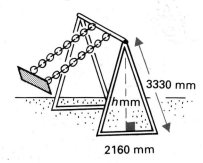

7 A plane flies 200 km east, then 480 km south. How far is it from the airport?

8 A ladder 12.5 m long is placed against the wall of a house. The foot of the ladder is 3.5 m from the foot of the wall. How high up the wall does it reach?

EXERCISE 6B

1 Larry made a big mistake. He took a short-cut across the rectangular field where Billy the goat lived. He had gone 20 metres along the path when he saw Billy following him.

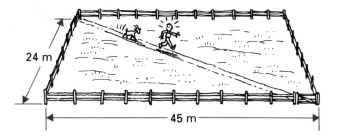

24 m

45 m

a How much further had he to go along the path?
b How much longer is it round two sides of the field than along the path?

2 Calculate the distance, to the nearest km, from:
a Merton to Newbay
b Newbay to Oldhaven
c Oldhaven to Merton.

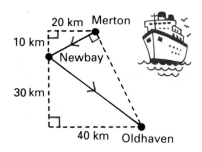

20 km Merton
10 km
Newbay
30 km
40 km Oldhaven

3 Sketch these diagrams, and draw one or two lines in each to make a right-angled triangle, so that you can calculate *y*.

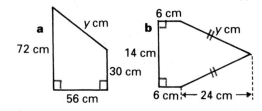

a y cm
72 cm
56 cm

b 6 cm
14 cm
30 cm
y cm
6 cm ⟵ 24 cm ⟶

4 How long is the base of the window box?

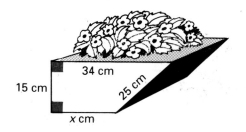

34 cm
15 cm
25 cm
x cm

5 The edge of this label is gold leaf. Calculate:
a *x*   **b** the perimeter of the label.

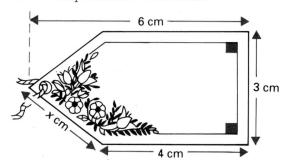

6 cm
3 cm
x cm
4 cm

6 Calculate the length of the sloping edge of this writing bureau.

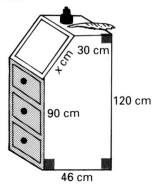

30 cm
x cm
120 cm
90 cm
46 cm

7 The fire engine has an extension ladder.

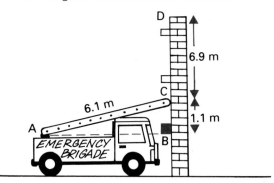

D
6.9 m
C
6.1 m
1.1 m
A
B
EMERGENCY BRIGADE

Calculate:
a the distance AB from A to the wall
b the length of ladder needed to reach from A to D.

8 How far is it, to the nearest yard, from the corner flag A to:
a player X   **b** player Y?

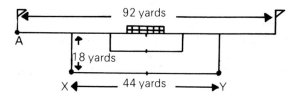

92 yards
A
18 yards
X ⟵ 44 yards ⟶ Y

CHECK-UP ON PYTHAGORAS

1 Calculate x in each right-angled triangle.

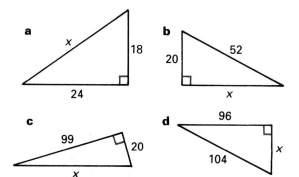

a x 18   24

b   52   20 x

c   99   20 x

d   96   104 x

2 What might be wrong with this calculation?

$$h^2 = 8^2 + 6^2$$
$$= 64 + 36$$
$$= 100$$
$$h = 10$$

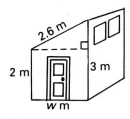

8   6 h

3 Calculate y.

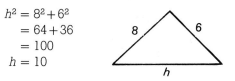

a   15   9 y

b   32 y 60

4 What length is the sloping bracket?

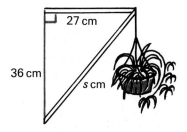

27 cm   36 cm s cm

5 Calculate the length of each diagonal of this rhombus.

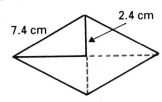

2.4 cm   7.4 cm

6 a Plot the points A(1, 4) and B(9, 10), and calculate the length of AB.

b C is the point (21, 15). Calculate the length of BC.

7 Each square glass pane has sides 1 metre long. Calculate the distances:
a AB   **b** AC
c BC, correct to 1 decimal place.

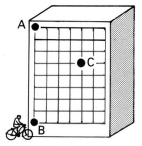

8 Calculate the width of this garden hut.

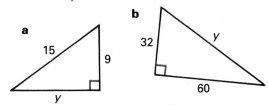

2.6 m   2 m   3 m w m

9 Calculate the length AB of the edge of the wing of this paper plane.

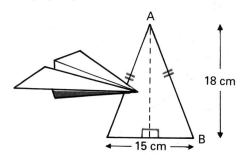

18 cm   15 cm

10 In $\triangle$AEC, EA = EC, and in $\triangle$CDE, DE = DC. Calculate the lengths of:
a EC   **b** DF

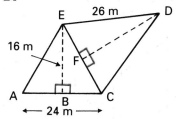

E   26 m   D   16 m   F   A   B   C   24 m

11 The stripe on the road sign is symmetrical about the line through B and C. Calculate:
a AB   **b** the perimeter of the stripe.

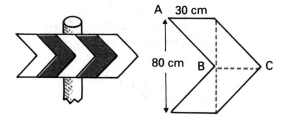

A   30 cm   80 cm   B   C

REVIEW: NUMBERS 2

LENGTH AND AREA

1 Write down the lengths of the lines OA, OB and AB in:
  a mm **b** cm.

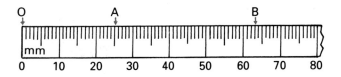

2 A playing card measures 8.8 cm by 5.7 cm.
  a Draw an accurate rectangle for the card.
  b Measure the length of its diagonal, correct to 1 decimal place.
  c Calculate the perimeter of the playing card.

3 Measure the diameter of the button and the perimeters of the domino and the brooch.

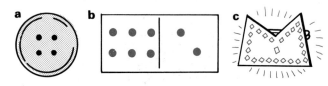

  Give your answers in:
  (i) millimetres (ii) centimetres.

4 A racing circuit is 7.5 km long.
  a How far will a car have travelled after 50 laps?
  b One car covers 435 km in a race. How many laps did it complete?

5 Two cars are 3.15 m and 2.87 m long.
  a Calculate the difference in their lengths; also their total length if parked end to end.
  b The cars are parked nose-to-tail in a garage 7 m long. How much space is left?

6 Twelve encyclopaedias, placed side by side, take up 44.4 cm of shelf space. Calculate their average thickness.

7 a Calculate the area of the triangle ABC where A is the point (3, 2), B is (7, 2) and C is (5, 8).
  b D is the point (5, 4). Calculate the area of:
  (i) △ABD (ii) V-kite ADBC.

8 How many 20 cm by 20 cm square tiles are needed to cover a rectangular floor 6 m long and 4 m broad?

9 Find the area of each rectangular object. Remember to include the units of area in your answers.

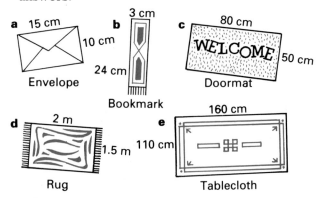

10 Calculate the areas of the shaded triangles.

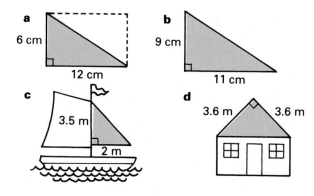

11 Calculate:
  a the breadth of an envelope 22 cm long, with an area of 242 cm²
  b the length of a stamp 20 mm broad, with an area of 900 mm².

12 Calculate the areas of these shapes, which are made of rectangles and right-angled triangles.

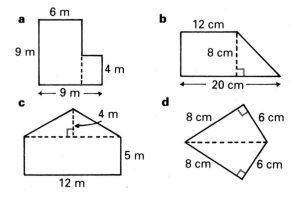

CIRCLES

1 Calculate:
  a the diameter of the inside of the tyre
  b the radius of the outside of the tyre.

17.5 cm

56 cm

2 Using $\pi = 3$, calculate the circumferences of the inside and the outside of the tyre in question **1**.

3 Taking $\pi = 3$, calculate:
  (i) the circumference   (ii) the area
  of each of these:

a

Button
(diameter 2 cm)

b

Clock face
(diameter 15 cm)

c

Cake
(radius 12 cm)

4 Sheena is a super skater. Here she cuts a perfect circle of radius 5 m.

Calculate, correct to 3 significant figures:
  a the circumference of the circle
  b its area.
     (Use the π key on your calculator.)

5 Calculate the circumference and area of the circular part of each musical instrument. Give your answers correct to 3 significant figures.

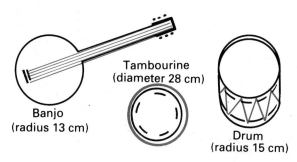

Tambourine
(diameter 28 cm)

Banjo
(radius 13 cm)

Drum
(radius 15 cm)

6 Each wheel of a bicycle has a circumference of 1.8 m. How far will the bicycle go in:
  a 1 turn   **b** 10 turns
  c 1000 turns   **d** $\frac{1}{2}$ turn of each wheel?

7 The waste-paper basket has a circular top and base. Calculate, correct to 3 significant figures:
  a the circumference of the top
  b the area of the base.

←30 cm→

←20 cm→

8 A circular table top has a radius of 1.4 m. Calculate, correct to 3 significant figures:
  a the circumference of the table
  b its area.

9 The diameter of this camera lens is 75 mm. Calculate its area, correct to 3 significant figures.

10 Calculate, correct to 3 significant figures, the circumference of:

  a the picture frame, with diameter 37 cm

  b the tin of shoe polish, with radius 4.5 cm

  c the TV aerial, with diameter 3.2 m.

11 Assume that the Earth's orbit round the sun is a circle with radius 93 million miles.
  a Calculate the length of the orbit, correct to 2 significant figures.
  b Write the number in standard form, $a \times 10^n$.

VOLUME

1 Calculate the volumes of these cuboids, made from small cubes with sides 1 cm long.

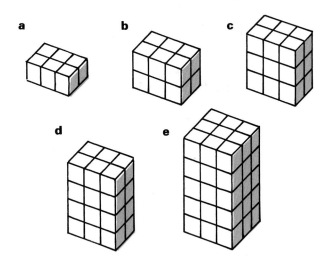

2 Calculate the volume of each box container. Include units in your answers.

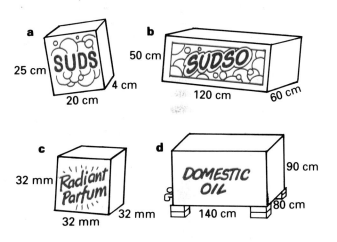

3 Find the volume of the oil tank in **2d** above in:
a millilitres **b** litres.

4 Miriam buys a 2-litre bottle of fabric conditioner for her washing machine.

 50 ml

a How many millilitres does the bottle hold?
b How many 50 ml capfuls will she get from it?

5 Megan needs a new freezer. The Coolcon model is 80 cm by 60 cm by 50 cm, and costs £220. The Ice Box model is 70 cm by 70 cm by 40 cm, and costs £190.
a Which freezer has the larger capacity in litres? By how many litres?
b Which gives more freezing space per £ of purchase price?

6 Tim has a number of toy cube bricks which are stored in this box. The edges of the bricks are all 8 cm long. How many bricks will fit:
a along one edge of the box
b in one layer
c in the box?

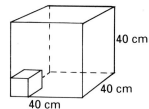

7 A straight stretch of motorway is 5 km long, and has a surface area of 140 000 m².

Calculate:
a the width of the motorway
b the volume of tarmacadam needed to cover it with a layer 0.1 m thick.

8 The side of each square in this net is 2.5 cm long.

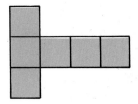

Calculate:
a the perimeter of the net
b the area of the net
c the volume of the cube made from the net.

9 A fishtank is 50 cm long, 40 cm broad and 30 cm deep.
a How many litres of water can it hold?
b 40 litres of water are poured into the empty tank. Calculate the depth of water in the tank.

RATIO AND PROPORTION

1 Peter has 15p, Paul has 60p and Kelly has 75p. Write these ratios of money in their simplest form:
  a Peter's:Paul's **b** Paul's:Kelly's
  c Kelly's:Peter's.

2 a Write down the number of faces, vertices and edges on this triangular pyramid.
  b Calculate, in their simplest form, the ratios of the number of:
    (i) faces:vertices
    (ii) vertices:edges
    (iii) edges:faces.

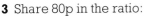

3 Share 80p in the ratio:
  a 1:1 **b** 4:1 **c** 2:3

4 Simplify each of these ratios:
  a 1 mm:1 cm **b** 5 mm:1 cm
  c 20 cm:1 m **d** 50 m:1 km

5 In a class of 30 students, the ratio of girls to boys is 3:2. How many in the class are:
  a girls **b** boys?

6 Greenfingers Garden Centre sells Ace potting compost in 24 kg bags. The compost consists of sand, peat and leaf mould in the ratio 2:3:1. How many kilograms in each bag consist of:
  a sand **b** peat **c** leaf mould?

7 Rob earns £24 for five hours as a porter in Greenwalls Hotel. How much does he earn in:
  a 1 hour **b** 3 hours **c** 4 hours?

8 Mike's GTX Special uses 35 litres of petrol for a journey of 329 km. Calculate the distance he could travel on 25 litres.

9 By using the scale 1:10, make a scale drawing of the outside of this frame.

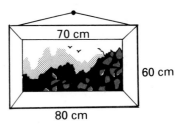

  a Use your drawing to find the length of a diagonal of the frame.
  b The inside of the frame is centrally placed. Add it to your drawing.

10 100 g of muesli contain 280 units of energy. Calculate:
  a the number of units of energy in 20 g of muesli
  b the weight of muesli needed to give 840 units of energy.

11 Motoring north, Sara's average speed was 60 km/h and her journey took six hours. Returning south, her average speed was 80 km/h. Calculate:
  a the length of her journey north
  b the time she took on her return journey.

12 In which of these tables are x and y in:
  a direct proportion **b** inverse proportion?

(i)

x	1	2	3	4	5
y	360	180	120	90	72

(ii)

x	2	4	6	8	10
y	18	36	54	72	90

13 Kath works as a hairdressing assistant at £3 an hour.
  a Copy and complete this table:

Number of hours	1	2	3	4	5	6	7
Earnings	3						

  b Draw a graph of Earnings against Number of hours.
  c Why would you expect the graph to be a straight line?
  d Why does the graph pass through the origin?

Reminders

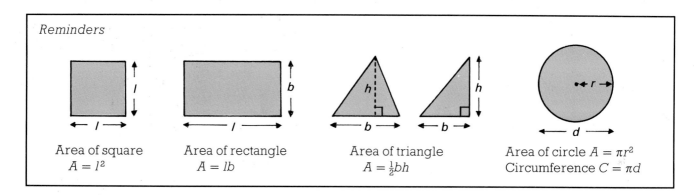

Area of square
$A = l^2$

Area of rectangle
$A = lb$

Area of triangle
$A = \frac{1}{2}bh$

Area of circle $A = \pi r^2$
Circumference $C = \pi d$

LOOKING BACK

1 Calculate the size of the shaded areas by counting the small squares:

a   **b**

c   **d**

2 Check your answers to question **1** by using a formula for each area (**d** to the nearest whole number).

3 Calculate the area for each of these shapes (**d** to the nearest cm²).

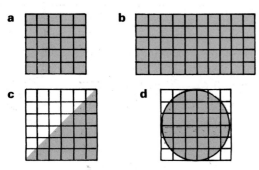

a Square — 3 cm

b Rectangle — 8 cm, 2 cm

c 12 cm, 5 cm, 13 cm

d 2 cm

4 Calculate the length of the perimeter of each shape in question **3** (**d** to the nearest cm).

5 Write each number below correct to: (i) the nearest whole number   (ii) 1 decimal place.
a 6.23   **b** 1.82   **c** 19.47

6 How many cubes are in each solid?

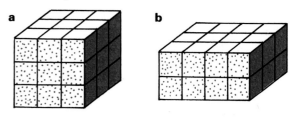

a   **b**

7 Calculate the volume of this cube and cuboid.

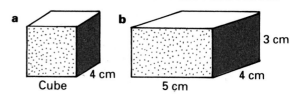

a Cube — 4 cm

b 5 cm, 4 cm, 3 cm

8 In Janet's room, calculate the area of:
a the poster on the wall
b the square record sleeve
c the record (to the nearest cm²).

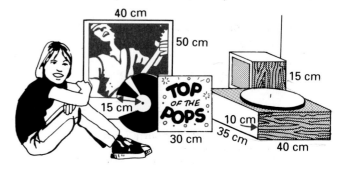
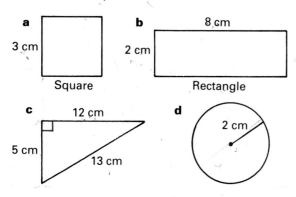

40 cm
50 cm
15 cm
15 cm
30 cm
10 cm
35 cm
40 cm

9 Calculate also the volume of:
a the record player   **b** the cube-shaped speaker.

RECTANGLES, TRIANGLES AND CIRCLES: PERIMETERS AND AREAS

EXERCISE 1A

In all the exercises in this chapter use the π key on your calculator and then round the answers to 3 significant figures.

1 Calculate the area of each rectangular pane of glass on offer at the glazier's.

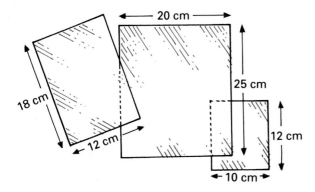

2 The glazier is called out to measure a broken window. The size is 2.5 m by 1.8 m. Calculate:
a the area of glass needed for the window
b the length of sealing strip to go round the edge.

3 A full-size snooker table is 12 feet by 6 feet.
a Calculate the area of the table top.

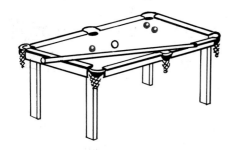

b A 'half-size' table is 6 feet by 3 feet. Calculate:
(i) its area
(ii) the fraction this area is of the full-sized table's area.

4 Calculate the areas of these rectangles. Watch the units.

	a	**b**	**c**	**d**
Length	15 mm	16 cm	7.5 m	3.8 m
Breadth	12 mm	9 cm	4 m	1.5 m
Area				

5 Red Cross Park has four rectangular lawns.
A: 50 m by 60 m
B: 50 m by 45 m
C: 60 m by 40 m
D: 45 m by 40 m.
Calculate:
a the area of each lawn
b their total area.

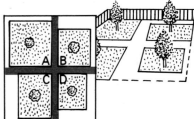

6 Copy and complete this table.

		1p	2p	5p	10p
Radius					
Diameter		20 mm			
Circumference					
Area					

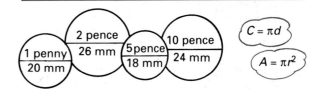

$C = \pi d$

$A = \pi r^2$

7 A roundabout is planned for a busy road junction. The radius of the central plot is 15 m.
Calculate:
a the area of the central plot
b its diameter
c its circumference.

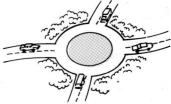

/BRAINSTORMER

Five medals are punched from a rectangle of metal.

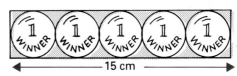

a *Write down the diameter and radius of one of the medals.*
b *Calculate the area of:*
(i) *the metal rectangle* (ii) *a medal*
(iii) *the wasted metal.*

EXERCISE 1B

1 These shapes are made from rectangles.
Calculate the area of each letter.

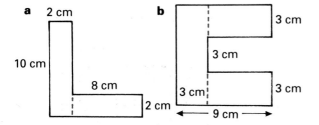

a 2 cm

10 cm

8 cm

b 3 cm

3 cm

2 cm

3 cm

3 cm

9 cm

2 The circular lily pond in the park is set in a square
paved area.
Calculate:
  a the area of the square
  b the radius of the pond
  c the area of the pond
  d the paved area.

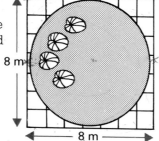

8 m

8 m

3 The High Street church needs a new stained glass
window.
Calculate:
  a the area of the square
  b the radius of the
    semi-circle
  c the area of the
    semi-circle
  d the area of the
    whole window.

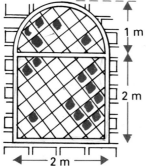

1 m

2 m

2 m

4 This sports field is rectangular, with semi-circular
ends.

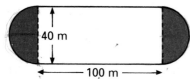

40 m

100 m

Calculate:
  a the circumference of the circle which makes up
    the ends
  b the perimeter of the sports field.

5 In the sports field in question **4**, calculate:
  a the area of the rectangle
  b the radius of each semi-circle
  c the area of the circle which makes up the ends
  d the total area of the sports field.

6 This picture frame is 5 cm wide all round.

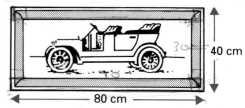

40 cm

80 cm

Calculate:
  a the area of the outer rectangle
  b the length and breadth of the rectangular
    picture
  c the area of the picture rectangle
  d the area of the frame (the shaded part).

7 The diagram shows a motor car's disc brake.
Calculate the area of:
  a the outer circle
  b the inner circle
  c the shaded brake
    disc.

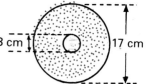

3 cm

17 cm

8 Calculate the areas of the ends of the shed and the
barn (each shape is made up of a rectangle and a
triangle).

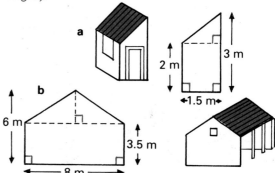

a

2 m

3 m

1.5 m

b

6 m

3.5 m

8 m

/ INVESTIGATION

*Kim fixes pins at A and B on the pinboard. She
makes triangles by putting five pins in the top row,
and elastic bands round the pins.*

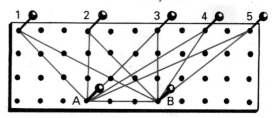

1   2   3   4   5

A   B

a *Calculate the area of each of the five triangles.*
b *Investigate the areas of the triangles formed if she
moves the five pins to points on other rows of dots.*

AREAS OF QUADRILATERALS

EXERCISE 2

(i) Rhombus and kite

The area of each triangle in the rhombus or kite
= ½ the area of its surrounding rectangle.

So the area of the whole rhombus or kite
= ½ the area of its surrounding rectangle
= ½ diagonal × diagonal

Rhombus

Kite

1 Calculate the area of each rhombus and kite as half the area of the surrounding rectangle.

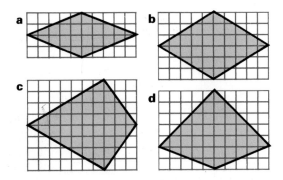

2 Calculate the area of each rhombus and kite using ½ diagonal × diagonal.

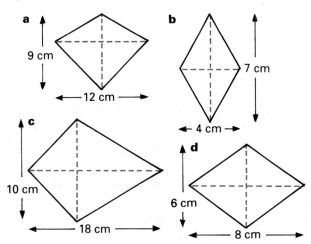

3 The end of this light shade is kite-shaped. Calculate the area of metal in each end.

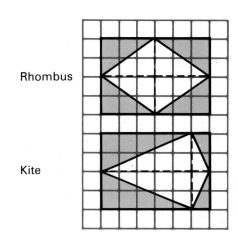

4 A Roman spear is needed for the school play. The head is cut from a surrounding rectangle of card. Calculate the area of:
a the rectangle
b the spear head.

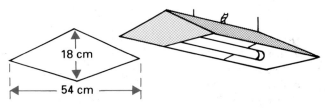

5 The new bridge is 750 m long and 100 m high. In order to measure wind resistance, the area of the three rhombus shapes is needed.

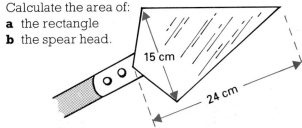

Calculate:
a the lengths of the diagonals of each rhombus
b the area of: (i) each rhombus   (ii) the bridge.

129

EXERCISE 3

(ii) Parallelogram

The area of the parallelogram
= the area of the rectangle. Why?

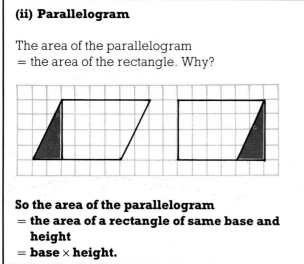

**So the area of the parallelogram
= the area of a rectangle of same base and
height
= base × height.**

1 Calculate the area of each parallelogram.

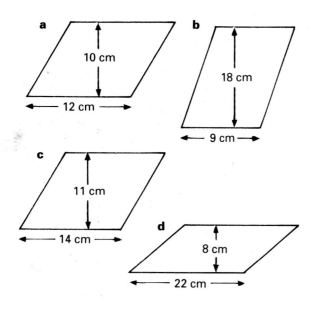

a 10 cm, 12 cm

b 18 cm, 9 cm

c 11 cm, 14 cm

d 8 cm, 22 cm

2 Each 'feather' on a dart is a parallelogram, and
each dart has three feathers. Calculate the area of:
a one feather
b feather needed for a set of three darts.

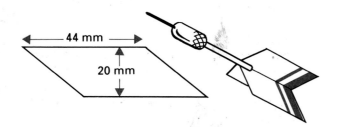

44 mm, 20 mm

3 The intersection of High Street and Broad Street is
a parallelogram. The Roads Department decides
to paint this area yellow to prevent drivers
stopping there. The cost of painting is £50 per m²,
and £1800 has been set aside to pay for the work.
Is this enough? Give reasons for your answer.

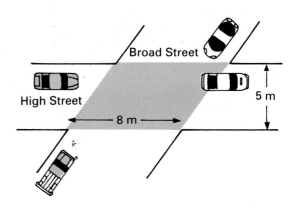

Broad Street
High Street
8 m
5 m

4 Find the areas of these shapes.

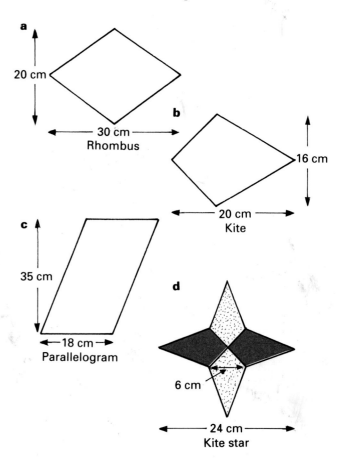

a 20 cm, 30 cm — Rhombus

b 16 cm, 20 cm — Kite

c 35 cm, 18 cm — Parallelogram

d 6 cm, 24 cm — Kite star

EXERCISE 4

(iii) Trapezium

The area of the trapezium
= area of the red rectangle
= 'length × breadth'
= **average length of parallel sides × distance between them.**

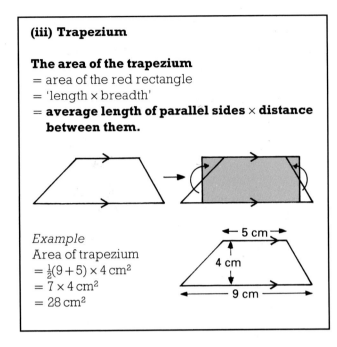

Example
Area of trapezium
$= \frac{1}{2}(9+5) \times 4 \text{ cm}^2$
$= 7 \times 4 \text{ cm}^2$
$= 28 \text{ cm}^2$

1 Calculate the area of each trapezium.

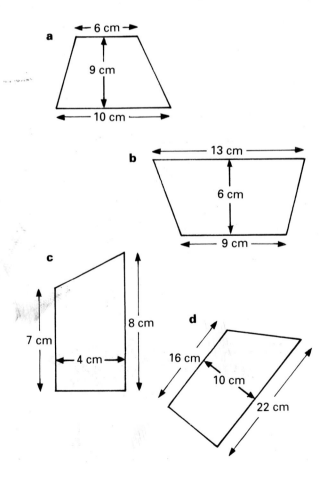

2 Architect Bill Jamieson is drawing plans for a house. Look at his drawings and calculate the areas of the trapezia in the roof and foundations and the area of the end view.

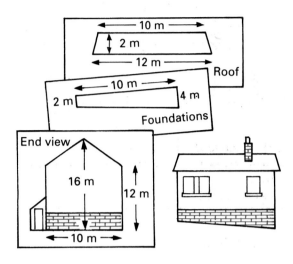

3 Summing up! Find the areas of these quadrilaterals.

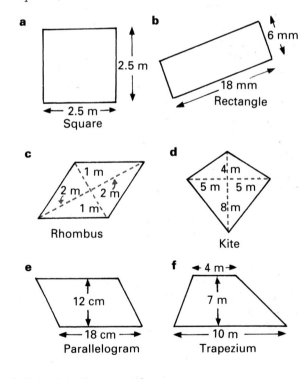

4 Calculate the area of:
  a a rhombus with diagonals 12 cm and 8 cm long
  b a parallelogram with base 25 cm long and height 10 cm
  c a trapezium with its parallel sides 11 cm and 7 cm long, and 5 cm apart
  d a kite with diagonals 56 cm and 24 cm long.

131

VOLUMES OF CUBES AND CUBOIDS

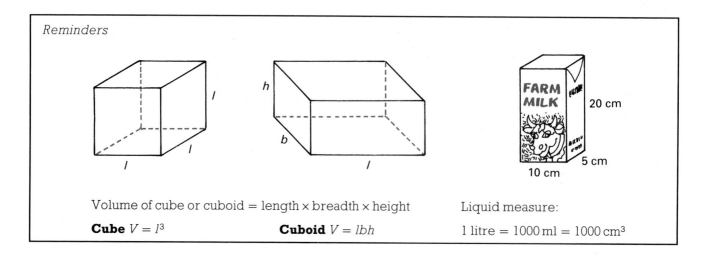

Reminders

Volume of cube or cuboid = length × breadth × height

Cube $V = l^3$ **Cuboid** $V = lbh$

Liquid measure:

1 litre = 1000 ml = 1000 cm³

EXERCISE 5

1 Calculate the volume of each packet.

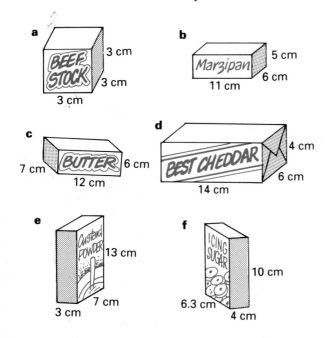

a 3 cm, 3 cm, 3 cm (BEEF STOCK)

b 5 cm, 6 cm, 11 cm (Marzipan)

c 7 cm, 6 cm, 12 cm (BUTTER)

d 4 cm, 6 cm, 14 cm (BEST CHEDDAR)

e 13 cm, 3 cm, 7 cm (CUSTARD POWDER)

f 10 cm, 6.3 cm, 4 cm (ICING SUGAR)

2 Calculate the volume of each carton in:
(i) cm³ (ii) litres (1 litre = 1000 cm³).

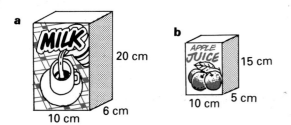

a 20 cm, 10 cm, 6 cm (MILK)

b 15 cm, 10 cm, 5 cm (APPLE JUICE)

3 The petrol tank in a car is a cuboid 70 cm by 30 cm by 20 cm.
  a Calculate its capacity in litres.
  b How far can the car travel on a full tank if it goes 9 km on 1 litre?

4 Each small cube in this large cube has sides 2 cm long.
  a How many small cubes are there?
  b Calculate the volume of:
   (i) a small cube
   (ii) the whole cube.

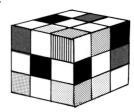

5 When this box of cereal is opened, there is a settling space 5 cm deep at the top.
Calculate the volume of:
  a the box
  b the space at the top
  c the cereal in the box.

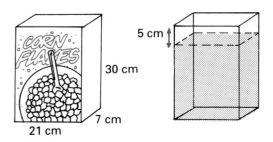

30 cm, 21 cm, 7 cm, 5 cm (CORN FLAKES)

6 The Shah family are installing central heating and have to estimate the volume of air in each room, in cubic metres.

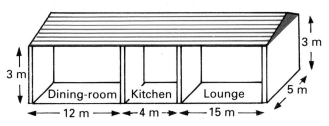

a Calculate the volume of each room.
b What is the fraction of the volume of:
 (i) kitchen : dining-room
 (ii) dining-room : lounge?

7 a Calculate the volume of:
 (i) the domino   (ii) the box.

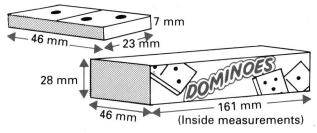

b How many dominoes will the box hold?
c How are the dominoes packed in the box?

INVESTIGATION

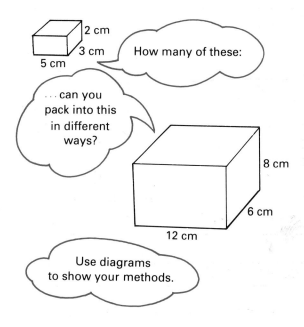

How many of these:

...can you pack into this in different ways?

Use diagrams to show your methods.

VOLUMES OF PRISMS

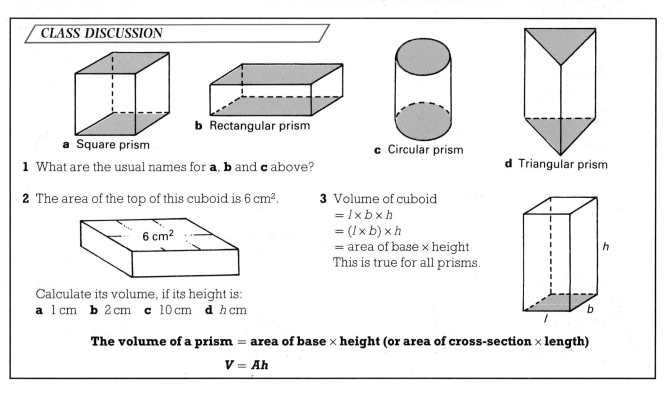

CLASS DISCUSSION

a Square prism
b Rectangular prism
c Circular prism
d Triangular prism

1 What are the usual names for **a**, **b** and **c** above?

2 The area of the top of this cuboid is 6 cm².

Calculate its volume, if its height is:
a 1 cm **b** 2 cm **c** 10 cm **d** h cm

3 Volume of cuboid
 $= l \times b \times h$
 $= (l \times b) \times h$
 $=$ area of base $\times$ height
 This is true for all prisms.

The volume of a prism = area of base × height (or area of cross-section × length)

$$V = Ah$$

EXERCISE 6

1 Calculate the volumes of these prisms:

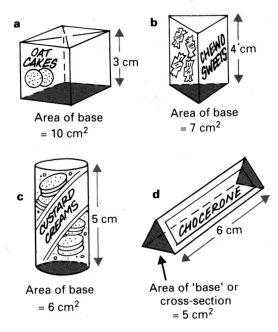

a
3 cm
Area of base
= 10 cm²

b
4 cm
Area of base
= 7 cm²

c
5 cm
Area of base
= 6 cm²

d
CHOCERONE
6 cm
Area of 'base' or
cross-section
= 5 cm²

2 Calculate the volumes of these prisms:

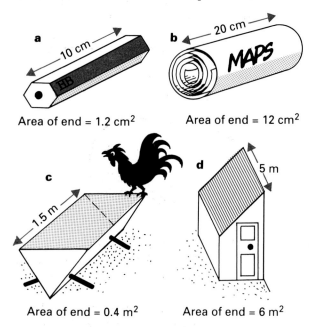

a
10 cm
Area of end = 1.2 cm²

b
20 cm
MAPS
Area of end = 12 cm²

c
1.5 m
Area of end = 0.4 m²

d
5 m
Area of end = 6 m²

3 Calculate:
   a the area of the end of this display unit
   b the volume of the unit, in cm³.

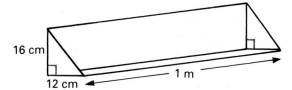

16 cm
12 cm
1 m

4 A solid glass prism like this is used in science to split light into the colours of the spectrum.

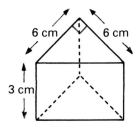

6 cm   6 cm
3 cm

Calculate:
   a the area of the base of the prism
   b the volume of glass in the prism
   c the weight of glass in the prism, given that 1 cm³ of glass weighs 2.7 g.

5 Calculate:
   a the area of the front of the tent (sketch it first, as an isosceles triangle)
   b the volume of the tent.

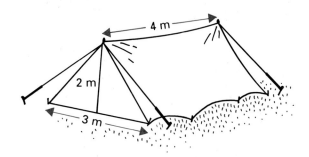

4 m
2 m
3 m

6 The owners of 'Sunnyside' are thinking of converting the roof-space into attic rooms.

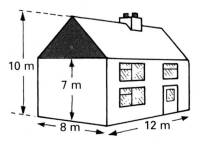

10 m
7 m
8 m   12 m

Calculate:
   a the area of the triangular part of the end wall
   b the volume of the roof space.

THE VOLUME OF A CYLINDER

EXERCISE 7

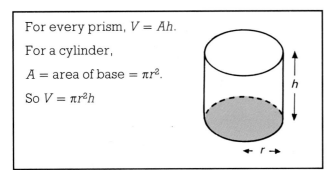

For every prism, $V = Ah$.

For a cylinder,

A = area of base = πr^2.

So $V = \pi r^2 h$

Putting π in the memory or constant facility of your calculator helps.

1 For each of these cylindrical objects:
  (i) write down the radius of the base
  (ii) calculate the volume.

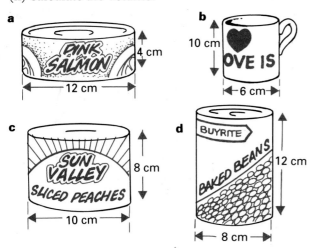

a PINK SALMON — 4 cm, 12 cm

b LOVE IS — 10 cm, 6 cm

c SUN VALLEY SLICED PEACHES — 8 cm, 10 cm

d BUYRITE BAKED BEANS — 12 cm, 8 cm

2 Which tub of moisturiser holds more? How much more? (Remember to find the radius first.)

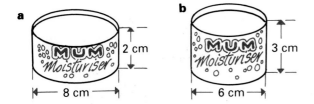

a MUM Moisturiser — 2 cm, 8 cm

b MUM Moisturiser — 3 cm, 6 cm

3 The Wilsons' central-heating oil is stored in a cylindrical tank.
Calculate:
a the area of a circular end
b the volume of the tank in cubic metres.

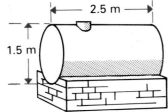

2.5 m, 1.5 m

4 Calculate the volume of each coin:

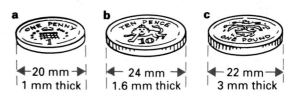

a ONE PENNY — 20 mm, 1 mm thick

b TEN PENCE — 24 mm, 1.6 mm thick

c ONE POUND — 22 mm, 3 mm thick

5 The DIY shop sells these wooden mouldings.

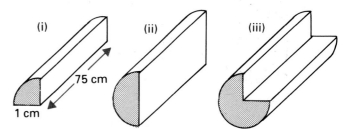

(i) 75 cm, 1 cm   (ii)   (iii)

They are cut from cylindrical rods 75 cm long, with 1 cm radius. Calculate the volume of:
a a rod of wood   **b** each moulding.

6 The ends of the bread-bin are quarter circular discs. Calculate:
a the area of one end of the bin
b the volume of the bin.

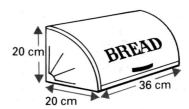

20 cm, 20 cm, 36 cm

7 Drains are being laid at the construction site. Each pipe is a concrete tube 5 m long. Its outside diameter is 50 cm, and its inside diameter is 30 cm. Calculate:
a the shaded area (outer circle − inner circle)
b the volume of concrete in one pipe, in cm³.

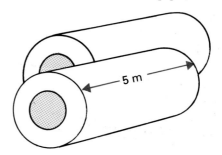

5 m

NETS AND SURFACE AREAS OF PRISMS

EXERCISE 8A

1 The box can be made from this net of squares of side 4 cm.

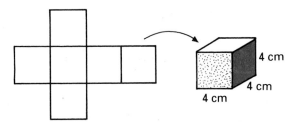

    a What is the area of:
        (i) each square   (ii) the whole net?
    b So what is the surface area of the cube?

2 Calculate the total surface area (six faces) of each cube:

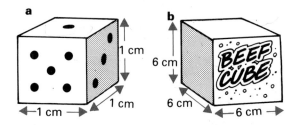

3 This box can be made from the net of rectangles.

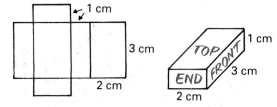

What is the area of:
  a the top of the box **b** the top and bottom
  c the front   **d** the front and back
  e one end   **f** both ends
  g the whole surface of the box?

4 Answer parts **a–g** of question **3** to find the surface areas of these packets.

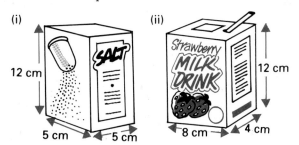

5 Both of these have just **five** faces. Calculate the total surface area of each one.

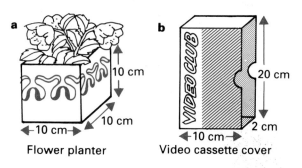

Flower planter   Video cassette cover

6 Calculate the area of material used to make the slide and the bookshelf.

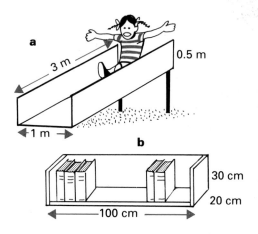

PRACTICAL PROJECT

Measure your maths book, and work out the length, breadth and area of a sheet of paper which would cover it, with 4 cm overlaps at the front and back.

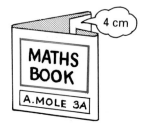

CHALLENGE

Find the area of card in a matchbox, including both the tray and the 'sleeve'. Illustrate by drawing nets, and marking lengths.

EXERCISE 8B

1

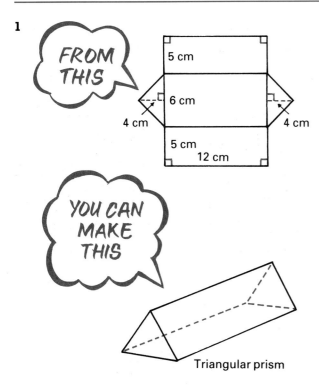

FROM THIS

YOU CAN MAKE THIS

Triangular prism

Calculate the area of:
a each rectangle
b each triangle
c the whole net.

2 Calculate:
a the area of each rectangle in this net
b the area of each triangle
c the total surface area of the triangular prism that can be made from the net.

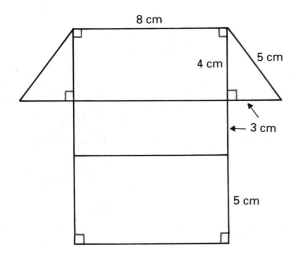

3 Calculate the total area of material needed for the roof, triangular ends and ground sheet of this tent.

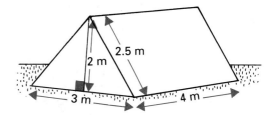

4 a List the shapes and areas of the pieces of wood needed to make this corner unit.

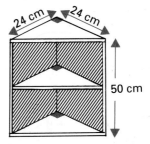

b Calculate the total area of wood required.

5

Jill is making cottages for her model village. Calculate the area of:
a each end of the building
b the total surface area of a cottage, including the floor.

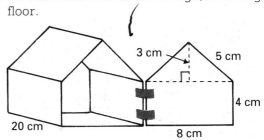

SURFACE AREA OF A CYLINDER

> *CLASS DISCUSSION*

Peel the label from a can of soup.

1 a What shape is it?
  b Where does its length come from?
  c What is a formula for the length?
  d Where does the breadth come from?
  e Write down a formula for the area of the label.

2 a What shape is each end of the can (top and bottom)?
  b Write down a formula for the area of each end.

3 What would the net of the can look like?

Summary

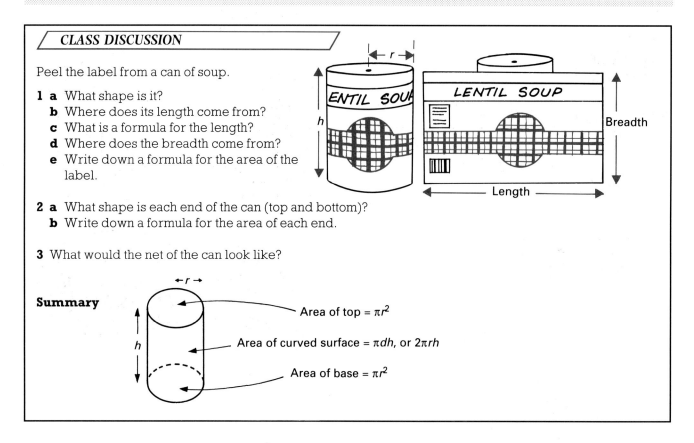

Area of top = πr^2

Area of curved surface = πdh, or $2\pi rh$

Area of base = πr^2

EXERCISE 9B

1 Calculate the area of each label. The distance right round the bottom edge of the label is given.

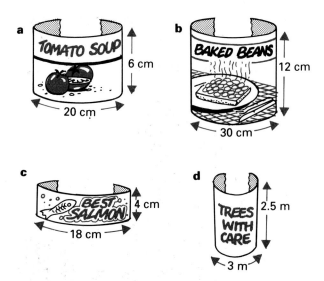

a TOMATO SOUP — 6 cm, 20 cm

b BAKED BEANS — 12 cm, 30 cm

c BEST SALMON — 4 cm, 18 cm

d TREES WITH CARE — 2.5 m, 3 m

2 Calculate:
  a the circumference of the top of the tin
  b the area of the label.

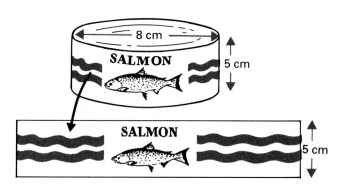

SALMON — 8 cm, 5 cm

SALMON — 5 cm

3 Calculate the curved surface area (round the sides) of these objects.

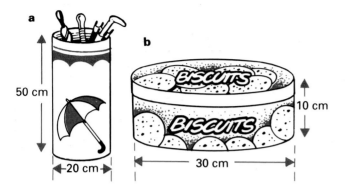

4 The height of the tea urn is 90 cm, and the radius of its base is 30 cm. Calculate the area of its side (the curved surface area).

5 The inside of the mug is 10 cm high, and the radius of its base is 3 cm. Calculate the inside area of:
a its base
b the curved surface.

6 A pipe running between two parts of a factory has to be lagged to keep out the frost. The pipe is 50 cm long and 12 cm in diameter. What area of pipe has to be covered?

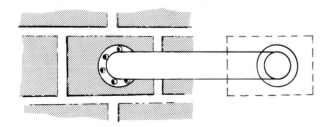

7 For each tin, calculate:
   (i) the area of the top
   (ii) the area of the curved surface
   (iii) the total surface area.

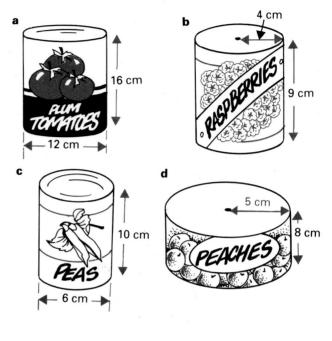

/ **PRACTICAL PROJECT**

a *Remove the labels from some cans. Measure their lengths and breadths (not counting any overlap). Calculate their areas.*
b *Measure the heights and diameters of the cans. Calculate their volumes and their total surface areas.*
c *Make a table for your results.*

CHECK-UP ON AREAS AND VOLUMES

1 Calculate the areas of these shapes:

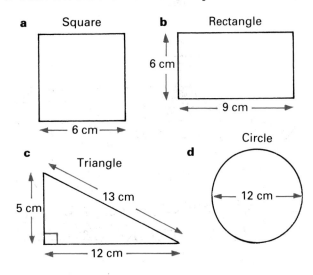

a Square

6 cm

6 cm

b Rectangle

6 cm

9 cm

c Triangle

5 cm

13 cm

12 cm

d Circle

12 cm

2 Calculate the perimeter of each shape in question **1**.

3 Calculate the areas of the kite and parallelogram.

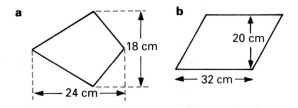

a

18 cm

24 cm

b

20 cm

32 cm

4 PQRS is a rhombus.
  a Use Pythagoras' Theorem to calculate QR.
  b Calculate:
   (i) the perimeter of the rhombus   (ii) its area.

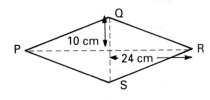

Q

P   10 cm

24 cm   R

S

5 Calculate the area and volume of the box which can be made from this net.

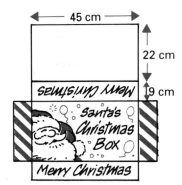

45 cm

22 cm

9 cm

Merry Christmas

Santa's
Christmas
Box

Merry Christmas

6 Calculate the volumes of the cube and cuboid.

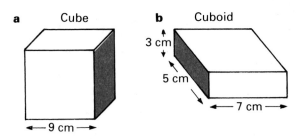

a Cube

9 cm

b Cuboid

3 cm

5 cm

7 cm

7 Calculate the total surface area of the solids in question **6**.

8 a What area of glass (top and three sides) is needed for this garden frame?
  b Calculate the volume of the frame.

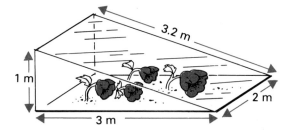

3.2 m

1 m

3 m

2 m

9 Calculate the volumes of the cylinder and prism.

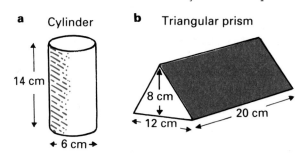

a Cylinder

14 cm

6 cm

b Triangular prism

8 cm

12 cm

20 cm

10 Calculate the curved surface areas of the drum and the umbrella stand.

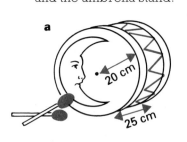

a

20 cm

25 cm

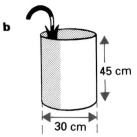

b

45 cm

30 cm

11 Calculate the volume and total surface area of this letter T.

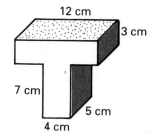

12 cm

3 cm

7 cm

5 cm

4 cm

COME TO THE DUNES HOTEL

FOR A CAREFREE HOLIDAY

		June	July	August
7 nights	Adult	£295	£361	£329
	Child	155	195	170
14 nights	Adult	366	459	405
	Child	201	275	253

1 Write down the cost of a holiday for:
  a one adult for 7 nights in July
  b one child for 14 nights in August
  c one adult and one child for 7 nights in June.

2 Calculate:
  a 10% of £50 **b** 25% of £3560 **c** £120 − £75.50

3 How much is:
  a a percentage increase of 5% on a wage of £250
  b VAT at 17.5% on a gas bill of £193.22?

4 Calculate the total cost of each of these.
  a Tony's check-out slip from the supermarket:

```
3lb tomatoes   @   75p/lb
1 cauliflower  @   67p
6lb potatoes   @   28p/lb
10 oranges     @   32p each  _____
Total                    £_____
```

  b Fiona's order form for her catalogue:

Item	Quantity	Cost
Sellotape	2 rolls	£1.55/roll
Envelopes	5 packets	99p/packet
Writing pad	4 pads	87p each
	Sub total	
	Postage	3.75
	Total	£

5 Alice Booth's basic rate of pay is £6.80 an hour.

  a Calculate her wage for 37 hours of work.
    She is paid 'time-and-a-half' for overtime.
  b How much is she paid for:
    (i) 1 hour's overtime
    (ii) a 37-hour week plus 7 hours of overtime?

6 Craig sells double glazing. His commission is $2\frac{1}{2}\%$ of sales. Calculate his commission on:
  a £7000 sales in May **b** £9200 sales in June.

7 How much more do you pay for the Night-light on HP?

NIGHT-LIGHT
PROTECTS YOUR HOME
£99.99 cash
or £10 deposit and
12 monthly payments
of £8.95

8

STEADY GROWTH
GOLD ACCOUNT
7%
Per annum

  a Jason got £702 interest in a year. How much was this (i) per month (ii) per week?
  b His sister Jenny puts £1800 into Steady Growth's Gold Account. How much interest will she get in a year?

PAYSLIPS

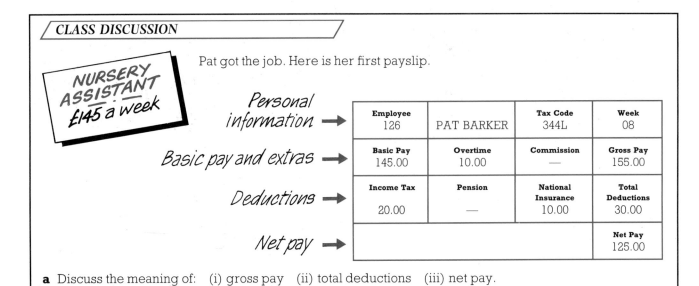

CLASS DISCUSSION

NURSERY ASSISTANT £145 a week

Pat got the job. Here is her first payslip.

Personal information →

Basic pay and extras →

Deductions →

Net pay →

Employee		Tax Code	Week
126	PAT BARKER	344L	08

Basic Pay	Overtime	Commission	Gross Pay
145.00	10.00	—	155.00

Income Tax	Pension	National Insurance	Total Deductions
20.00	—	10.00	30.00

			Net Pay
			125.00

a Discuss the meaning of: (i) gross pay   (ii) total deductions   (iii) net pay.
b Check the calculations for Pat's gross pay, total deductions and net pay.

EXERCISE 1A

Calculate the missing entries.

1 Basic pay   £220.00
   +Overtime   56.00

   Gross pay   _____

2 Basic pay   £175.20
   +Bonus   80.30

   Gross pay   _____

3 Income tax   £46.50
   +National Insurance   21.50

   Total deductions   _____

4 Income tax   £86.35
   +Pension   15.75

   Total deductions   _____

5 Gross pay   £250.50
   −Total deductions   75.20

   Net pay   _____

6 Gross pay   £196.10
   −Total deductions   63.60

   Net pay   _____

7 Basic pay   £235.00
   +Overtime   42.00

   Gross pay

   −Total deductions   65.00

   Net pay   _____

Calculating net pay

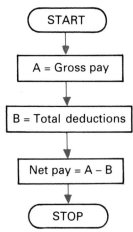

START

↓

A = Gross pay

↓

B = Total deductions

↓

Net pay = A − B

↓

STOP

8 George Gibbs is a chef at The Old Steakhouse.

Calculate his:

a gross pay   **b** total deductions   **c** net pay.

Employee 128	GEORGE GIBBS		Tax Code 516H	Week 17
Basic Pay 270.00	**Overtime** 8.50		**Other Allowances** —	**Gross Pay**
Income Tax 42.39	**Pension** —		**National Insurance** 21.15	**Total Deductions**
				Net Pay

9 Melanie Moss is a courier for Swimsun Travel.

Calculate her:

a gross pay   **b** total deductions   **c** net pay.

Employee 248	MELANIE MOSS		Tax Code 378L	Week 50
Basic Pay 303.28	**Overtime** 18.47		**Other Allowances** —	**Gross Pay**
Income Tax 59.86	**Pension** 12.87		**National Insurance** 25.04	**Total Deductions**
				Net Pay

EXERCISE 1B

1

Calculate Penny's bonus:

Employee 021	PENNY CARTER		Tax Code	Week 3
Basic Pay 132.50	**Overtime** —	**Commission** —	**Bonus** ?	**Gross Pay** 141.50

2 Calculate Paul's commission for the month:

Employee 205	PAUL BAKER		Tax Code	Month 7
Basic Pay 725.80	**Overtime** 28.40	**Commission** ?	**Bonus** —	**Gross Pay** 846.60

3

a How much did Anwar pay towards his pension?

Income Tax 32.82	Pension ?	National Insurance 15.91	Total Deductions 61.95
			Net Pay ?

b Anwar's gross pay was £220.35. Calculate his net pay.

4 Bram Ngema is a car salesman for Delux Motors.
This is his monthly salary slip:

Employee 043	BRAM NGEMA		Tax Code 525H	Month 7
Basic Pay 1235.50	**Overtime** —	**Commission** 163.85	**Bonus** 23.30	**Gross Pay**
Income Tax 218.09	**Pension** 71.13	**National Insurance** 111.05	**Other Deductions** 4.80	**Total Deductions**
				Net Pay

Calculate Bram's:
a gross pay   **b** total deductions   **c** net pay.

5 Alan Jackson also works for Delux Motors.
a Make out his monthly payslip, using all this
information.
Employee number: 044
Tax code: 516H, Month 7
Basic pay: £1420.00
Overtime: £78.00
Income tax: £237.75
Pension: £74.90
National Insurance: £117.83

b Complete Alan's payslip by calculating and
entering his gross pay, total deductions and net
pay.

INCOME TAX

Example

a Liz, single:

Annual salary	£19 700
Personal allowance	3 500
Taxable income	£16 200

b John, married:

Annual salary		£17 500
Personal allowance	£3 500	
Married allowance	1 500	
	5 000	5 000
Taxable income		£12 500

EXERCISE 2

1 Write down the tax-free personal allowance for:
 a Habib, who is single
 b Tim, who is married, and receives the married couple's allowance as well as his personal allowance.

2 Calculate the taxable income for:
 a Emma, single, earning £17 000
 b Ralph, single, earning £15 600
 c Nicola, married and claiming the married allowance, earning £21 100
 d Joe, personal allowance and other allowances of £760, salary £18 125.

3 Ken earns £5600 a year, and his tax allowance is £3500. Calculate his taxable income.

4 Omar Kay, an engineer, is on £18 650 a year. He claims a personal allowance and a married couple's allowance. Calculate:
 a his total tax allowance
 b his taxable income.

5 Tabitha Holme's gross income last year was £9460. Her tax allowance consisted of her personal allowance plus £220. Calculate:
 a her total tax allowance   **b** her taxable income.

6 Calculate the taxable income, if any, for these people who have part-time jobs.

 a Fiona, single, a secretary, earning £3250 a year

 b Neil, single, a nurse, earning £4375 a year

 c Depak, claiming the personal and married allowances, earning £5520 a year

 d Mairi, claiming the personal and married allowances, earning £4980 a year.

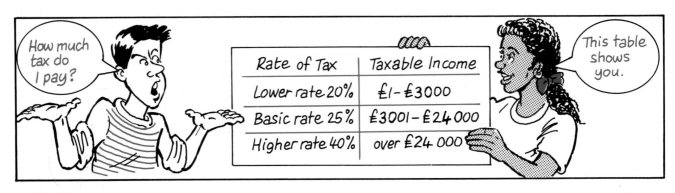

Example

Rhona Ryan, a photographer, earned £16 240 last year.
She is not married. Calculate:
a her taxable income   **b** the tax she has to pay.

a Income	£16 240		**b** Tax	£3000 at 20%	£600
Allowance	3 500			9740 at 25%	2435
Taxable income	£12 740			Total tax	£3035

EXERCISE 3

1 Copy and complete:

  a Income   £12 000
      Allowance   3 500

      Taxable income   £ _____

  b Tax £3000 at 20%   £ _____
          5500 at 25%

         Total tax   £ _____

2 Copy and complete:

  a Income   £18 200
      Allowances   5 000

      Taxable income   £ _____

  b Tax £3000 at 20%   £ _____
          . . . at 25%

         Total tax   £ _____

3 Copy and complete this table:

	Income	Allowance	Taxable income	Tax at 20%	Tax at 25%	Tax to pay
a	6000	3500				
b	10 000	4000				
c	16 700	5700				

4 Jim Jones' gross income last year was £10 000. His tax allowances total £4260. Calculate:
  a his taxable income
  b the income tax he pays for the year.

5 Debbie Malcolm is a part-time nurse earning £5825. Her allowances total £3620. Calculate:
  a her taxable income
  b the tax Debbie pays in the year.

6 Anita Robson gets the personal tax allowance, plus other allowances of £580. For a year when she earns £15 180, calculate:
  a her taxable income   **b** the tax she has to pay.

7 Miss Shona Bates is a waitress. In her annual income tax return she enters her wage as £8540, and 'tips' (also taxable) as £830. Calculate the amount of tax due:
  a annually   **b** weekly.

8 Peter earns £220 a week as a fork-lift truck driver. He claims both personal and married allowances. Calculate:
  a his gross pay for a year
  b his taxable income
  c the total tax he has to pay annually, and weekly
  d his weekly pay after tax is deducted.

/ **INVESTIGATIONS**

1 Find out what the personal and married couple's tax allowances are for this year.

2 Investigate the present rates of tax.

3 Calculate the answers to questions 7 and 8 of Exercise 3 using the information you have found in Investigations 1 and 2 above.

/ **CHALLENGES**

1 Use this graph to read off the tax due on gross salaries of:
  a £2000   **b** £10 000   **c** £16 000   **d** £20 000
  e £30 000

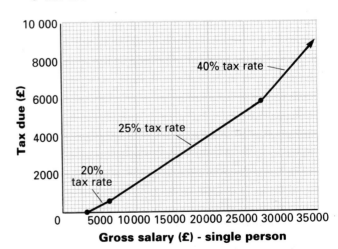

2 Check your answers by calculation, assuming a personal tax allowance of £3500.

LIFE INSURANCE

Which kind of
LIFE INSURANCE
policy should
I have?

Look at
these two types
of policy...

Whole Life Policy
You pay throughout your whole life.
Your dependants get the money when you die.

Endowment Policy
You pay for a certain number of years.
You get the money after this time, or your dependants get it if you die before the time is up.

What are the advantages and disadvantages of each kind of policy?
(See also the tables of costs below.)

The Safe and Secure Insurance Company uses these tables to calculate people's premiums.

Monthly premiums for every £1000 insured

Whole Life (with profits)

Age		Non-smoker	Smoker
Male	Female		
16–25	16–32	1.90	2.30
26	33	1.90	2.35
27	34	1.95	2.45
28	35	1.95	2.55
29	36	2.00	2.65
30	37	2.05	2.70
31	38	2.10	2.80
32	39	2.15	2.95

Endowment (with profits)

Age		10 years		20 years	
Male	Female	Non-smoker	Smoker	Non-smoker	Smoker
16–25	16–32	9.65	11.29	4.58	5.36
26	33	9.66	11.30	4.60	5.39
27	34	9.67	11.31	4.61	5.40
28	35	9.67	11.31	4.62	5.40
29	36	9.68	11.33	4.63	5.41
30	37	9.69	11.34	4.64	5.42
31	38	9.70	11.35	4.65	5.44
32	39	9.72	11.38	4.67	5.46

EXERCISE 4

1 Write down the monthly premiums for these £1000 policies.
  a Whole life, for:
    (i) a 26-year-old male, non-smoker
    (ii) a 39-year-old female, smoker.
  b Endowment, for:
    (i) a 21-year-old male smoker, for 10 years
    (ii) a 20-year-old female non-smoker, for 20 years.

2 Why are the monthly premiums in the table:
  a greater as the starting age increases
  b less for females than males
  c more for smokers than non-smokers?

3 Melanie, aged 38 and a non-smoker, takes out a whole life policy for £1000.
  a What is her monthly premium?
  b What would her monthly premium be for a whole life policy for:
    (i) £2000   (ii) £3000   (iii) £5000   (iv) £10 000?

4 Mr Clarke, just turned 30, is a moderate smoker. For £2.70 a month he can insure his life for £1000. When he dies his wife will get £1000, plus profits. What monthly premium would he pay for a £10 000 policy?

5 Mrs Clarke, 5 years younger than her husband, is completely against smoking. What would her monthly premium be for a whole life policy for £10 000?

6 Calculate the monthly premiums for:

	Name	Age	Policy	Term	Sum insured
a	Justin Case (male, non-smoker)	26	Whole life	Life	£10 000
b	Fallon Downie (female, non-smoker)	22	Endowment	20 years	£6000
c	Al Dunn (male, smoker)	18	Endowment	10 years	£5000
d	I. McClean (female, non-smoker)	38	Whole life	Life	£25 000

7 Graham, aged 21, is a smoker. He wishes to take out a 20 year endowment policy for £1000.
  a What is his monthly premium?
  b What would his premium be for a 20 year endowment policy for:
    (i) £2000   (ii) £4000   (iii) £5000   (iv) £12 000?

8 Dale Thomson (31), a keen sportsman, doesn't smoke. He takes out a 20 year endowment policy with profits, giving £8000 cover.

  a Calculate his annual premium.
  b How much less would he pay for a whole life policy?

9 Nobby Norris is a professional footballer. He is 23 years old and a smoker. He takes out a 10 year endowment for £25 000.
  a What is his annual premium?
  b How much less would it be if he didn't smoke?

BRAINSTORMER

Christine, a 26-year-old dentist, finds she can save £80 a month. She decides to put this into life insurance. What choices has she? How much cover can she get (to the nearest £100)?

HOLIDAYS ABROAD

If you are going on holiday abroad you have to buy **currency** (francs, pesetas, dollars, etc.) in Britain or in the country you are visiting. The **exchange rate** for buying foreign currency changes from day to day. This list gives an idea of what you could get for £1 on a particular day:

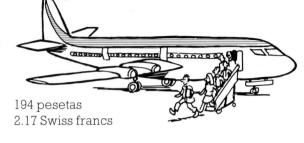

1.45 dollars	8.45 francs	2.44 marks	194 pesetas
250 escudos	2500 lire	350 drachmas	2.17 Swiss francs

Match these countries with their currencies above:

Germany, Switzerland, USA, Greece, France, Spain, Portugal, Italy

EXERCISE 5A

1 If you changed £5 into each of the currencies above how much of each would you receive?

2 Diana works in a bank, selling foreign currency. Use the memory, or constant facility, on your calculator to find how many:
  a marks she would issue for:
   (i) £75   (ii) £77   (iii) £1250
  b pesetas she would issue for:
   (i) £500   (ii) £152   (iii) £85
  c lire she would issue for:
   (i) £50   (ii) £9   (iii) £1500.

3 Before leaving for a camp-site in Brittany, Neil and his three friends changed £150, £180, £140 and £165 into francs.
How many francs did each receive from the bank?

4 Mark Fleming drew this graph before going on holiday to the Greek Island of Cos.

He found it useful when changing pounds to drachmas. It also let him judge how expensive things were to buy in Cos.

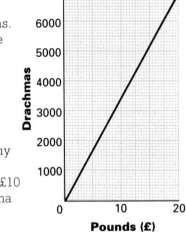

a Use the graph to find out how many drachmas:
 (i) Mark got for £10
 (ii) his sister Fiona got for £14.

b Mark and Fiona went shopping. Everything was priced in drachmas. Use the graph to change the prices into pounds, to the nearest pound.

(i) Necklace 2000 drachmas

(ii) Sandals 1400 drachmas

(iii) Tankard 1000 drachmas

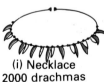

(iv) Earrings 4500 drachmas

(v) Handbag 5000 drachmas

(vi) Wallet 6000 drachmas

Conversion of currency

To change £s to foreign currency:

| £s | → | × Exchange rate | → | Foreign currency |

To change foreign currency to £s:

| Foreign currency | → | ÷ Exchange rate | → | £s |

Example

For a holiday in France the Crawfords changed £1200 into francs at the rate of 8.3 francs to the pound. They spent 9000 francs and changed the rest back to pounds at 8.9 francs to the pound. How much did they get?

£1200 = 1200 × 8.3 francs = 9960 francs

960 francs = £$\dfrac{960}{8.9}$ = £107.86

They got £107.86.

$$\begin{array}{r} 9960 \\ -9000 \\ \hline 960 \text{ francs left} \\ \hline \end{array}$$

EXERCISE 5B

1 Change to £s:
  a 1750 escudos **b** 100 francs **c** 50 dollars.

2 This table shows the weekly wages of five boys who work in shops in different countries.

Name	Andrew	Pierre	Wilbur	Mañuel	Karl
Wage	£142.50	1480 francs	$195	28 000 pesetas	385 marks
Rate to the £	—	8.45	1.45	194	2.44

  a Which country do you think each boy comes from?
  b Change their wages into pounds, and put them in order, starting with the highest.

3 Kate and Jenny went cycling in France.

  a They changed £225 to francs at 8.2 francs to the pound. How many francs did they get?
  b At the end of their holiday they had 155 francs left: 8.8 francs bought £1. How much did they get for their 155 francs?

4 Emily is going to Disneyworld. She decides to draw a pounds–dollars exchange graph, using these scales and axes. Copy them on squared paper.
  a Taking an exchange rate of £1 = $1.40, you can draw the line joining the points (0, 0) and (40, 56). Why?

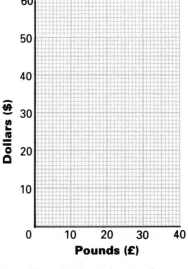

  b Copy and complete this table, using your graph. Give answers to the nearest whole number.

£s	7	10	25	32				
$s					7	20	45	66

INVESTIGATIONS

1 Find the countries, and rates of exchange, for these currencies: yen, rupee, schilling, kroner, rouble, florin, ryal, ecu.

2 Compare today's rates of exchange with the ones given on page 150. Make lists of the countries where the pound is now worth more, and the ones where it is now worth less.

CHECK-UP ON MONEY MATTERS— PERSONAL FINANCE

1 Calculate the missing entries:

a Basic pay   £210.00
   Overtime   40.50

   Gross pay   £ _____

b Gross pay   £288.20
   Total deductions   65.20

   Net pay   £ _____

2 Calculate Mr Quick's gross pay, total deductions and net pay.

Employee 25	G. R. QUICK	Tax Code 344L	Week 12
Basic Pay 152.00	**Overtime** 22.50	**Allowances** 7.50	**Gross Pay** ?
Income Tax 43.41	**Pension** 9.10	**National Insurance** 12.46	**Total Deductions** ?
			Net Pay ?

3 Andrea earns £178 a week, and pays 6% of this in superannuation.
How much is her superannuation?

4 Ken is a traffic warden, and earns £7200 a year. His tax allowance is £3500. Calculate his taxable income.

5 Nicola Walker earns £17 400 a year as a librarian. Her tax allowances total £3950. Calculate:
a her taxable income
b the tax due. (Use the tax rates on page 146.)

6 Mr Inglis' monthly salary is £1250. His personal tax allowance is £3500. Calculate:
a his annual salary
b his taxable income
c the amount of tax he pays
d his annual income after tax.

7 Mike Milligan, a teacher of physical education, is 26 years old and a non-smoker.

a He takes out a whole life insurance policy for £7000. How much is his monthly premium? (See the table on page 148.)
b Mr Milligan also wishes to take out a 20 year endowment insurance for £3500. Calculate his monthly premium.
c How much will he pay altogether in premiums each year?

8 a Luke changes £400 to German marks at 2.44 marks to the £. How many marks does he get?
b He then changes 90 marks back to £s at 2.50 marks to the £. How many £s this time?

REVIEW: LETTERS AND NUMBERS 2

EQUATIONS 1

1 Solve these equations:
  a $x+8 = 12$ **b** $x-5 = 1$ **c** $x-1 = 8$
  d $y+9 = 12$ **e** $y+1 = 10$ **f** $y-10 = 10$
  g $t+8 = 15$ **h** $u-4 = 10$ **i** $t+4 = 4$

2 Make equations for these pictures, and solve them to find v and w, the numbers of marbles in the bags.

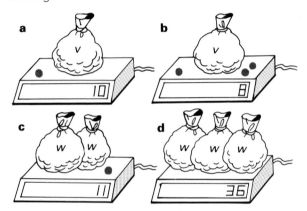

3 Make an equation for each balance, then solve it.

  a
  | $x+3$ | 9 |

  b
  | $y-2$ | 5 |

  c
  | $t+6$ | 14 |

  d
  | $u-10$ | 2 |

4 Make equations for these, then solve them:

  a

  b
  $n \leftarrow -6 \leftarrow 3$

5 Use the patterns in the rows and columns to make equations in a, b, c and d. Then solve the equations.

	A	**B**	**C**	**D**
1	5	6	7	$a+1$
2	$b-3$	8	9	10
3	9	10	$c+7$	12
4	11	12	13	$d-8$

6 Solve:
  a $2x+1 = 15$ **b** $3y-1 = 14$
  c $4m+3 = 7$ **d** $5n-6 = 4$
  e $3x+2x = 10$ **f** $4y-3y = 5$
  g $d+d+d = 12$ **h** $e+e-e = 8$

7 Make equations for these pictures, and solve them.

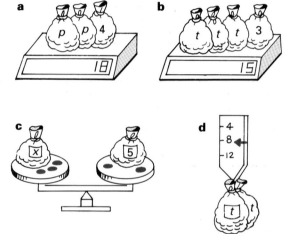

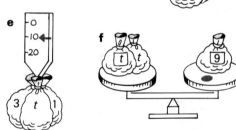

8 The edges of a cuboid are x cm, $2x$ cm and $4x$ cm long.
  a What is the total length of the edges, in terms of x?
  b If the total length is 28 cm, make an equation and find x.
  c Write down the lengths of the sides of the cuboid.

9 Solve these equations:
  a $5p-2 = 13$ **b** $6t+3 = 9$ **c** $8u-2 = 14$
  d $9v+7 = 16$ **e** $2x+4 = 10$ **f** $3y-5 = 10$

10 a $3x+2x+x = 6$ **b** $5y+y-y = 10$
  c $u+u+2u = 12$ **d** $v+2v+3v = 30$

EQUATIONS 2

1 Solve these equations:
  a $x - 3 = 2$ **b** $2x = 18$ **c** $3x - 1 = 5$
  d $2y + 3 = 13$ **e** $10 - y = 4$ **f** $12 - 2y = 0$

2 Write down:
  (i) the number of weights on each tray
  (ii) the number after the action shown is taken.

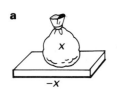

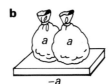

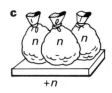

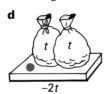

3 What entries go into the empty circles?

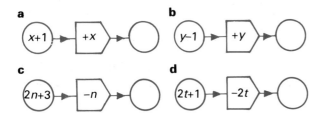

4 Solve these equations:
  a $2x = x + 6$ **b** $3y = 2y + 5$ **c** $4t = t + 9$
  d $2y = 6 - y$ **e** $5x = 6 - x$ **f** $3n = 20 - n$
  g $5p = 2p + 3$ **h** $6t = t + 10$ **i** $7u = 20 - 3u$

5 Make an equation for each pair of equal canes,
  and solve it. Write down the lengths of the canes
  (in centimetres).

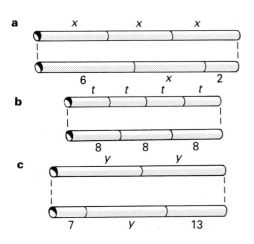

6 Make an equation for each picture, and solve it.
  Check your solution.

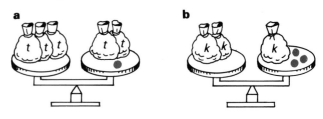

7 The nth terms of two sequences are given:
  $4, 7, 10, \ldots, 3n + 1$; and
  $40, 41, 42, \ldots, n + 39$.
  If the nth terms are equal, make an equation and
  solve it to find n.

8 Make an equation for each picture, and solve it.
  Check your solution.

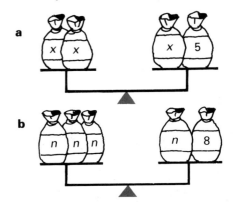

9 Make an equation for each *pair* of shelves, and
  solve it. Then find the length of each shelf. Units
  are centimetres.

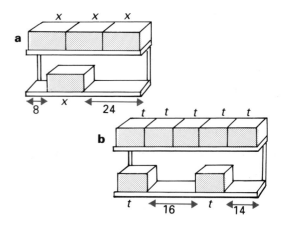

10 Solve:
  a $2x + 3 = x + 5$ **b** $4x + 2 = 2x + 8$
  c $4u - 7 = u - 1$ **d** $5v + 6 = 14 + v$
  e $9d + 3 = 5d + 11$ **f** $12t + 20 = 2t + 70$

FORMULAE AND SEQUENCES

1 a Make a formula for the distance d from A to B along the route shown (distances are in metres).

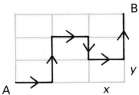

b Use the formula to calculate the distance when $x = 50$ and $y = 30$.

2 Make a formula for:
   a the number of people, N, on a bus which started with 20 passengers, after x got on and y left
   b the amount, £A, left from £40 after three CDs were bought at £x each
   c the time, T hours, for a journey in three stages, lasting x, y and z hours
   d the length, L metres, of a branch m metres long after a part n metres long is cut off.

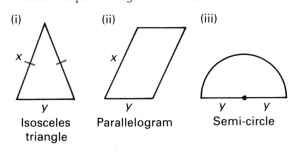

3 a Write down formulae for the perimeters P of these shapes. Lengths are in cm.

(i) Isosceles triangle
(ii) Parallelogram
(iii) Semi-circle

b Calculate the perimeters when $x = 15$ and $y = 10$. (Give (iii) to the nearest cm.)

4 Describe a possible rule used to form each sequence below:
   a $3, 7, 11, 15, \ldots$ **b** $3, 1, -1, -3, \ldots$
   c $1, 3, 9, 27, \ldots$ **d** $0, -1, -2, -3, \ldots$

5 a The nth term of a sequence is $2n + 1$. Write down the first three terms.
   b The nth term of another sequence is $5n - 5$. Find its first three terms.

6 Find an nth term formula for each sequence, and check it for $n = 1, 2$ and 3.
   a $2, 4, 6, 8, \ldots$ **b** $2, 3, 4, 5, \ldots$
   c $1, 4, 7, 10, \ldots$ **d** $7, 15, 23, 31, \ldots$

7 Construct difference tables for these sequences, and use them to calculate the next three terms in each.
   a $5, 9, 13, 17, \ldots$ **b** $3, 5, 8, 12, \ldots$
   c $36, 32, 28, \ldots$ **d** $1, 4, 9, 16, \ldots$

8 Jane made up this table of the number of diagonals in shapes with various numbers of sides. Check it by drawing the diagonals in a quadrilateral and a pentagon.

Number of sides	3	4	5	6
Number of diagonals	0	2	5	9

Assuming that the pattern of differences continues, how many diagonals has an octagon (8 sides)?

9 a Find formulae for the perimeter P and area A of the garden parallelogram shape in (i) and the running track in (ii), which has semi-circular ends.

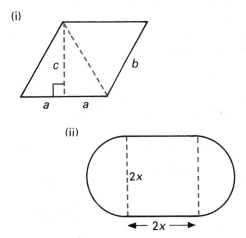

(i)

(ii)

b Use your formulae to calculate the perimeters and areas when $a = 3$, $b = 5$, $c = 4$ and $x = 40$. (Give (ii) to the nearest whole number.) The lengths are all in metres.

155

EQUATIONS AND INEQUATIONS

1 Solve these equations:
  a $4x = 12$ **b** $y + 5 = 6$ **c** $t - 3 = 9$
  d $12 - 2x = 0$ **e** $4y + 6 = 10$ **f** $10 - t = 10$

2 Make an equation for each of these, and solve it.

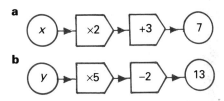

3 Solve:
  a $2(y + 3) = 12$ **b** $3(t + 2) = 12$ **c** $2(u - 2) = 2$
  d $5(x - 1) = 10$ **e** $4(n - 2) = 20$ **f** $6(v - 1) = 0$
  g $4(x + 2) = 12$ **h** $2(x - 1) = 8$ **i** $5(x + 1) = 5$

4 Solve:
  a $2x = x + 4$ **b** $3y = 8 - y$ **c** $3t + 1 = 2t + 6$

5 Make an equation for these two diagrams, and find the value of x for each.

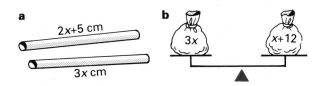

6 Make equations for these pictures, and solve them. Weights are in kg.

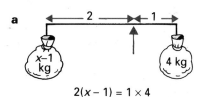

$$2(x - 1) = 1 \times 4$$

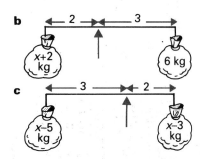

7 True or false?
  a $2 < 1$ **b** $-1 < 0$ **c** $1 > 0$
  d $3 > -3$ **e** $-2 > -1$ **f** $-1 < 1$

8 Write down an inequation for the weights in each picture below.

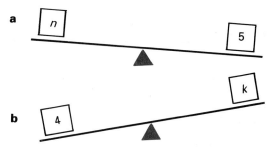

9 Write down an inequation for each picture below.

The weight of this bag is more than 5 kg.

The volume of liquid in this bottle is less than 2.5 litres.

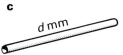

This straw is less than 18 mm long.

There are more than 5 kg of sand here.

10 a Find the nth terms of these sequences:
    (i) $1, 3, 5, 7, \ldots$ (ii) $20, 21, 22, 23, \ldots$
  b If the nth terms are equal, make an equation and solve it. Check that the two nth terms have the same value.

11 a (i) Write down an expression for the area of this rectangle.

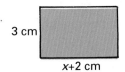

    (ii) If the area is $12 \, \text{cm}^2$, make an equation, and find x.
  b (i) Find an expression for the perimeter of the rectangle.
    (ii) If the perimeter is 16 cm, make an equation, and find x.

12 Write down the solutions of these inequations from the given sets of numbers:

	Inequation	*Set of numbers*
a	$x > 3$	$\{1, 2, 3, 4, 5\}$
b	$y < 1$	$\{-2, -1, 0, 1, 2\}$
c	$z > -3$ and $z < 3$	$\{-5, -4, \ldots, 4, 5\}$

11 FORMULAE AND SEQUENCES

LOOKING BACK

1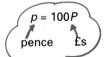
$p = 100P$
pence → £s

Calculate p when:
a $P = 5$ **b** $P = 20$

2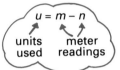
$u = m - n$
units used ← meter readings

Calculate u when:
a $m = 300$ and $n = 100$
b $m = 750$ and $n = 125$

3
$C = 6n + 20$
cost of party ← number of people

Calculate C when:
a $n = 10$ **b** $n = 25$

4 Write down a formula for the width W of each picture, $W = \ldots$

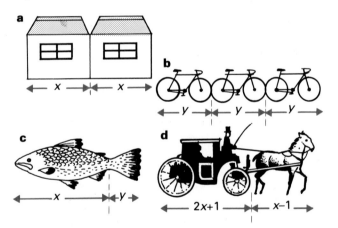

5 Write down three more terms in each sequence:
a 5, 6, 7, 8, . . .   **b** 2, 4, 6, 8, . . .
c 29, 28, 27, 26, . . .   **d** 5, 10, 15, 20, . . .

6 Find the eighth term of each sequence in question **5**.

7 a How many triangles of matches are in each of the next two pictures in this sequence?

 . . .

b How many matches are in each of the next two pictures?

8 How many dots are in the next two squares in this sequence?

 . . .

9 What terms go in the circles?

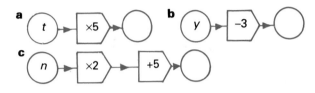

10 Which numbers would the computer print out for these programs? (* means 'times'.)
a 01 FOR M = 1 TO 5   **b** 10 FOR N = 1 TO 6
   02 PRINT 10*M   11 PRINT N*N
   03 GOTO 01   12 GOTO 10

11 The formula for the nth term of a sequence is $T = 4n + 1$. Write down the first five terms.

12 Write down a formula for the perimeter P of each shape.

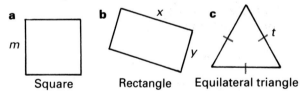

Square   Rectangle   Equilateral triangle

13 a A book has 150 pages. You have read 90 pages. How many are left?
b A book has p pages. You have read q pages. n pages are left. Write down a formula for n.

ALL SORTS OF FORMULAE

Example

a Formula for distance flown: $D = ST$

Given $S = 350$ and $T = 3$, $D = 350 \times 3 = 1050$

b Formula for speed: $S = \dfrac{D}{T}$

Given $D = 900$ and $T = 2$, $S = \dfrac{900}{2} = 450$

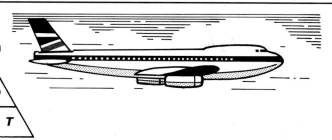

EXERCISE 1A

Twenty questions!
In each one, write down the formula, then calculate the value asked.

Puzzle
Can you see which picture goes with which formula?

Question	Formula for:	You are given:	Calculate:
1	Temperature: $T = C + 273$	$C = 80$	T
2	Distance: $D = ST$	$S = 310,\ T = 4$	D
3	Voltage: $V = IR$	$I = 7,\ R = 6$	V
4	Side of a square: $L = \sqrt{A}$	$A = 49$	L
5	Speed: $S = \dfrac{D}{T}$	$D = 500,\ T = 4$	S
6	Heat: $Q = m \times s \times t$	$m = 120,\ s = 1,\ t = 8$	Q
7	Density: $D = \dfrac{m}{v}$	$m = 240,\ v = 16$	D
8	Kilometres: $K = \dfrac{8M}{5}$	$M = 20$	K
9	Perimeter: $P = 2x + 2y$	$x = 15,\ y = 8$	P
10	Area: $A = t^2$	$t = 2.5$	A
11	Cooking time: $T = 15 + 8W$	$W = 5$	T
12	Velocity: $v = u + at$	$u = 20,\ a = 10,\ t = 3$	v
13	Distance fallen: $d = 5t^2$	$t = 4$	d
14	Energy: $E = \frac{1}{2}mv^2$	$m = 10,\ v = 5$	E
15	Pendulum: $T = 2\sqrt{L}$	$L = 625$	T
16	Temperature: $F = \dfrac{9C}{5} + 32$	$C = 10$	F
17	Volume: $V = \pi r^2 h$	$r = 6,\ h = 2$	V
18	Pressure: $R = \dfrac{F}{A}$	$F = 1000,\ A = 25$	R
19	Profit: $P = s - c$	$s = 4.50,\ c = 2.75$	P
20	% profit: $P = \dfrac{s - c}{c} \times 100\%$	$s = 30,\ c = 20$	P

EXERCISE 1B

1 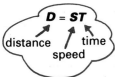 Calculate D when:
a $S = 500$, $T = 4$
b $S = 375$, $T = 2$

2 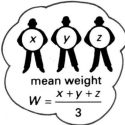 Calculate W when:
a $x = 50$, $y = 60$, $z = 70$
b $x = 45$, $y = 55$, $z = 62$

3 Calculate each perimeter, using the given formula.

a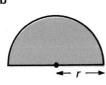

b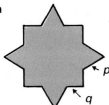

$P = 8p + 8q$
Put $p = 3$, $q = 1.5$.

$P = 2r + \pi r$
Put $r = 5$; calculate P correct to 1 decimal place.

4 Calculate each area, using the given formula.

a

b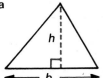

$A = \frac{1}{2}bh$
Put $b = 12$, $h = 10$.

$A = \pi r^2$
Put $r = 4$; calculate A correct to 1 decimal place.

5 Calculate each volume, using the given formula.

a

b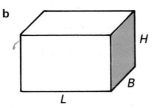

$V = L^3$
Put $L = 10$.

$V = LBH$
Put $L = 15$, $B = 9$, $H = 10$.

6 The resistance R to a current in this wire is $R = t + 4$.

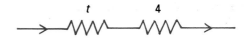

Calculate R when: **a** $t = 9$ **b** $t = 6.8$

7

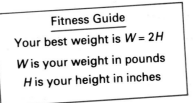
Fitness Guide

Your best weight is $W = 2H$

W is your weight in pounds

H is your height in inches

Calculate the best weight for:
a Alice, who is 62 inches tall
b Alec, who is 66 inches tall
c yourself.

8 The higher up you are, the farther you can see. From a height of h feet the distance, D miles, to the horizon is $D = 1.4 \times \sqrt{h}$ approximately.
Calculate D for a height of:
a 16 feet **b** 100 feet.

9 The farther you are from the lamp, the less bright the light. At d metres the illumination I is $I = 4 \div D^2$.
Calculate I when:
a $d = 1$
b $d = 2$
c $d = 10$

10 The formula $N = \dfrac{PH}{50}$ gives the number of rolls of wallpaper needed for a room where the perimeter of the floor is P feet and the height is H feet. How many rolls are needed to paper this room?

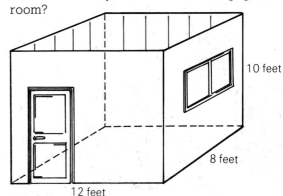

10 feet

8 feet

12 feet

INVESTIGATIONS

The Highway Code tells you to leave plenty of space in front of you when driving. Why is this?

Cars can't stop dead – drivers can!
A good driver, good weather,
broad daylight, dry roads, car in
good condition... now read on...

1 Danger ahead

Before you brake, you have to think about braking. This takes time, and distance.

Rule: *Speed s mph* ⟶ *Thinking distance s feet.*

s mph

s feet

Write down the thinking distances for speeds of:
a *10 mph*   **b** *30 mph*   **c** *50 mph*
d *70 mph*   **e** *100 mph.*

2 Foot goes on brake

Rule: *Speed s mph* ⟶ *Braking distance* $\frac{s^2}{20}$ *feet.*

s mph

$\frac{s^2}{20}$ feet

Calculate the braking distances for speeds of:
a *10 mph*   **b** *30 mph*   **c** *50 mph*
d *70 mph*   **e** *100 mph*

3 Rule: *Stopping distance, D feet =*
Thinking distance + Braking distance

Formula: $D = s + \dfrac{s^2}{20}$

a *Calculate the stopping distances for the speeds in questions **1** and **2**.*
b *Which one is just over the length of a football field (300 feet)?*

4 Graphs

a *(i) Copy and complete the table.*

Speed in mph	0	10	20	30	40	50
Thinking distance in feet						
Braking distance in feet						
Stopping distance in feet						

(ii) Copy the axes. Draw the graphs.

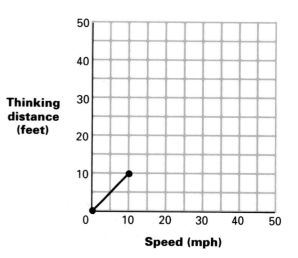

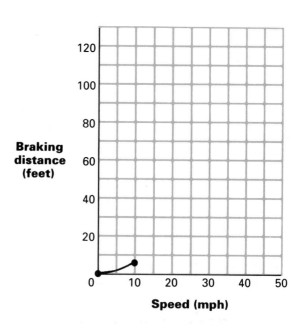

b *Draw a third graph for the stopping distance at each speed.*
c *Write a sentence about each graph.*

MAKE UP YOUR OWN FORMULAE

Look at these formulae. Each has three main parts.

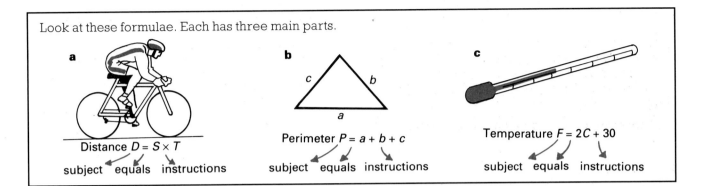

a Distance $D = S \times T$
subject equals instructions

b Perimeter $P = a + b + c$
subject equals instructions

c Temperature $F = 2C + 30$
subject equals instructions

EXERCISE 2A

Make sure your formulae have three parts, like the ones above.

1 Write down a formula for the perimeter P of each shape, $P = \ldots$.

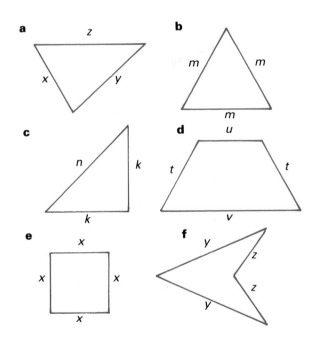

2 Write down a formula for the weight W of each train, $W = \ldots$.

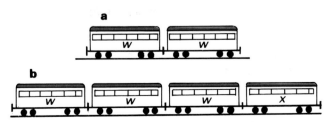

3 Write down a formula for the weight of each lorry and its load, $W = \ldots$.

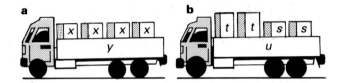

4 Write down a formula for the size of $\angle$ PQR in each diagram, $S = \ldots$.

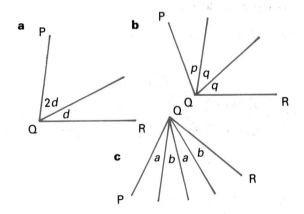

5 Each book has p pages. Write down a formula for the number of pages, N, in:
a 6 books **b** x books.

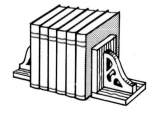

6 Each class has u pupils. Write down a formula for the number of pupils, N, in:
a 3 classes **b** t classes.

7 The swimming pool is rectangular.

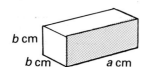

y metres

x metres

a Write down a formula for its area, $A\,\mathrm{m}^2$.
b Calculate A when $x = 50$ and $y = 15$.
c The pool in **a** is z metres deep. Write down a formula for its volume, $V\,\mathrm{m}^3$.

8 a Write down a formula for the volume, $V\,\mathrm{cm}^3$, of this brick.

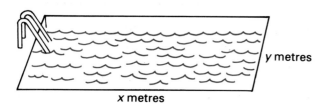

b cm
b cm
a cm

b Calculate its volume when $a = 20$ and $b = 10$.

9 Use each table to copy and complete the formula.

a

Number (N)	1	2	3	4
Cost (C)	2	4	6	8

$C = \ldots \times N$

b

Time (T)	1	2	3	4
Distance (D)	20	40	60	80

$D = \ldots \times T$

c

Number of cm (C)	100	200	300	400
Number of m (M)	1	2	3	4

$M = \ldots \times C$

10 a Copy and complete this formula for Pythagoras' Theorem:
$x^2 = \ldots \ldots$

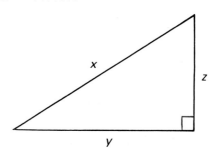

x
z
y

b Calculate x when:
(i) $y = 12$ and $z = 9$ (ii) $y = 6$ and $z = 2.5$.

EXERCISE 2B

1 Copy and complete the formulae given by these rules:

a

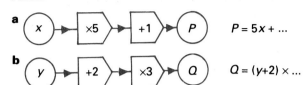

$P = 5x + \ldots$

b

$Q = (y+2) \times \ldots$

2 Find formulae for these:

a

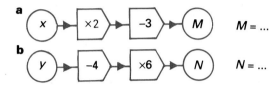

$M = \ldots$

b

$N = \ldots$

3 a Chris was given three videos for his birthday. They ran for 1, $1\frac{1}{2}$ and 2 hours. Calculate their total running time.

b Make a formula for the total running time, T hours, of videos lasting p, q and r hours.

4 a Marco has £50, and spends 6 lots of £4. How much has he left?

b If he had £p, spent 3 lots of £t and had £m left, make a formula for m.

5 Make a formula for:

a S, the sum of the weights of the bags

b D, the difference between their weights ($x > y$)

c A, the average weight.

6 The Mach number, M, for a fast jet aircraft is the speed of the aircraft, A, divided by the speed of sound, S.

a Copy and complete: $M = A \div \ldots$

b Calculate M when:
(i) $A = 2250$, $S = 750$ (ii) $A = 3330$, $S = 740$.

7 This square metal plate has a circular hole cut in it. Find a formula for the area A cm^2 of metal left.

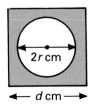

2r cm

d cm

8 To find the surface area A of the football, square the radius r, then multiply by 12.

a Copy and complete: $A = r^2 \times \ldots$

b Calculate A when $r = 15$.

CHALLENGE

V = Number of vertices (corners)

F = Number of faces

E = Number of edges

a Copy and complete:

Solid	V	F	E
Cuboid	8	6	12
Square pyramid			
Triangular prism			
Tetrahedron			
Pentagonal prism			
Pentagonal pyramid			

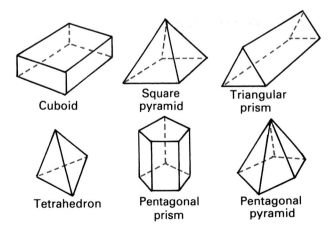

Cuboid   Square pyramid   Triangular prism

Tetrahedron   Pentagonal prism   Pentagonal pyramid

b Discover an equation connecting V, F and E for all of these solids.

SEQUENCES

Example
Find a formula for N, the nth number in each sequence, and check it.
a 5, 7, 9, 11, . . .   **b** 2, 5, 8, 11, . . .

a 5   7   9   11 . . .
    2   2   2   So compare multiples of 2.

    2   4   6   8 . . . $2n$

Sequence numbers are 3 greater. So $N = 2n + 3$

Check
Next 2 terms in sequence: 13, 15
Using the formula: $n = 5, N = 2 \times 5 + 3 = 13\checkmark$
                     $n = 6, N = 2 \times 6 + 3 = 15\checkmark$

b 2   5   8   11 . . .
    3   3   3

    3   6   9   12 . . . $3n$ (Multiples of 3)

Sequence numbers are 1 less. So $N = 3n - 1$

Check
Next 2 terms in sequence: 14, 17
Using the formula: $n = 5, N = 3 \times 5 - 1 = 14\checkmark$
                     $n = 6, N = 3 \times 6 - 1 = 17\checkmark$

EXERCISE 3A

1 Copy and complete:

    3   5   7   9
       2 . . . . . .

Multiples of 2:   2   4   6   8 $\rightarrow 2n$
Sequence 1 greater, so $N = 2n + \ldots$

Check
Next 2 terms in sequence: 11, . . .
Formula: $n = 5, N = 2 \times 5 + 1 = \ldots$
           $n = 6, N = \ldots = \ldots$

2 Show that a formula for N, the nth number in the sequence 1, 3, 5, 7, . . . , is $N = 2n - 1$, and check it.

3 Find a formula for N, the nth number in each sequence, and check it.
   a 1, 4, 7, 10, . . .   **b** 4, 6, 8, 10, . . .
   c 3, 7, 11, 15, . . .   **d** 7, 10, 13, 16, . . .

4 a Find a formula for the number of coins, N, in the nth collection.

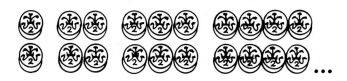

   b How many would there be in the 15th collection?

5

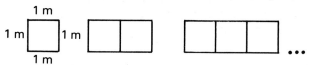

Engineers are testing and costing different shapes of frame for a new bridge.
   a Copy and complete the table for this shape:

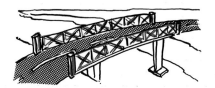

Number of squares (n)	1	2	3	4	5
Number of girders (G)	4	7			
Perimeter (P)		6			

   b Find a formula for:
      (i) G in terms of n (ii) P in terms of n.

6 Repeat question **5** for these designs of bridge frames:

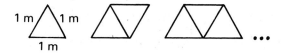

7 Repeat question **5** for these frames:

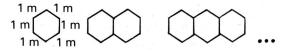

EXERCISE 3B

1 Find a formula for the *n*th term, *N*, of each
sequence, and check it.
  a 9, 16, 23, 30, . . . **b** 4, 9, 14, 19, . . .
  c 5, 10, 15, 20, . . . **d** 1, 7, 13, 19, . . .

2 a Find a formula for the number of coins, *N*, in the
*n*th group.

  b How many coins are in the hundredth group?

3 All the surfaces of these solids, except the bases,
have to be painted.

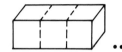

  a Copy and complete this table.

Number of cubes (*n*)	1	2	3
Number of painted squares (*F*)			

  b Find a formula for *F* in terms of *n*.
  c How many faces have to be painted on the
  twentieth solid?

4 a Copy and complete this table for the
scaffolding towers.

Number of floors (*n*)	1	2	3
Number of joints (*J*)	6		
Number of poles (*P*)	7		

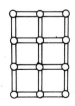

  b Find formulae for:
    (i) the number of joints (*J*)
    (ii) the number of poles (*P*), in the *n*th tower.
  c How many joints and poles are needed for:
    (i) the sixth tower (ii) the first six towers?

5 Fences are made of sections like this.

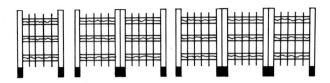

  a Copy and complete the table.

Number of sections (*n*)	1	2	3
Number of posts (*P*)	2		
Number of crossbars (*C*)	3		
Number of palings (*A*)	4		

  b Find a formula for the number of:
    (i) posts (ii) crossbars (iii) palings
    in a fence with *n* sections.

INVESTIGATION

$$2 \quad 4 \quad 7 \quad 11 \quad 16 \rightarrow 22 \rightarrow 29$$
$$\quad 2 \quad 3 \quad 4 \quad 5 \rightarrow 6 \rightarrow 7 \qquad \text{First differences}$$
$$\quad\quad 1 \quad 1 \quad 1 \rightarrow 1 \rightarrow 1 \qquad \text{Second differences}$$

If the differences are constant you can 'build up' the
sequence, to get 22, 29, . . .
Copy these sequences, and calculate their
differences. Then extend each sequence by four
terms:
  a *3, 7, 11, 15, . . .* **b** *4, 7, 10, 13, . . .*
  c *1, 3, 6, 10, . . .* **d** *2, 6, 12, 20, . . .*
  e *10, 11, 15, 22, . . .* **f** *1, 2, 5, 11, 21, . . .*

CHECK-UP ON FORMULAE AND SEQUENCES

1 $D = ST$. Calculate D when $S = 55$ and $T = 2$.

2 $T = \dfrac{D}{S}$. Calculate T when $D = 120$ and $S = 15$.

3 $y = 3x + c$. Calculate y when $x = 7$ and $c = 9$.

4 Sue is a sales executive. Her travelling expenses, £E, are given by $E = \dfrac{15N}{100}$, where N is the number of km she travels. Calculate her expenses for:
a 20 km **b** 50 km **c** 189 km.

5 The formula $K = 8M \div 5$ changes miles to kilometres. Use it to change to kilometres:
a 5 miles **b** 20 miles **c** 100 miles.

MILEND 10 miles/16 km   SOUTHEND 5 miles/8 km

6 The temperature $T°C$ at a height h m is $T = t - \dfrac{h}{100}$, where $t°C$ is the ground temperature. Calculate T when:
a $t = 20$, $h = 200$ **b** $t = 15$, $h = 100$.

7 Use the formula in question **6** to find the temperature at a height of 1000 m when the ground temperature is 10°C.

8 Write down formulae for:
(i) the perimeter P (ii) the area A
of these shapes.

a

2x

2x
Square

b

u

v+3
Rectangle

9 Calculate the perimeter and area of the square and rectangle in question **8** when $x = 10$, $u = 5$ and $v = 5$.

10 Mr Wilson buys records at £c each and sells them at £s each. Write down a formula for his profit £p on each record.

11 2 points for a win, 1 for a draw. Write down a formula for the total points, P, for x wins and y draws.

12 Make a formula for each of these:

a
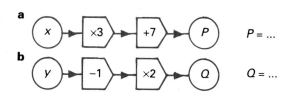

$x \rightarrow \times 3 \rightarrow +7 \rightarrow P$ $P = \ldots$

b

$y \rightarrow -1 \rightarrow \times 2 \rightarrow Q$ $Q = \ldots$

13 Find a formula for the nth term, N, of each sequence, and check it for the fifth and sixth terms.
a $8, 11, 14, 17, \ldots$ **b** $1, 6, 11, 16, \ldots$

14

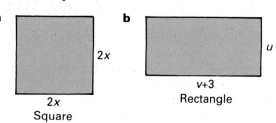

H–C–H   H–C–C–H   H–C–C–C–H ...

a Copy and complete this table.

Number of Cs (n)	1	2	3
Number of Hs (H)	4		
Number of Cs and Hs (T)	5		

b Find formulae for H and T in terms of n.
c Calculate the number of:
(i) Hs   (ii) Cs and Hs
in the 20th arrangement.

12 PROBABILITY

When a dice is rolled there are six possible results, but only one favourable result for Sandra, a '3'.

I need a 3 to win.

She has one chance in six of winning.
Her probability of winning is $\frac{1}{6}$; P(win) = $\frac{1}{6}$.

Where there are several equally likely results,

the probability of a favourable result $= \dfrac{\textbf{number of favourable results}}{\textbf{number of possible results}}$.

LOOKING BACK

1 Calculate:
  a P(head)
  b P(head or tail)

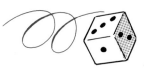

  c P(1)
  d P(7)
  e P(even number)

  f P(a year chosen at random is a leap year)
  g P(a student chosen at random from 3 girls and 2 boys will be a girl).

2 Copy this scale, and mark and label points **a**, **b**, **c**, ... to show the probabilities in question **1**.

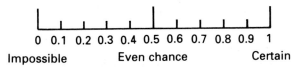

0 0.1 0.2 0.3 0.4 0.5 0.6 0.7 0.8 0.9 1
Impossible   Even chance   Certain

3 Calculate the probability that the spinner will stop at:
  a 6
  b an odd number
  c 7 or 8
  d more than 4
  e 0
  f less than 9

4 There are 2 white marbles and 3 red marbles in the bag. One is taken out at random. The tree diagram shows the probabilities of 'red' or 'white'.

  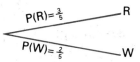

P(R) = $\frac{3}{5}$ —— R
P(W) = $\frac{2}{5}$ —— W

Draw tree diagrams for these bags:

a **b** **c**

5 P(letter arrives next day) = 0.9.
  a Amita posts 20 cards. How many should arrive the next day?
  b How many, if she posts 15?

6 What can you say about tomorrow's weather, if:
  a P(snow) = 0 **b** P(snow) = 0.5 **c** P(snow) = 1?

7

Survey? Experiment? Past data?
Counting? Equally likely outcomes?

Which method would you use to estimate or calculate the probability that:
  a a student in the school has blue eyes
  b a student has had measles
  c your MP will be re-elected at the next General Election
  d Ben will pick a blue marble from a bag of marbles with mixed colours?

167

EXERCISE 1A

1 a List all the possible outcomes when a dice is rolled.
  b Write down the value of each of these:
  P(1), P(2), P(3), P(4), P(5), P(6) and
  P(1)+P(2)+P(3)+P(4)+P(5)+P(6).

2 You either win or lose when the arrow spins freely.
  Calculate:
  a P(W)
  b P(L)
  c P(W)+P(L).

3

The four cards are shuffled, and placed face down. Campbell closes his eyes and picks a card.

  a How many possible results are there?
  b Calculate the probability that he picks the:
    (i) Ace   (ii) King   (iii) Queen   (iv) Jack
  c What is the value of P(A)+P(K)+P(Q)+P(J)?

4 In this game you roll a dice onto one of the squares. Calculate:
  a P(W) **b** P(R) **c** P(B)
  d P(W)+P(R)+P(B).

W	R	W
R	B	R
B	R	B

5 Avril chooses a letter at random from the word PERCENTAGE. What is the probability that she'll choose:
  a a vowel   **b** a letter that is not a vowel?

6 Weather forecast:
  'A 20% probability of rain'.
  What is the probability that it won't rain?

7 The probability of a traffic jam somewhere in town is 0.2. What is the probability that there will be no traffic jam?

8 The probability that Hassan will have flu this winter is $\frac{1}{5}$. What is the probability that he won't have flu?

9 Draw tree diagrams for the probabilities in questions **6**, **7** and **8**, like the one in question **4** of Looking Back.

EXERCISE 1B

1

It's Tracy's turn to roll the dice. What is the probability that she will:
a go up the ladder **b** not go up the ladder?

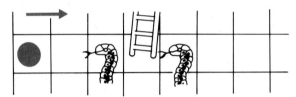

2 What is the probability that Tracy will:
a go down a snake **b** not go down a snake?

3 What is the probability that Tracy will miss both the ladder and the snakes?

4 The probability of winning a raffle is $\frac{1}{100}$. Calculate the probability of not winning:
a as a fraction **b** as a percentage.

5 The bar graph shows class 3B's votes for the best video game of the year.
A = *Superstar*, B = *Gremlin*, C = *Galaxy*,
D = *Victory*

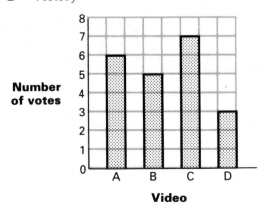

Calculate the probability that a student from the class, chosen at random, voted for:
a *Superstar* **b** *Victory*.

6 Based on United's past results, P(Win) = 0.6 and P(Lose) = 0.3. Why is P(Win) + P(Lose) not equal to 1? Explain fully.

7 Winning squares are B3 (£2), D2 (£1) and E4 (£1). If you choose one square at random, what is the probability of winning:
a £2 **b** £1 **c** nothing?

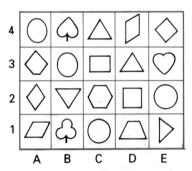

/ A PROBABILITY GAME

a *Roll a dice twice. The first score is the x-coordinate, and the second is the y-coordinate. Repeat this 50 times, and note the number of times the 'point' lies in the shaded area. Calculate the fraction of times this happens.*

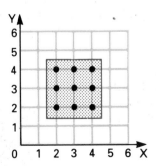

b *Calculate the probability of the point being in the shaded area. Compare this with your answer in a.*

COMBINING PROBABILITIES

When two coins are tossed we can show the possible outcomes:
 (i) in a list: (H, H), (H, T), (T, H), (T, T)

(ii) in a table of outcomes:

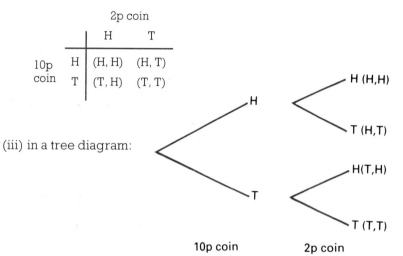

		2p coin	
		H	T
10p coin	H	(H, H)	(H, T)
	T	(T, H)	(T, T)

(iii) in a tree diagram:

```
                              H (H,H)
                    H
                              T (H,T)

                              H (T,H)
                    T
                              T (T,T)
        10p coin        2p coin
```

P(both heads) = $\frac{1}{4}$, P(both tails) = $\frac{1}{4}$, P(one head and one tail, in any order) = $\frac{1}{2}$

EXERCISE 2A

1 Sally spins her racket to decide who serves first. The racket is equally likely to fall smooth side up (S), or rough side up (R).

a Copy and complete this table for the outcomes of spinning the racket for two games.

		Second game	
		S	R
First game	S	(S, S)	(S, . . .)
	R	(R, S)	(R, . . .)

b How many outcomes are there?

2 a For the data in question **1**, calculate:
  (i) P(S, S) (ii) P(R, R)
  (iii) P(one S and one R, in any order).
 b Copy and complete this tree diagram.

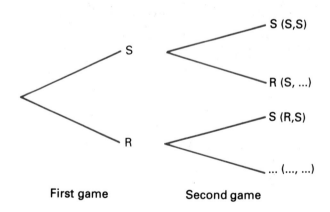

```
                              S (S,S)
                    S
                              R (S, ...)

                              S (R,S)
                    R
                              ... (..., ...)
        First game      Second game
```

3 The cards in each half of the tray are placed face down, and one card is drawn at random from each half.

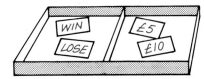

a Copy and complete the table of outcomes.

	£5	£10
W	(W, 5)	(W, . . .)
L	(L, . . .)	(. . . , . . .)

b How many outcomes are there?

4 a For the data in question **3**, calculate:
(i) P(win £10)   (ii) P(lose £10)
(iii) P(does not win £10).
b Copy and complete this tree diagram.

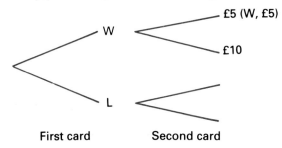

First card   Second card

5

Norma was moving house. Both gas and electricity readers were due to check the meters that day, and equally likely to call morning or afternoon.
a Copy and complete the table.

		Electricity reader	
		E (am)	E (pm)
Gas reader	G (am)	G (am), E (am)	
	G (pm)		

b Calculate P(both readers called in the afternoon).

6 Two square spinners can each score 1, 2, 3 or 4.
a How many outcomes are possible? (See the table.)
b Calculate: (i) P(1, 1)   (ii) P(2, 2)
(iii) P(both spinners show the same number)
(iv) P(the sum of the two scores is more than 5).

		Blue			
		1	2	3	4
Red	1	(1, 1)	(1, 2)	(1, 3)	(1, 4)
	2	(2, 1)	(2, 2)	(2, 3)	(2, 4)
	3	(3, 1)	(3, 2)	(3, 3)	(3, 4)
	4	(4, 1)	(4, 2)	(4, 3)	(4, 4)

7 Terry is going to the beach. He chooses one of his three T-shirts, and a pair of shorts from the two pairs that he has.
a Copy and complete the table.

		Shorts	
		Blue (B)	White (W)
T-shirts	Red (R)	(R, B)	(R, . . .)
	Yellow (Y)	(Y, . . .)	
	Green (G)	(G, . . .)	

b How many possible outfits are there?
c Calculate:
(i) P(Y, W)   (ii) P(at least one green garment)
(iii) P(both the same colour)
(iv) P(different colours).

8 The coin is tossed and the spinner is spun. This table shows all possible outcomes.

		Spinner		
		1	2	3
Coin	H	(H, 1)	(H, 2)	(H, 3)
	T	(T, 1)	(T, 2)	(T, 3)

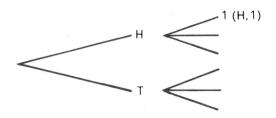

a Copy and complete the tree diagram.

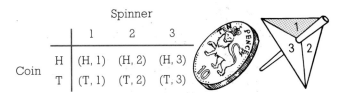

b How many outcomes are there?
c Calculate:
(i) P(H, 3)   (ii) P(T, 2)   (iii) P(T; 1, 2 or 3)

EXERCISE 2B

1 Moya has two spins.
  a Copy and complete the tree diagram.

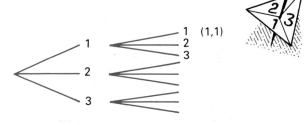

First spin   Second spin

  b Calculate:
  (i) P(3, 3)   (ii) P(2 and 3, in any order)
  (iii) P(total of 4)   (iv) P(total more than 4).

2

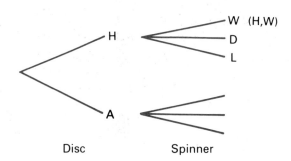

FORECAST A FOOTBALL RESULT

The disc has H(Home) on one side, and A(Away)
on the other. The spinner is marked W(Win),
L(lose) and D(Draw).
  a Copy and complete the table of outcomes when
  the disc is tossed and the spinner is spun.

	W	D	L
H			
A			

  b Calculate:
  (i) P(a home win)   (ii) P(a win)
  (iii) P(a draw).
  c Copy and complete the tree diagram.

```
        ┌─── W  (H,W)
    H ───┼─── D
   /     └─── L
  /
  \
   \
    A ───┤
        └───

 Disc        Spinner
```

3 A red dice and a black dice are rolled.

  a Copy and complete the table of outcomes.

		Black			
		1	2	3	4
Red	1	(1, 1)	(1, 2)	(1, 3)	
	2	(2, 1)	(2, 2)		
	3	(3, 1)			

  b Calculate:
  (i) P(3, 3)   (ii) P(at least one 3)
  (iii) P(the same score on both dice).

4 a Make a table like the one in question **3**, but
  enter the sum of the two scores in each space.
  b List P(2), P(3), . . . , P(12).
  c Which total is most likely?

5 a Make another table like the one in question **3**,
  but enter the product of the two scores in each
  space.
  b Calculate:
  (i) P(odd number)   (ii) P(even number)
  (iii) P(12)   (iv) P(total greater than 19)
  (v) P(multiple of 3).

P(*A* OR *B*)

Example
When the Wheel of Fortune is spun,
P(winning £10) = 0.1
P(winning £5) = 0.3
P(winning £10 or £5) = 0.4

Notice that P(winning £10 or £5) = 0.4 = 0.1 + 0.3.
= P(winning £10) + P(winning £5).

You can add the probabilities when the two events cannot happen at the same time (i.e. they are **mutually exclusive**.)

In this example, you cannot win £10 and £5 in one spin.

For two events that cannot happen at the same time, P(*A* or *B*) = P(*A*) + P(*B*)

EXERCISE 3

1 A coin is tossed. Calculate:
  a P(H)   **b** P(T)   **c** P(H or T).

2 A dice is rolled. Calculate:
  a P(1)   **b** P(2)   **c** P(1 or 2).

3 Patrick picks a card at random. Calculate:
  a P(Ace)   **b** P(King)   **c** P(Ace or King).

4 The weather forecaster says that there is a 10% probability of snow and a 30% probability of rain.

Calculate:
  a P(snow or rain)   **b** P(no snow or rain).

5 A letter is chosen at random from the word ENTERTAINMENT. Calculate:
  a P(E)   **b** P(A)   **c** P(E or A)   **d** P(N)
  e P(T)   **f** P(N or T)   **g** P(vowel)
  h P(consonant)
  i P(vowel or consonant).

6 Michelle estimates that the probability that her hockey team will win their next game is 0.2, and the probability that they will draw is 0.5.
Calculate:
  a P(win or draw)   **b** P(lose).

7 Calculate these probabilities when the spinner stops:

a P(B) **b** P(W) **c** P(B or W) **d** P(R)
e P(R or B) **f** P(B or W or R).

8 Paul sleeps 8 hours a day. Scott phones him from America at a random hour. Calculate:

a P(Paul is asleep) **b** P(Paul is awake)
c P(Paul is asleep or awake).

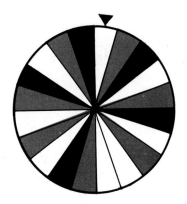

9 Calculate the probability that a month chosen at random will start with M or J.

10 Peter chooses a date at random from the calendar for a party. Calculate the probability that he chooses:

a a Saturday **b** a Sunday
c a Saturday or Sunday.

APRIL

M	5	12	19	26
T	6	13	20	27
W	7	14	21	28
T	1	8	15	22	29
F	2	9	16	23	30
S	3	10	17	24
S	4	11	18	25

11 A lucky dip box contains 20 packets of Crinkly Crisps and 30 packets of Curly Crisps. Amy chooses one at random. Calculate:

a P(Curly) **b** P(Crinkly)
c P(Curly or Crinkly).

12 A spinner has seven equal sections in the colours of the rainbow: R, O, Y, G, B, I, V. Calculate, for each spin:

a P(R) **b** P(R or O) **c** P(R or O or Y)
d P(R or O or Y or G or B or I or V).

BRAINSTORMER

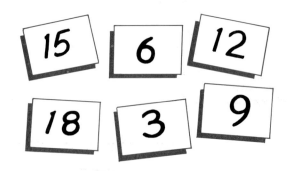

A card is chosen at random. Calculate:

a *(i) P(6) (ii) P(12) (iii) P(6 or 12)*
b *(i) P(3) (ii) P(odd number)*
(iii) P(3 or odd number).
Explain why P(3) + P(odd number) is not equal to P(3 or odd number).

EXPERIMENT AND PROBABILITY

CLASS DISCUSSION/EXERCISE 4

> Very often, the only way to estimate the probability of an event is to carry out an experiment.

1 Estimate the probability of left-handedness in the population.
What do you think: 0.1, 0.2, 0.3, . . . ?
  a Try it for your own class. Copy and complete:

	Number	Decimal fraction
Left-handed		
Right-handed		
Total		

  b Larger samples were used to provide the data in these tables. Calculate the decimal fraction of left-handed people in each sample.

(i)
LH	12
RH	48
Total	

(ii)
LH	27
RH	123
Total	

(iii)
LH	100
RH	525
Total	

  c Draw a bar graph of the results on squared paper, using these scales:

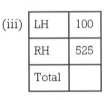

Fraction who are left-handed

Sample: Class, (i), (ii), (iii)

With larger and larger samples the fraction gets closer and closer to 0.15. So the probability that a person chosen at random is left-handed is 0.15.

> In a survey or an experiment, the larger the random sample, the closer we get to the probability.

2 Find the probability of 'Pin up' when a drawing pin is dropped onto a flat surface.

  a Guess the probability.
  b Do the experiment 40 times, recording the results in a tally table.
  c Calculate the fraction of 'Pin up' outcomes for your pin.
  d In an experiment, Nick recorded the number of 'Pin ups' every 40 drops. Calculate the fractions of 'Pin ups', correct to 2 decimal places.

Number of 'Pin ups' so far	18	32	43	51	64
Total number of drops	40	80	120	160	200
Fraction of 'Pin ups'	0.45				

  e Estimate P('Pin up') for Nick's drawing pin.
  f Continue the experiment with your pin until you are confident that you can give P('Pin up') for it, correct to 2 decimal places.

/ *PRACTICAL PROJECTS* /

1 Recording data as above, carry out experiments which will enable you to estimate the probability of:
  a cutting an Ace, King, Queen or Jack in a pack of cards
  b obtaining:
    (i) an odd number when you roll a dice
    (ii) a score of 10 with two dice.

2 Calculate the probability for 1a and b, and compare the results with your experimental estimate.

FORETELLING THE FUTURE—EXPECTATION

Example 1
How many heads would you expect to get if
you tossed a coin 50 times?
P(H) = $\frac{1}{2}$
Number of heads expected
= P(H) × number of tosses
= $\frac{1}{2}$ × 50
= 25

Example 2
P(rainy day in September) = 0.3
Estimate the number of dry days in the month.
P(dry day) = 0.7
Number of dry days expected
= 0.7 × 30
= 21

EXERCISE 5A

1 A coin is tossed.
  a Calculate P(Tail).
  b How many tails would you expect in 100 tosses?

2 A dice is rolled.
  a Calculate P(5).
  b How many 5s would you expect in 100 rolls of
    the dice?

3 The probability of passing a national examination
in French is 0.7. 1200 students take the exam.
How many would be expected to pass?

4 Based on last season's results, Rovers' manager
predicts that in the new season P(Win) = 0.5 and
P(Draw) = 0.2.
  a Write down P(Defeat).
  b How many wins, draws and defeats should the
    manager expect in 40 games?

5 a Calculate P(W) for a spin of this wheel.

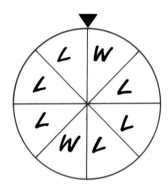

  b How many wins would you expect in 20 spins?
  c The prize for a win is 50p. How much money
    would you expect to win from 12 spins?
  d Each spin costs 20p. Would you expect to make
    a profit or loss in 12 spins?

6 A card is drawn at random from a full pack, and is
then replaced.
  a Calculate P(Ace).
  b How many aces would you expect in 100
    draws?

7 a What is the probability that a person chosen at
    random was born on a Monday?
  b How many students in a class of 35 would you
    expect to have been born on a Monday?

8 120 people were asked to name a month at
random. How many would you expect to choose a
month starting with J?

9 A letter is chosen at random from the word
TELEVISED.
  a Calculate P(Vowel)
  b In 100 choices, how many would you expect not
    to be vowels?

EXERCISE 5B

1 In the Modern Music workshop a sample of 80 CDs is selected and three are found to be faulty.
  a Estimate the probability of a faulty disc in their production line, as a decimal.
  b 4800 discs are sent to High Street stores. How many faulty ones should Modern Music expect to have to replace?

2 a For this spinner, calculate:
    (i) P(A)   (ii) P(A or B).
  b In 60 spins, how many:
    (i) As would you expect
    (ii) As or Bs would you expect?

3 a Draw a tree diagram for the possible outcomes when two coins are tossed.
  b Calculate the probability of (H, H) or (T, T).
  c How many outcomes (H, H) or (T, T) would you expect in 100 tosses of two coins?

4 A survey shows the usual lunchtime drinks chosen by 100 students.
How many of each should be ordered for a canteen supplying 750 students?

Drink	Number
Tea	12
Cola	44
Milk	20
Orange	24

5 Corny Cereals offer a 50p voucher which may be used on the next purchase. The company sells 5000 boxes of cereal each week. Surveys show that the probability of a purchaser using a voucher is 0.6. How much will the scheme cost the company per week?

6 Sunshine Insurance cover garden fetes against losses due to rain. From past experience, they know that the probability of a loss is 0.05. They insure 6000 events and promise to pay £1000 for each loss. How much does the company need to charge for each event if it is to break even?

/ **CHALLENGE** /

As you spin two barrels on the fruit machine, you see that each barrel has 1 cherry, 1 lemon and 1 orange on it.

a *(i) List all possible outcomes on the two barrels.*
    (ii) Write down P(C, C).
b *(i) List all possible outcomes for three barrels.*
    (ii) Write down P(C, C, C).
c *For three cherries you win £2, but each attempt costs 10p. Will you win or lose overall?*

/ **INVESTIGATION** /

Bob invents a cricket game. This is the net of the dice he uses. A player rolls the dice, and totals the 'runs' scored and the number of 'wickets'. When ten wickets have fallen the other player has a turn. The player with most runs wins.

	1 RUN	
2 RUNS	**6** RUNS	**3** RUNS
	WICKET	
	4 RUNS	

a *Investigate the scores a player might make.*
b *Play the game with a friend.*
c *Invent your own sports game using spinners, dice, etc. Explain the rules and most likely scores.*

CHECK-UP ON PROBABILITY

1 Diana approaches a roundabout. She's not sure which of the other exits to take, and in a panic chooses one at random.

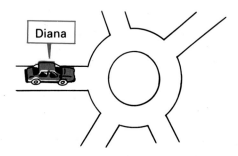

Calculate the probability that it is:
a the right one   **b** a wrong one.

2 In a survey of 80 cars, 24 are red. Calculate the probability that a car chosen at random from the group is red.

3 Steven reckons that the probability of success with his first serve is 0.75. What is the probability that his first serve fails?

4 A bag contains 7 red, 8 white and 10 blue marbles. One is taken out at random. Calculate:
a P(red)   **b** P(blue)   **c** P(red or blue)
d P(not red or blue)   **e** P(white).

5 A letter is chosen at random from the word MATHEMATICS. Calculate:
a P(vowel)
b the number of vowels chosen in 100 random choices.

6 The Safety First Insurance Company estimates that the probability of injury in a skiing holiday is 0.02. How many injuries should they expect in a party of: **a** 100 skiers   **b** 1500 skiers?

7 Guests at Petra's party choose an ice cream and a soft drink.
a Copy and complete:
(i) the table of outcomes
(ii) the tree diagram.

		Cola	Lime	Orange
Ice cream	Vanilla	(V, C)		
	Raspberry			

Soft drink

b If the ice creams and soft drinks are chosen at random, calculate: (i) P(cola)   (ii) P(vanilla).

8 Mo's torch needs two batteries, placed end to end in the torch with the ' + ' signs towards the bulb. Without thinking, she drops the batteries into the torch.

a Sketch all possible positions of the batteries in the torch.
b Calculate the probability that the bulb in the torch lights up first time.

9 In a game a dice is rolled and a coin is tossed. A head counts as 1 and a tail counts as 2. This is multiplied by the score on the dice.
a Copy and complete this table of scores.

	1	2	3	4	5	6
Head (1)	1	2	3			
Tail (2)	2	4				

Dice

b Calculate the probability of scoring:
(i) 9   (ii) 6   (iii) 8 or more.

10 From sales figures, the probability of a driver buying a Super Spectre car is 0.003. How many might you expect to see in a carpark holding 1150 cars?

REVIEW: SHAPE AND SPACE

ANGLES 1

1 Say whether each marked angle is acute, right, obtuse, straight or reflex (between 180° and 360°).

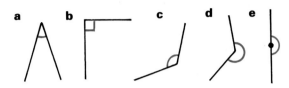

a   **b**   **c**   **d**   **e**

2 What type of angle is each of these?
   a 160°   **b** 99°   **c** 90°   **d** 10°   **e** 180°

3 Write down the sizes of angles AOB, COD, AOC, BOC and DOB:

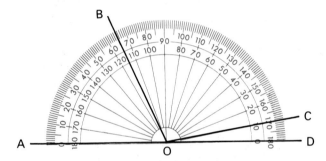

4 Estimate, then measure, the sizes of these angles: ∠PQR = ..., etc.

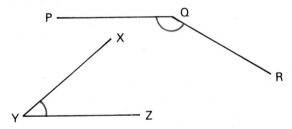

5 Draw an angle of:
   a 80°   **b** 110°

6 Name, and calculate the sizes of, the angles marked with arcs:

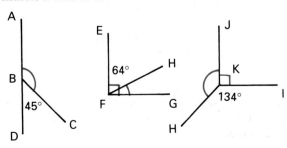

7 How many degrees are there in the smallest angle between:
   a N and NE
   b SW and SE
   c W and S
   d NW and E?

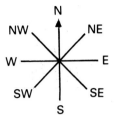

8 Through how many degrees does the dial turn clockwise from off to turn on the:
   a grill   **b** oven   **c** light   **d** defrost?

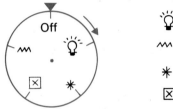

☀ Light
∿ Grill
✳ Defrost
⊠ Oven

9 On this rectangular farm gate, name:
   a the horizontal lines
   b the vertical lines
   c the two smallest acute angles.

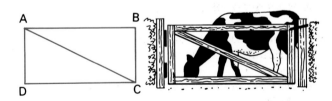

10 Construct △DEF with base DE = 8 cm, ∠FDE = 45° and ∠FED = 60°.
Measure: **a** FD   **b** FE   **c** ∠DFE.

11 On this diagram of rugby posts name:
   a a pair of parallel lines
   b two pairs of perpendicular lines.

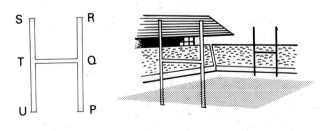

12 The reflex angle MON at a point O is 190°.
Calculate the size of the obtuse angle MON.

ANGLES 2

1 Show these pairs of angles in sketches:
   a supplementary angles
   b complementary angles
   c vertically opposite angles
   d (i) corresponding angles   (ii) alternate
      angles, in pairs of parallel lines.

2 a In the diagram below, name:
      (i) the supplement of ∠CBD
      (ii) the complement of ∠CBD.
   b If ∠CBD = 35°, calculate:
      (i) ∠DBE   (ii) ∠DBA.

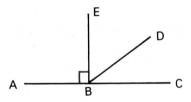

3 Name the angle which is:
   a vertically opposite ∠KMN
   b corresponding to ∠KMN
   c alternate to ∠KMN.

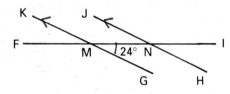

4 In the diagram for question **3**, ∠GMN = 24°.
   Calculate:
   a ∠KMN   **b** ∠FMK   **c** ∠JNM   **d** ∠HNI

5 Calculate *x* in each diagram.

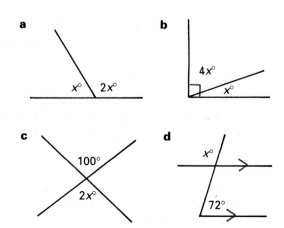

6 Calculate *a*, *b* and *c* for this diagram of a folding
   chair.

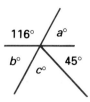

7 Sketch this TV aerial,
   and mark pairs of
   vertically opposite
   angles.

8 Make two sketches of this aerial.
   a Mark sets of corresponding
      angles on one sketch.
   b Mark pairs of alternate angles
      on the other sketch.

9 Copy this workbench diagram, and fill in the
   sizes of all the angles.

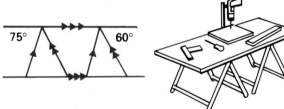

10 This dolls' house design is symmetrical about
   AB. Make a sketch, and fill in all the angles.

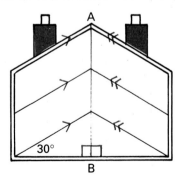

11 Four angles of *x*°, 2*x*°, 3*x*° and 4*x*° make up a
   complete turn at a point. Make an equation, solve
   it and find the sizes of the angles.

RECTANGLES AND SQUARES

1 a Draw accurately:
   (i) a square of side 5 cm
   (ii) a rectangle 6 cm by 4 cm.
 b Measure the lengths of the diagonals in each, correct to 1 decimal place.

2 a Sketch a square and a rectangle.
 b What properties does a square have that a rectangle does not have? Think about their:
   (i) sides   (ii) diagonals   (iii) symmetry.

3 a In this square, name:
   (i) two pairs of parallel sides
   (ii) eight right angles.

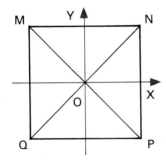

 b (i) If O is at the origin, and N is the point (5, 5), write down the coordinates of P, Q and M.
   (ii) Calculate the area of the square.

4 Copy the rectangle below, and fill in the lengths of as many lines, and the sizes of as many angles, as you can.

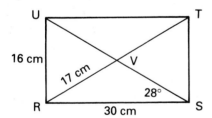

5 a Copy this square, and fill in the lengths of as many lines and the sizes of as many angles as you can.

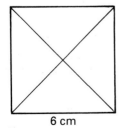

 b Calculate the area of each small triangle.

6 The boxing ring has sides 5 m long. There are three parallel strands of rope round the outside. Calculate the total length of rope needed for the ring.

7 a Find the total length of wood needed to make these gates.

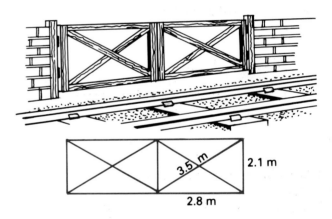

 b Sketch the diagram, and mark sets of parallel lines and equal angles.

8 a Plot the points A(1, 3), B(4, 0) and C(7, 3).
 b Complete the square ABCD and write down the coordinates of:
   (i) D   (ii) the centre of the square.

9 Draw the reflection in the *x*-axis of the square in question **8**, and write down the coordinates of its vertices.

10 Two shapes are congruent if they are identical in shape and size. Name all the sets of congruent triangles in the rectangle in question **4**.

TRIANGLES

1 Which of these could be sets of angles in a triangle?
 a 160°, 10°, 10° **b** 90°, 70°, 40° **c** 45°, 60°, 75°

2 Look at the triangles below, then say which type of triangle each one is—right-angled, isosceles, equilateral or obtuse-angled.

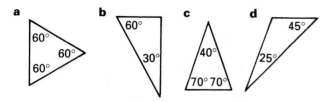

3 Calculate $a, b, c, \ldots$

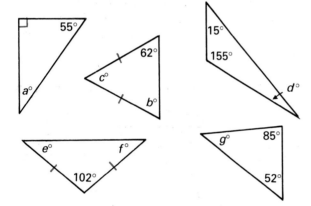

4 Calculate the areas of these triangles.

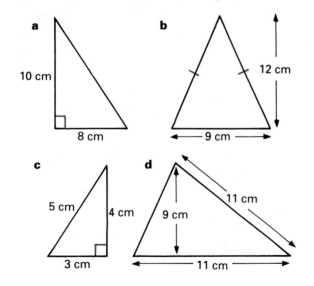

5 Is it possible to have a triangle with:
 a two acute angles
 b two obtuse angles
 c two right angles?

6 Copy these diagrams, and fill in all the angles.

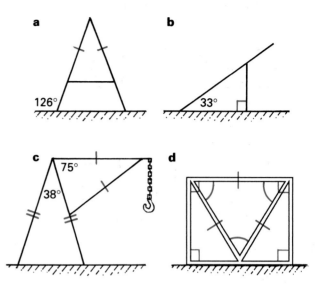

7 Calculate:
 a the length of AB
 b the area of:
  (i) △ACD (ii) △ABE
  (iii) quadrilateral BCDE.

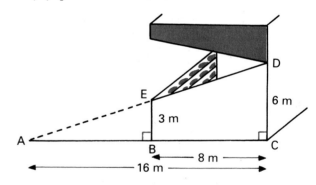

8 Calculate the area of:
 a rectangle ABCF
 b △AFE
 c trapezium ABDE.

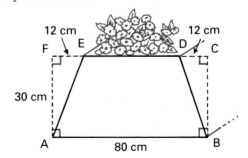

9 a Plot the points P(4, 2), Q(8, 2), R(6, 7).
 b Calculate the area of △PQR.

182

TILING AND SYMMETRY

1 Copy and extend these tiling patterns on squared paper. Colour them if you wish.

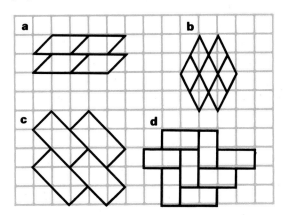

2 Shapes **a** and **b** below are symmetrical about both the *x* and *y*-axes. Write down the coordinates of all their other vertices.

a

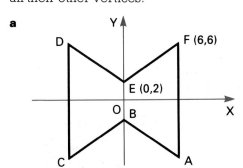

b

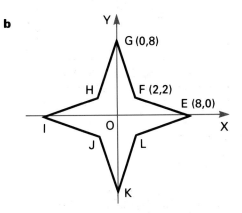

3 How many lines of symmetry has each shape in question **2**?

4 a Plot these points on squared paper, and join them up in order.
(4, 1), (1, 1), (1, 4), (−1, 4), (−1, 1), (−4, 1), (−4, −1), (−1, −1), (−1, −4), (1, −4), (1, −1), (4, −1), (4, 1).
b Describe the type of turn symmetry that this shape has.

5 (i) How many lines of symmetry does each shape have?
(ii) Describe the turn symmetry of each shape.

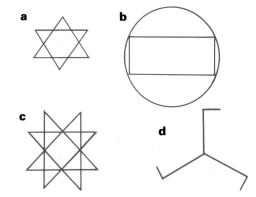

6 Copy these dots and axes of symmetry on squared paper, or on tracing paper. Then mark the images of the dots under reflection in the axes of symmetry.

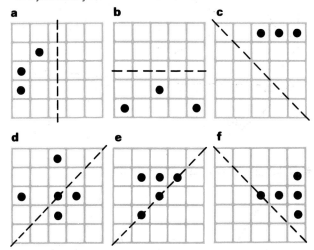

7 Say whether each shape below has:
(i) line symmetry; and if so, how many lines?
(ii) turn symmetry; and if so, which type?

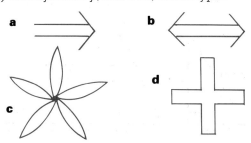

8 a Draw the line joining P(3, 1) to Q(1, 3).
b Draw the reflection of PQ in:
(i) the *x*-axis (RS) (ii) the *y*-axis (TU).
c Write down the coordinates of R, S, T and U.

QUADRILATERALS

1 (i) Sketch or trace each quadrilateral, and use dotted lines to show any lines of symmetry.

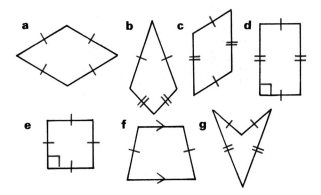

(ii) Which type of quadrilateral is each of the above?

2 a Plot the points A(3, 0), B(8, 0), C(7, 4) and D(2, 4). What shape is quadrilateral ABCD?
b Find the coordinates of the point of intersection of its diagonals.

3 Sketch these quadrilaterals, and fill in the sizes of as many angles, and the lengths of as many sides, as you can. The lengths are in cm.

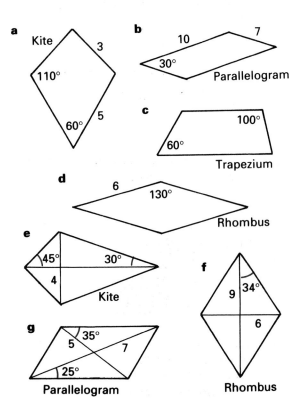

4 The church window has lead strips along the edges and diagonals of its rhombus shape. Calculate the total length of lead strip needed.

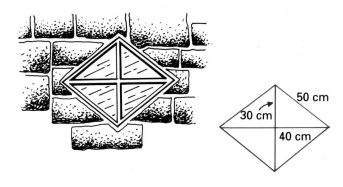

5 A lantern is made from four congruent kites. Calculate the total length of edging needed.

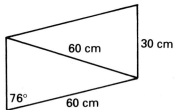

6 A metal framework is made in the shape of a parallelogram.
a Make a sketch, and fill in all the angles and lengths.

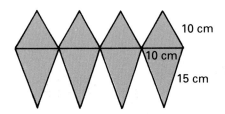

b Calculate the total length of metal strip needed.

7 A wooden trapezium-shaped panel is symmetrical about the dotted line.
a Sketch it, and fill in all the angles and lengths.
b Calculate its perimeter.

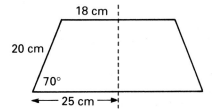

THREE DIMENSIONS

1 (i) Name the shapes shown in these diagrams.
(ii) Describe the faces of each one.

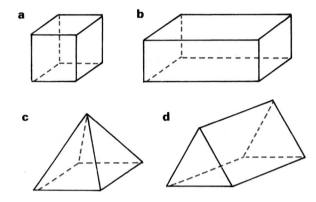

a   **b**   **c**   **d**

2 Name the shapes shown in these diagrams.

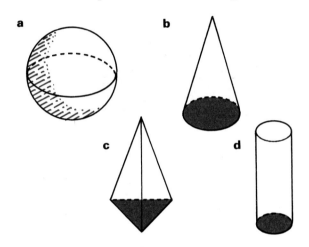

a   **b**   **c**   **d**

3 Calculate the total length of wire needed to make these skeleton models.

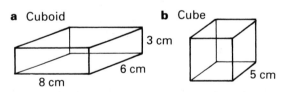

a Cuboid   8 cm   6 cm   3 cm
b Cube   5 cm

4 This shape is made from 1 cm cubes.

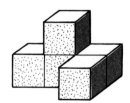

a How many cubes have been used?
b How many 1 cm² faces are on the outside (including the base)?
c Draw the view of this shape from:
(i) the front
(ii) the right-hand side   (iii) above.

5 a Calculate the volume of the box, in cubic centimetres.

CHESS SET   18 cm   8 cm   5 cm

b Calculate the area, in cm², of the:
(i) front face   (ii) lid   (iii) side.
c Calculate the total area of the six faces.
d Sketch a net of the box.

6 On this house, name:
a the vertical edges
b the vertical faces
c four lines parallel to BC
d a face congruent to IEF
e four lines which are perpendicular to AB.

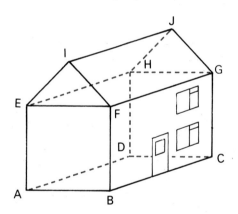

7 Clyde has drawn a net of 2 cm squares to make a box, but finds that it doesn't work.

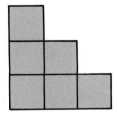

a By moving one square, can you make the net of a cube for him? Show this in a sketch.
b Calculate: (i) the area of the net
(ii) the volume of the box.

DISTANCES AND DIRECTIONS

1 Sue redesigns her rectangular lawn by cutting quarter-circle plots from each corner. Make a scale drawing of her new lawn using a scale of 1 cm to 1 m.

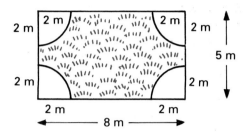

2 Use a scale of 1 cm to 5 km to make a scale drawing of this ship's route from P to Q to R.

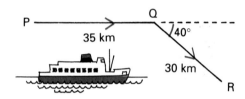

3 a Make a scale drawing of the end of this hut. Use a scale of 1 cm to 20 cm.

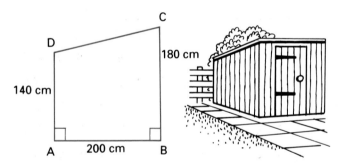

b Measure CD, correct to 1 decimal place. Using the scale, calculate the actual length of the sloping edge of the roof.
c Measure the angles BCD and ADC to the nearest degree.

4 Write down the 3-figure bearings of these directions from O.

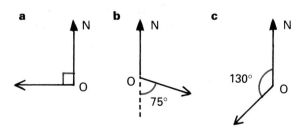

5 These five places are at the corners and centre of a large square area.

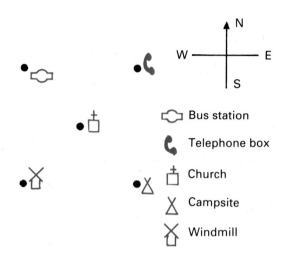

- Bus station
- Telephone box
- Church
- Campsite
- Windmill

a What is the direction of:
  (i) the windmill from the bus station
  (ii) the church from the campsite
  (iii) the telephone box from the church?
b Which place is:
  (i) N of the campsite
  (ii) NW of the church
  (iii) SW of the church?

6 a Find the bearing from Allford to:
  (i) Dipmouth (ii) Buxsea (iii) Cowton.

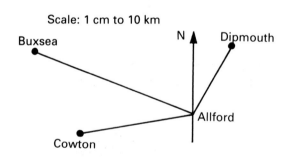

Scale: 1 cm to 10 km

b Find the distance, in km, from Allford to each of the other villages.

7 Becky sailed 16 km on a bearing of 120°, then 24 km on a bearing of 250°.
  a Use a scale of 1 cm to 4 km to make a scale drawing.
  b How far is she now from her starting point, to the nearest 0.1 km?
  c What is the bearing of her starting point from her finishing point, to the nearest degree?

TOPICS TO EXPLORE

1 Scale drawings

a Make a scale drawing of this sports pitch. Use a scale of 1 cm to 10 feet.

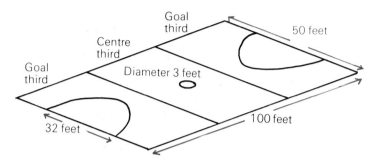

b Make a scale drawing of these traffic lights. Colour them if you wish.
Scale: 1 cm to 10 cm.

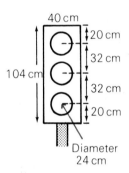

c Make a scale drawing of the front, end and sloping roof of this house. Choose your own scale.

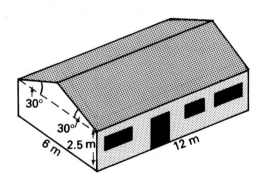

2 Hidden words

The words below, which are all about a circle, are hidden in the rectangle of letters. They may be horizontal, vertical or diagonal, in either direction.

ARC
AREA
CENTRE
CHORD
CIRCUMFERENCE
DIAMETER
RADIUS
PI
SECTOR
SEGMENT
SEMICIRCLE
TANGENT

a Copy, or trace, the rectangle of letters, and draw a line round each word.

E	C	N	E	R	E	F	M	U	C	R	I	C
S	S	A	R	C	O	N	D	R	A	A	T	R
S	E	C	T	O	R	R	T	E	O	D	A	A
O	G	C	N	E	O	A	R	T	S	I	N	T
M	M	D	E	H	G	A	H	E	G	U	G	E
G	E	L	C	R	I	C	I	M	E	S	C	O
R	N	M	A	T	H	S	P	A	R	T	E	N
A	T	A	N	G	E	N	T	I	I	I	N	T
D	A	C	T	I	O	N	A	D	D	R	O	C

b Draw one or two circles, and mark the parts described by the words.
c This book's title is hidden in the rectangle (not necessarily in the same line). Can you find it?

3 Design symmetry

a Copy the pattern on squared paper, or use tracing paper.

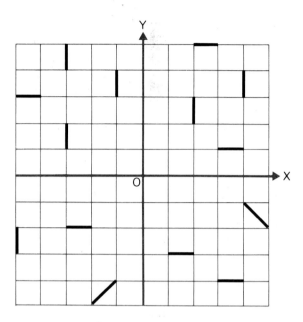

b Choose one of the black lines. Reflect it in the *x*-axis, then in the *y*-axis, then in the *x*-axis, and so on, until you are back to the start.
Do this for every black line until you have four polygons.

c Design your own shape on a squared grid, and break it up into different parts. It could be a geometric shape, or an animal, or . . . . Ask a friend to try to put it together again as in parts **a** and **b**.

4 Which would you choose?

Phyllis saw two advertisements that interested her. But she had a problem. Which job would have the better salary by the end of six years? No quick answers here—use paper, pencil and calculator!

a Copy and complete this table for the first job.

Year	1	2	3	4
Salary (£)	20 000	20 500	21 000	2

b The second job needs a more difficult calculation. Copy and complete the table.

Year	1	2	3	4
Increase	—	1500	1650	
Salary (£)	15 000	16 500	18 150	

c Draw graphs of the salaries over six years on the same diagram, using the axes and scales shown.

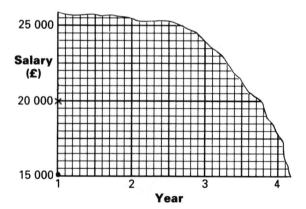

d How would you advise Phyllis? Would it make any difference if you calculated the *total* sum of money earned over six years? Write a sentence about your advice for Phyllis.

5 Silly circle patterns

a You'll need a coin and plenty of paper. Circles can't tile, but you can make regular patterns. Copy the sets of circles in pencil, then turn them into the pictures. Use colour if you wish.

(i)

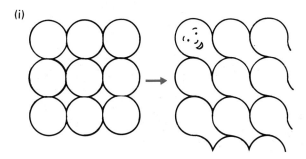

(ii)

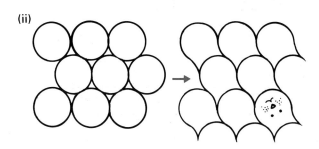

(iii)

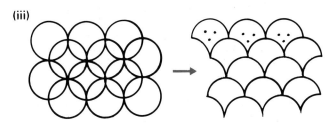

b These shellfish come from a pattern of equal circles. Can you draw them?

c Draw other patterns of circles and designs of your own.

6 Football scores

a List all possible half-time scores in the Rovers v. United game. Try to arrange them in a methodical way.

Repeat this for two or three different full-time scores.

b If the final score is 'Rovers m United n', can you make a formula in terms of m and n for the number of possible half-time scores?

7 How to win a magazine competition

Win £1000! All you have to do is to choose the eight items on this list that you would find most useful, and list them in order 1 to 8. How can you be sure of submitting a correct entry?

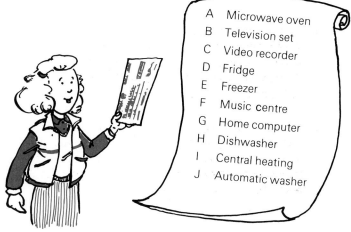

A Microwave oven
B Television set
C Video recorder
D Fridge
E Freezer
F Music centre
G Home computer
H Dishwasher
I Central heating
J Automatic washer

Think it out!
Two items, A and B, can be listed in two ways, AB and BA. In how many ways can A, B, C be listed, two at a time? Make lists to find out. You should be able to find six ways.

A quicker way
a With A, B, C, the first place in the list can be filled in three ways, and *then* the second place can be filled in two ways. So both places can be filled in $3 \times 2 = 6$ ways.
b With 4 items A, B, C and D, three places can be filled in $4 \times 3 \times 2 = 24$ ways.
c Now find how many entries you would have to send in to the competition to be sure of winning. A magazine costs £1.50. Can you see any snags?

8 Some clever constructions

Pencil, ruler and compasses only!

a *Refresh your memory*
   (i) Draw a straight line, and construct its perpendicular bisector.
   (ii) Draw an angle, and construct the line which bisects it.

b Two rocks, 80 m apart, to steer between. So Bob plays it safe. He steers the *Mary Anne* on a course which keeps an *equal distance* from the rocks on either side. Make a scale drawing to show his course.
(*Scale:* 1 cm = 10 m).

c Rocks safely past, the *Mary Anne* enters the harbour on a course which keeps the *same distance* from each wall.
Make a drawing to show the *Mary Anne*'s course.

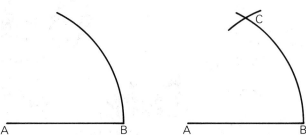

d *Eight points of the compass*
   (i) Draw a line WE 8 cm long.
   (ii) Construct its perpendicular bisector, NS.
   (iii) Construct the bisectors of the angles between: N and E; N and W.
   (iv) Finish the drawing, and name the eight points.

e *Special angles—60° and 30°*
   (i) Follow these two steps to construct an angle of 60°.

   (ii) Check that AB = BC = AC. Why is ∠BAC = 60°?
   (iii) Using ∠BAC, construct angles of 30°.

f *Construct a clockface*
Make a rough sketch.
Think how you would construct the hands at:
(i) 3 o'clock (ii) 2 o'clock (iii) 1 o'clock.
Now do this accurately using your ruler and compasses. Construct a full clockface.

9 A corner-cabinet design

Make rough sketches of a cabinet you wish to design to fit into the corner of a room.

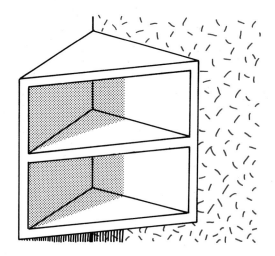

Decide what its dimensions will be, and make scale drawings of the top, front and sides.
How many shelves do you want? Will it have a door?
Make a list of all the items you need, including their sizes.
Calculate the shelf area, and the volume of your cabinet.

10 A whirl of right-angled triangles

a Look at this whirl of right-angled triangles. Draw it like this:
  (i) Draw OA = 2 cm
  (ii) With set-square or protractor, make a right angle at A.
  (iii) Draw AB = 2 cm and join OB.
  (iv) Make another right angle at B.
  (v) Draw BC = 2 cm and join OC.
  (vi) Continue the whirl as far as you can.

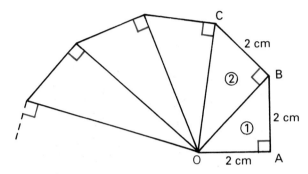

b Call each 2 cm length 1 unit.
  So OA = AB = BC = . . . = 1 unit.
  (i) *Triangle 1*: OAB.
     By Pythagoras' Theorem,
     $$x^2 = 1^2 + 1^2$$
     $$= 1 + 1$$
     $$= 2$$
     $$x = \sqrt{2}$$

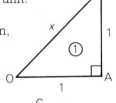

  (ii) *Triangle 2*: OBC.
     Copy and complete:
     $$y^2 = (\sqrt{2})^2 + 1^2$$
     $$= 2 + 1$$
     $$= \ldots$$
     $$y = \ldots$$

  (iii) Copy and complete this table for the first ten triangles:

Triangle	1	2	3	4
Length of hypotenuse	$\sqrt{2}$	$\sqrt{3}$	$\sqrt{4} = 2$	

  (iv) What is the length of the hypotenuse for triangle n?
  (v) For some triangles the length of the hypotenuse is an exact number of units. For example, for triangle 3, the length is $\sqrt{4} = 2$ units. List the triangle numbers of the first five triangles which have an exact hypotenuse.
  (vi) What is the ratio of the area of triangle 2 to the area of triangle 1? Of triangle 21 to triangle 20? Of triangle $(n+1)$ to triangle n?

11 Quadrilateral clues—a kind of detective game

a On squared paper make careful drawings of: a rectangle, a square, a kite, a rhombus, a parallelogram and a trapezium.
b Keep your eye on your drawings, and follow the clues in the flowchart to find which kind of quadrilateral is hiding in each box . . .

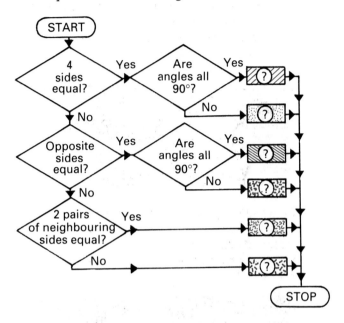

12 A statistical survey

Choose a topic:

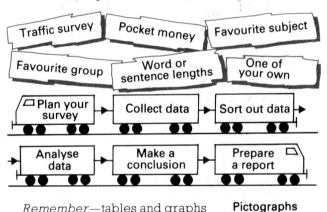

Remember—tables and graphs are always useful.

Frequency tables and tallies

Line graphs

Bar graphs

Pictographs

Pie charts

Mean Median Mode
Range
Percentages

Could your survey be used, improved or extended?

REVISION EXERCISE ON CHAPTER 1: CALCULATIONS AND CALCULATORS

1 Round to 1 decimal place:
  a 3.14 **b** 8.16 **c** 10.05 **d** 0.46

2 Round to 1 significant figure:
  a 17 **b** 234 **c** 660 **d** 3199

3 a Which of these is the best estimate for 12×37?
  (i) 40 (ii) 400 (iii) 4000
  b Which of these could be correct?
  (i) 437 (ii) 4004 (iii) 452 (iv) 444
  c Check with your calculator.

4 Estimate first, then calculate:
  a 19×42 **b** 48×116 **c** 243×8.1
  d 22.8×197.6

5 £100 is shared out equally among six prize-winners in a competition. How much does each winner get?

6

The bathroom scales had not been zeroed properly. As a result every reading was 3.4 kg over. Use the calculator memory, or constant facility, to find the correct weights.

Reading	42.3	51.7	58.0	63.7	68.9	75.0
Correct weight						

7 Calculate the volumes of the cube and cuboid, correct to 2 significant figures.

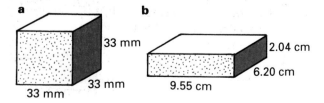

a 33 mm, 33 mm, 33 mm
b 2.04 cm, 6.20 cm, 9.55 cm

8 a *No calculator here!* Which of the following could be 18^2?
  (i) 36 (ii) 180 (iii) 226 (iv) 324
  b Check with your calculator.

9

These plates have radii of 8 cm, 10 cm and 13 cm.
  a Use the formula $A = \pi r^2$ to calculate their areas, correct to 2 decimal places.
  b Another plate has area 600 cm². Use the formula $r = \sqrt{(A \div \pi)}$ to find its radius, correct to 2 decimal places.

10 Write these numbers in standard form:
  a a local charity mystery tour raised £2400
  b the speed of light is 300 000 000 m/s
  c the weight of the Earth is 6 600 000 000 000 000 000 000 tonnes
  d a sheet of fine paper is 0.085 mm thick
  e a photographic film is 0.0007 mm thick.

11 Write these displays in standard form, and then in full:

  a   **b**   **c**

1.6 03   2 05   7 -02

12 Jon says he can find the nth number in the Fibonacci sequence 1, 1, 2, 3, 5, 8, 13, . . . by using $(1.618)^n \div \sqrt{5}$, correct to the nearest whole number.
  Check this for $n = 1, 2, 3, 4, 5, 6, 7, 8$. Does this prove that it always works?

REVISION EXERCISE ON CHAPTER 2: SHAPE AND SPACE

1 Calculate *x* in each diagram:

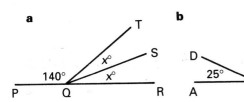

2 What is:
  a the length of AB
  b the size of ∠ACB?

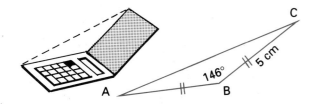

3 Copy this diagram, and fill in the sizes of all the angles.

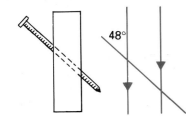

4 Calculate *x* in each diagram.

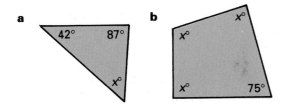

5 MN is an axis of symmetry. Name:
  a a line equal in length to
    (i) AB (ii) HG (iii) DE
  b an angle equal to
    (i) ∠FGH (ii) ∠PIL (iii) ∠NDE
  c a shape congruent to ABCP.

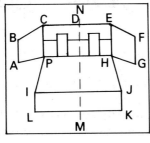

6 Copy these quadrilaterals. For each:
  (i) say what type it is
  (ii) fill in all the angles
  (iii) use dotted lines to draw any axes of symmetry.

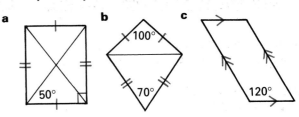

7 a If ABCD is a square on this grid, write down the coordinates of C and D.

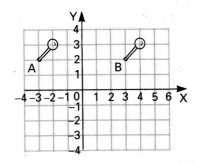

  b If ABEF is a rectangle on the grid with area 30 squares, find the coordinates of E and F.

8 Copy the diagram, and draw the image of △ABC under:
  a reflection in the *x*-axis
  b a rotation about O of 180°.

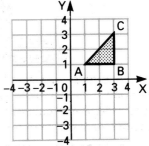

9 Each edge of a dice is 15 mm long.
  a Draw a net for making the dice.
  b Calculate the surface area and volume of the dice.

10 a Sketch the path traced by P on the door handle when it is pressed down to open the door.
  b What is the path of P as the door opens?

REVISION EXERCISE ON CHAPTER 3: MONEY MATTERS— SAVING AND SPENDING

1 Sheila got this job for six weeks.

> **• OFFICE TEMP FOR HOLIDAYS •**
> **MUST TYPE**
> **37 hour week — £3.75 an hour**
> **Apply to BOX 101 in writing**

  a What is the hourly rate of pay?
  b Calculate her weekly wage.
  c How much did she earn in the six weeks?

2

Alan works in a shoe repair/key cutting shop. His basic pay is £7.40 an hour. His overtime rates are: weekday, time-and-a-quarter; Saturday, time-and-a-half; Sunday, double time.
Calculate his overtime pay for:
  a 1 hour on Tuesday   **b** 3 hours on Saturday
  c 7 hours on Sunday.

3 Sanjay is a car salesman. His salary is £6000 per annum, plus 8% commission on sales. His sales for the year came to £200 000. Calculate his total earnings for the year.

4 Jill invested £460 in the Monument Building Society for one year. The rate of interest was $6\frac{1}{2}\%$ per annum.

MONUMENT BUILDING SOCIETY
$6\frac{1}{2}$ % M S B

  a How much interest did she expect to receive?
  b Tax was deducted at 25p in the £. How much interest did she actually get?

5 Use the chart to find the price of each item in the data. (Use the memory or constant facility.)

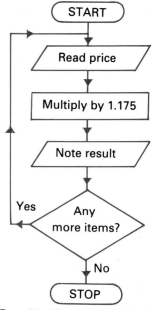

```
        START
          │
          ↓
     Read price  ←──────┐
          │             │
          ↓             │
  Multiply by 1.175     │
          │             │
          ↓             │
     Note result        │
          │             │
          ↓          Yes│
      Any        ───────┘
    more items?
          │
          │ No
          ↓
        STOP
```

Data (£): 20, 12, 8, 3, 1.50, 0.60

6 Calculate the cost of this phone bill:

Call charges	£15.80
Rental charges	19.94
Subtotal	
VAT at 17.5%	
Total due	

7 Mr Abraham never looked forward to his winter electricity bill. Calculate entries A, B, C, D and E to find how much he had to pay.

Meter reading		Charges	Amount (£)
Present	Previous		
22853	21645	Standing charge A units at 7.55p	6.50 B
		SUB TOTAL VAT at 17.5%	C D
		TOTAL DUE	E

8 How much cheaper is the camera if you pay cash for it?

> **CAMERA**
> **£79.99 CASH**
> **H P DEPOSIT £24 AND**
> **12 WEEKLY PAYMENTS**
> **OF £5.35**

REVISION EXERCISE ON CHAPTER 4: SCALE DRAWINGS AND SIMILAR SHAPES

1 An aircraft flies 120 km east, then 50 km south.
  a Show its route on a scale drawing, taking 1 cm to 10 km.
  b Use your scale drawing to estimate:
    (i) its distance from base
    (ii) its bearing back to base.

2 Copy and complete the table of scale factors.

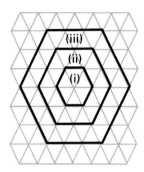

Enlargements from		Reductions from	
(i) to (ii)		(iii) to (i)	
(i) to (iii)		(ii) to (i)	
(ii) to (iii)		(iii) to (ii)	

3 The model bridge is made to a scale of $\frac{1}{10\,000}$. It is 5 cm long.

Calculate:
  a the enlargement scale factor for the real bridge
  b the length of the bridge
    (i) in cm   (ii) in metres.

4 Magic Cards make standard cards and junior cards. The junior cards are scaled down by a factor of 0.4.
Calculate the lengths of the diagonals of the diamond at the centre of the junior ace.

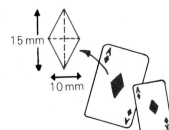

5 A map has a representative fraction (scale factor) of 1 : 25 000. A coastline is 4 cm long on the map. Calculate its real length in:
  a cm **b** m **c** km.

6 Martin's speaker cabinet has two circular speakers. The scale factor of the enlargement from one to the other is 4.

  a The diameter of the small one is 3 cm. Calculate the diameter of the larger one.
  b If the radius of the larger speaker was 6 cm, what would the radius of the smaller speaker be?

7 These two road signs are similar.

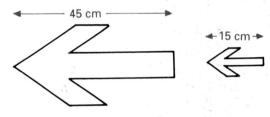

  a What is the reduction scale factor?
  b The larger sign is 24 cm high. What is the height of the smaller sign?

8 The rectangular gates are similar. Lengths are in metres.

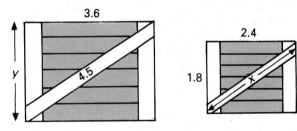

Calculate:
  a (i) the reduction scale factor   (ii) x.
  b (i) the enlargement scale factor (ii) y.

9 a Explain why △s ABC and ADE are similar.

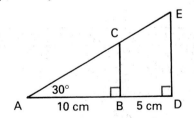

  b What is the enlargement scale factor from △ABC to △ADE? (Careful!)
  c BC = 5.8 cm. Calculate the length of DE.
  d If AC = 11.6 cm, calculate AE.

REVISION EXERCISE ON CHAPTER 5: GOING PLACES

1 a Speed = 55 km/h **b** Distance = 120 km
Time   = 5 h   Speed   = 24 km/h
Distance = ?   Time   = ?

2 How far will the car travel in $1\frac{1}{2}$ hours?

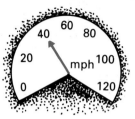

3 a Action Rovers football supporters' coach travels 220 miles to an away game in 5 hours. Calculate its average speed.
  b The coach returned at an average speed of 55 mph. How long did the return journey take?

4 A mountain rescue helicopter left its base at 11 30 hours and reached the accident at 13 30 hours. Its average speed was 148 km/h. How far had it to fly?

5 Use the mileage chart to find how long these journeys take.
  a Hendon to Airlie at 10 mph
  b Patch to Airlie at 20 mph
  c Hendon to Patch at 40 mph.

Distances in miles

Hendon		
50	Airlie	
60	40	Patch

6 The Dobson family have been on holiday.

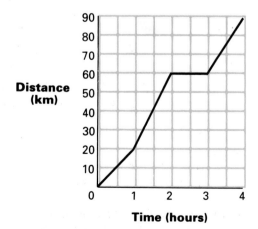

a How far did they travel?
b How long did the journey take?
c How far from home were they after $1\frac{1}{2}$ hours?
d How long did they stop for lunch?
e Calculate the average speed for each of the four parts of their journey.

7 A train travelling at an average speed of 50 km/h takes 2 hours 30 minutes for the journey from Aberdeen to Perth. What is the distance between the two towns?

8 The pilot knows that he can fly 1890 km at an average speed of 630 km/h. How long will the flight take?

9 *Timetable* (Bus Route 1)

Ayton	09 00
Poole	10 00
Poole	10 15
Barton	12 00

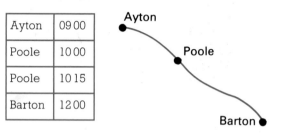

a Fill in the missing entry in the table.
b How long does the bus take from
  (i) Ayton to Poole
  (ii) Poole to Barton?

Distances in km

Ayton		
40	Poole	
	64	Barton

10 A troop of soldiers march at a steady speed of 6.5 km/h. How far do they go in 48 minutes? (Express 48 minutes as a decimal fraction of an hour first.)

11 Cardiff is 190 km from Exeter. The times taken for the journey by car, van and coach are: car, 2 hours; van, 3 hours 20 minutes; coach, 2 hours 30 minutes.
Calculate the average speed of each vehicle.

REVISION EXERCISE ON CHAPTER 6: BRACKETS AND EQUATIONS

1 Remove the brackets:
  a $4(x+2)$ **b** $5(y-1)$ **c** $2(3-t)$
  d $8(1-n)$ **e** $3(2x+5)$ **f** $4(1-3y)$

2 a Write down two expressions for the area of the front of this ghetto-blaster.

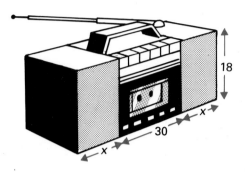

  b Calculate the area when $x = 12$, and units are cm.

3 Write the OUT entries with and without brackets.

a

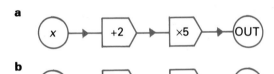

b

4 Remove the brackets, and tidy these up.
  a $3(x+5)-10$ **b** $5(x-1)+6$
  c $8+2(p+1)$ **d** $7+3(q-2)$

5 Solve the equations:
  a $x+6 = 12$ **b** $y-7 = 5$ **c** $8x = 64$
  d $u-8 = 8$ **e** $2v+1 = 11$ **f** $7t-3 = 11$

6 Solve:
  a $4(y-1) = 36$ **b** $3(s+4) = 15$
  c $5(k-3) = 20$ **d** $8(m+3) = 40$

7 Write down an equation with brackets for each part, then solve it.

a

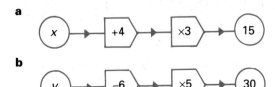

b

8

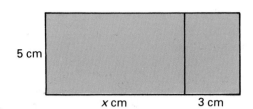

The area of the largest rectangle is 55 cm². Make an equation, solve it and find the length of the rectangle.

9 Make an equation for this balance and solve it to find the left-hand weight, in kg.

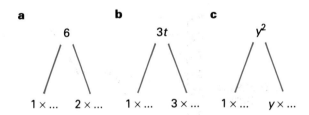

10 Solve:
  a $3(x+2)+1 = 7$ **b** $4(y-1)+1 = 13$
  c $2(1+a)-2 = 10$ **d** $6(1+c)-3 = 15$

11 The price of a newspaper increases from 45p to $(45+x)$p. Six papers now cost 318p. Make an equation, and find the price increase for each paper.

12 Copy and complete these diagrams to show the missing factors.

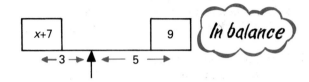

a 6: $1 \times \ldots$ $2 \times \ldots$
b $3t$: $1 \times \ldots$ $3 \times \ldots$
c y^2: $1 \times \ldots$ $y \times \ldots$

13 Factorise:
  a $2x+4$ **b** $3y-6$ **c** $4z+4$
  d $9+3t$ **e** $15-5u$ **f** $21+14v$

14 Write down the highest common factor of:
  a 9 and 12 **b** 20 and 30 **c** 12 and 18

15 Factorise fully:
  a $6x+8$ **b** $6x+12$ **c** $6x+x^2$
  d $9y-15$ **e** $4t+8$ **f** $2u^2-8u$

REVISION EXERCISE ON CHAPTER 7: HANDLING DATA

1 a Use the flowchart to process the given data.
b Suggest a title for the flowchart.

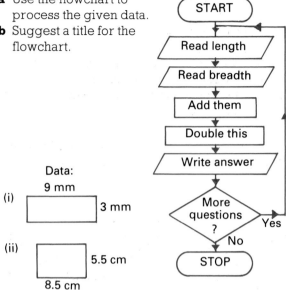

Data:

(i)

9 mm

3 mm

(ii)

5.5 cm

8.5 cm

2 a Which three features are linked by this 3-D bar graph?

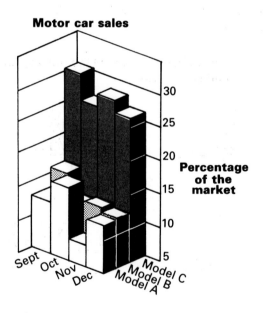

Motor car sales

Percentage of the market

Sept, Oct, Nov, Dec — Model A, Model B, Model C

b What percentage of sales had model C in September?
c Which was model A's best month?
d Which model had most sales?

3 Seven babies were weighed at the Health Centre: 5.5, 7, 8, 6, 7.5, 6, 9 kg.
a Calculate:
  (i) the range of weights
  (ii) the mean and median weights.
b Write down the modal weight.

4 A sample of 25 g packets of Energy Oats weighed: 22, 24, 26, 27, 23, 24, 30, 27, 28, 28, 23, 28, 25, 25, 26, 25, 27, 25, 25, 27, 26, 24, 26, 29, 25, 25, 24, 25, 27, 26 g.

a Make a frequency table:

Weight (g)	Tally	Frequency	Weight × frequency
22			

b Calculate the mean weight, correct to 1 decimal place.
c What are the modal and median weights?

5 Copy the data in question **4** in a table like this, and calculate the mean again.

Weight (g)	Mid-value	Frequency	Mid-value × frequency
22–24	23	7	
25–27			
28–30			
Total			

6 Chris asks his friends about the time they spend watching television and doing homework in a typical week.

TV (h)	16	18	10	5	11	9
Homework (h)	7	4	10	14	9	12

9	4	13	17	11	7
11	15	8	6	8	12

a Calculate, correct to 1 decimal place, the mean number of hours spent on each activity.
b Draw axes for a scatter diagram, and plot the point M showing the two means.
c Draw the best-fitting line through M.
d Describe any connection between the two activities.

REVISION EXERCISE ON CHAPTER 8: PYTHAGORAS

1 Calculate:
 a the area of the square on AB
 b the length of each side of △ABC.

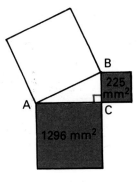

2 Calculate a, b, c, d, correct to 1 decimal place.

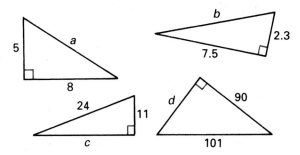

3 Calculate these lengths, correct to 1 decimal place:

a 5 cm, 3 cm — The diagonal of the rectangle

b 4 cm — A side of the square

4 What is the length of the wire supporting the tree?

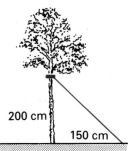

200 cm
150 cm

5 AB = 7 m. If the ladder is 10 m long, how far above B can it reach, to the nearest centimetre?

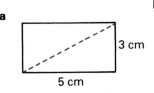

6 a Draw axes OX and OY, and draw lines from the origin to:
 A(10, 0), B(9, 5), C(8, 6), D(7, 7), E(6, 8), F(4, 9) and G(0, 10).
 b Calculate the lengths of the lines, correct to 1 decimal place when not exact.
 c Say which of the points A, . . . , G lie on a circle, centre O, radius 10 units.

7 Copy these diagrams, and draw lines which give you right-angled triangles for the calculations.

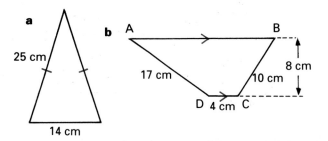

a 25 cm, 14 cm

b A, B, 17 cm, 10 cm, 8 cm, D 4 cm C

Calculate the height of the isosceles triangle.

Calculate the length of side AB of the trapezium.

8 Calculate the slanting edge of the rocker, correct to 3 significant figures.

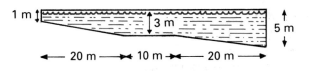

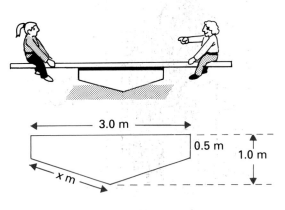

3.0 m, 0.5 m, 1.0 m, x m

9 This is the cross-section of Sunsea swimming pool. Calculate the total length of the floor of the pool, to the nearest metre.

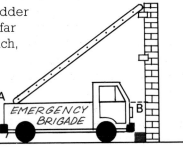

1 m, 3 m, 5 m
20 m, 10 m, 20 m

REVISION EXERCISE ON CHAPTER 9: AREAS AND VOLUMES

1 The sports field is rectangular. Calculate:
  a its perimeter
  b its area in
    (i) m² (ii) hectares (1 ha = 10 000 m²).

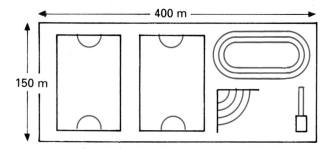

2 The end of Rovers' sports stand is to be painted blue, with white doors. Calculate the area to be painted each colour.

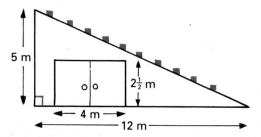

3 Calculate the area of grass in a trapezium-shaped field like this.

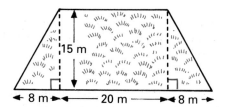

4 a Use Pythagoras' Theorem to calculate the hypotenuse of each triangle in question **3**.
  b Calculate the perimeter of the field.

5 The top of the cooker is square, with sides 40 cm long. Each ring has a diameter of 16 cm. Calculate the shaded area of the top.

6 The bricks are cubes of side 5 cm.
  a Calculate the volume of:
    (i) a brick (ii) the box.
  b How many bricks will fit into the box?

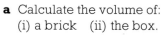
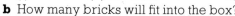

7 Calculate the area of material used to make this Disc Tidy (four surfaces).

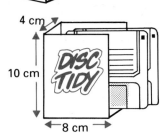

8 Each prism is 25 cm long. Given the areas of their cross-sections, calculate the volumes of the prisms.

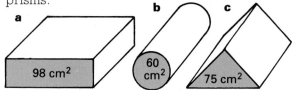

9 Calculate:
  a the area of the end of the tent
  b the volume of the tent.

10 The pan is cylindrical. Calculate:
  a the area of the base
  b the capacity of the pan in:
    (i) cm³ (ii) litres.

11 The height of the beaker is 18 cm and the radius of its base is 4 cm. It is half full of liquid. Calculate:
  a the volume of liquid
  b the area of beaker in contact with the liquid.

REVISION EXERCISE ON CHAPTER 10: MONEY MATTERS—PERSONAL FINANCE

1

Julia Winters is a nursery assistant. Calculate her gross pay, total deductions and net pay for week 28.

Employee 058	JULIA WINTERS		Tax Code 411H	Week 28
Basic Pay 180.00	**Overtime** —	**Commission** —	**Bonus** —	**Gross Pay**
Income Tax 30.00	**Superannuation** 9.00	**National Insurance** 12.00	**Other Deductions**	**Total Deductions**
				Net Pay

2

Jake Maloney is a salesman. Calculate his gross pay, total deductions and net pay for month 5.

Employee 042	JAKE MALONEY		Tax Code 523H	Month 5
Basic Pay 1200.00	**Overtime** —	**Commission** 144.00	**Bonus** 25.00	**Gross Pay**
Income Tax 285.00	**Superannuation** 72.00	**National Insurance** 107.53	**Other Deductions** 14.20	**Total Deductions**
				Net Pay

3 Gita is personnel manager at Hifly Airways. Her gross pay in January was £1720. How much superannuation had she to pay, at 4.5% of her gross pay?

4 Use the tax information on pages 144 and 146 to help you to copy and complete Mr Williams' tax calculation.

Allowances:

Personal	£ ____	Gross pay	£15 800
Married couple	1500	Allowances	____
Total	£ ____	Taxable income	£ ____

Tax due: 20% of £3000 £ ____
25% of . . . ____
Total tax £ ____

5 Make a similar calculation for a single person with a gross salary of £12 800.

6 Peter Wilson is 31, and decides to take out a whole life policy worth £15 000 to protect his family. Use the table on page 148 to calculate his monthly and his annual premiums. He doesn't smoke.

7 If, instead, Peter Wilson chooses a 10 year endowment policy for £15 000, how much will he pay monthly?

8 Joy and Alan are spending a holiday in France and Germany. They decide to change £500 into francs, at 8.45 francs to the £, and £500 into marks, at 2.48 marks to the £. How many of each will they receive?

9 £1 = 1.44 dollars. How many £s will a tourist get for 3450 dollars?

REVISION EXERCISE ON CHAPTER 11: FORMULAE AND SEQUENCES

1 Choose the correct formula below, and calculate:
  a the volume of a rectangular box 15 cm by 12 cm by 9 cm
  b the circumference of a circle of diameter 8 mm, correct to 1 decimal place
  c the length of the hypotenuse in a right-angled triangle with sides 30 cm and 16 cm long
  d the area of a rectangular runway 950 m long and 75 m wide.

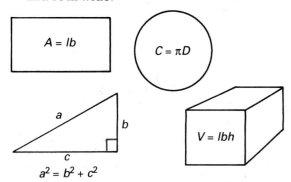

$A = lb$

$C = \pi D$

$a^2 = b^2 + c^2$

$V = lbh$

2 a Write down formulae for
    (i) the perimeter P cm
    (ii) the area A cm^2
      of the window.
  b Calculate P and A when $x = 12$.

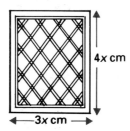

4x cm

←—3x cm —→

3 a Make a formula for this 'rule'. Take a Fahrenheit temperature F, subtract 32, then divide by 2. You'll then have the approximate Celsius temperature C.
  b Use your formula to find C when:
    (i) $F = 50$ (ii) $F = 32$.

4 Calculate the first three terms of sequences which have nth terms:
  a $5n+2$ **b** $2n-1$ **c** n^2+n-1

5 Calculate the values asked:

	Formula	Given	Calculate
a	$y = x+c$	$x = 9, c = 8$	y
b	$a = b \div c$	$b = 60, c = 8$	a
c	$d = 2t^2$	$t = 10$	d
d	$p = 5q-r$	$q = 6, r = 5$	p
e	$s = 2\sqrt{t}$	$t = 900$	s
f	$u = 20-x+y$	$x = 7, y = 12$	u

6 Phil is a fitness fanatic. He raises the weight by pulling the ends of the cord. The formula for the force he needs is $F = \dfrac{WL}{4s}$.
W is the weight, L the length of the cord, s the sag. Calculate F when $W = 50$, $L = 120$, $s = 15$.

7 Make a formula for P.

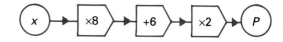

x → ×8 → +6 → ×2 → P

8 The Smiths are off to the seaside. They travel for 3 hours at x km/h and 2 hours at y km/h. Write down a formula for the distance D km that they travel.

9 Find a formula for N, the nth term of each sequence.
  a 7, 10, 13, 16, . . .   **b** 2, 8, 14, 20, . . .

10 A child's construction set makes these frames.

a Copy and complete this table:

Frame number (n)	1	2	3
Number of small △s (T)	2		
Number of joints (J)	4		
Number of rods (R)	5		

b Find formulae, in terms of n, for the number of triangles, joints and rods in the nth frame. Check by drawing diagrams for frames 4 and 5.
c How many joints and rods are in:
  (i) the eighth frame
  (ii) a set from which you can make all the frames 1 to 8?

REVISION EXERCISE ON CHAPTER 12: PROBABILITY

1 A letter is chosen at random from the word PASSPORT. Calculate:
a P(T) **b** P(S) **c** P(T or S).

2 Simon is 90% certain of getting a job this year. What is his probability of failure?

3

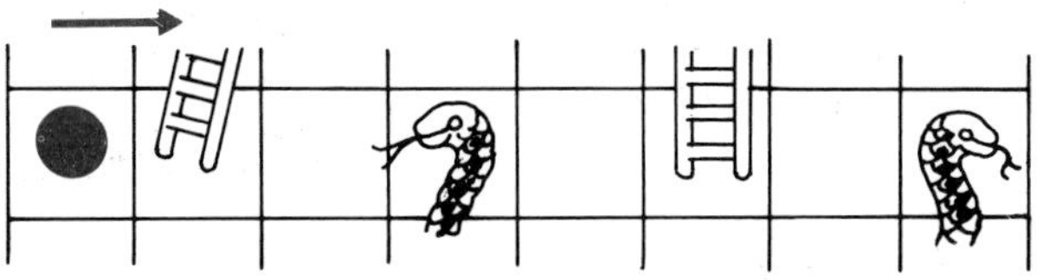

Tracy rolls a dice. Calculate:
a P(snake)
b P(ladder)
c P(no snake or ladder)
d P(a snake or ladder).

4 Rebecca had to draw lots to choose a day for the school outing in June. Calculate the probability that it falls:
a on a Friday
b at a weekend
c in the first half of the month.

JUNE

S	S	M	T	W	T	F
1	2	3	4	5	6	7
8	9	10	11	12	13	14
15	16	17	18	19	20	21
22	23	24	25	26	27	28
29	30					

5 On average, Ben is late for school one morning each week.
a What is the probability that he will be on time?
b How often will he be on time in a six week period?

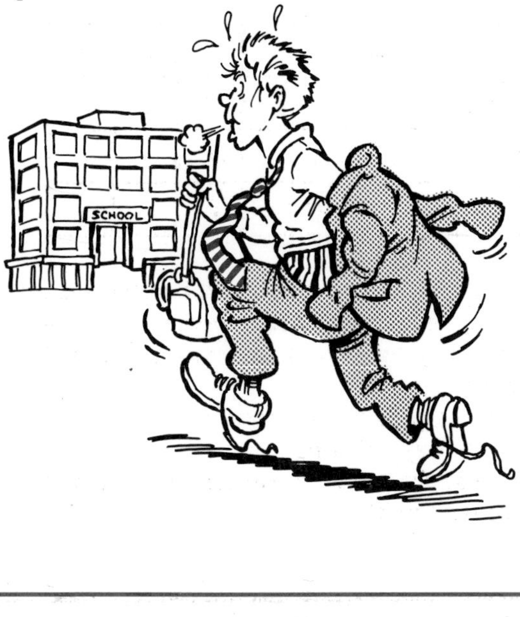

6 The faces on two dice are marked 1, 1, 2, 3, 4, 5. When the dice are rolled, the two scores are added together.
a Copy and complete the table.
b Calculate:
(i) P(2) (ii) P(9)
(iii) P(2 or 9)
(iv) P(score > 5)

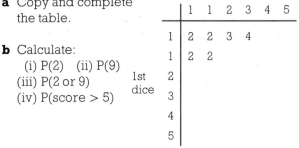

2nd dice

		1	1	2	3	4	5
1st dice	1	2	2	3	4		
	1	2	2				
	2						
	3						
	4						
	5						

7 A five-sided and a three-sided spinner are spun. Copy and complete the tree diagram for all possible outcomes.

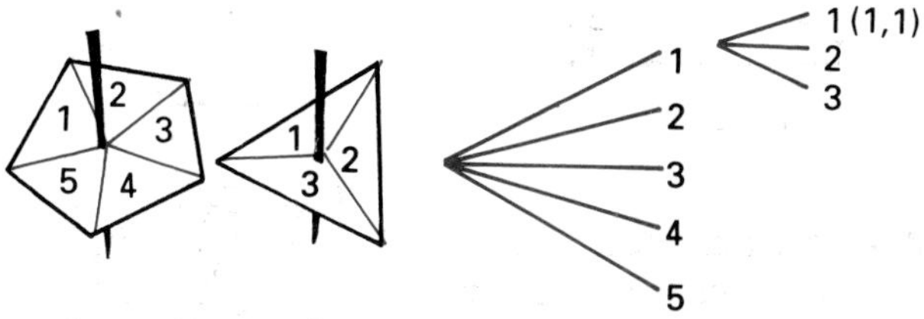

8 There are 820 students at City High School. 287 wear spectacles.
a Calculate the probability that a student chosen at random in the school wears spectacles.
b How many students in a class of 32 would you expect to wear spectacles?

9 In medical trials, a drug is successful in 85% of cases. Calculate:
a P(failure)
b the number of patients in a group of 36 who are not likely to benefit.

10 The Kings and Queens from a pack of cards are placed, face down, in two piles, and one card is taken from each pile.
a Copy and complete this table of outcomes.

Queens

		C	D	H	S
Kings	C	(C, C)	(C, D)		
	D	(D, C)			
	H				
	S				

b Calculate:
(i) P(King of Spades and Queen of Spades)
(ii) P(King and Queen of the same suit).

ANSWERS

1 CALCULATIONS AND CALCULATORS

Page 1   Looking Back

1a 36.3 **b** 20.9 **c** 425 **d** 28 **e** 111 **f** 289 **g** 12 **h** 0.06
i 200 **2a** 13 **b** 30 **c** 6 **d** 18 **e** 7 **f** 3 **g** 4 **h** 6 **i** 5
3a (i) 4 (ii) 7 (iii) 13 **b** (i) 1.4 (ii) 5.2 (iii) 0.9 **c** (i) 30
(ii) 4.0 (iii) 0.8 **4 Across**: **2** BEG **5** BESIEGE **6** Ill
Down: **1** LEGIBLE **3** LEG **4** EGG

Page 2   Exercise 1

1a 2.4 cm **b** 8.7 cm **2a** 136.8 **b** 20.2 **c** 451.8 **d** 2047.1
3a 2.2 **b** 6.4 **c** 8.0 **d** 1.9 **e** 0.9 **4a** 5.8 s **b** 12.3 m
c 107.4 litres **5a** 1.23 **b** 5.11 **c** 11.14 **d** 102.20
6a £1.35 **b** £0.75 **c** £12.11 **d** £101.13
7a 10.8 **b** 9.6 **c** 1.2 **8a** 1.04 **b** 33.06 **c** 25.80 **d** 0.09
9a 0.78 m **b** 8.34 m **10a** £57 **b** £57.10 **c** £57.14
11a 10.6 cm **b** 6.4 cm^2

Page 3   Exercise 2

1a 80 **b** 30 **c** 20 **d** 200 **e** 500 **2a** 360 **b** 120 **c** 3500
d 0.14 **3a** 30 cm **b** 80 h **c** 6 kg **d** 0.02 g
4a 11 **b** 3.3 **c** 0.67 **5a** 79 **b** 28 **c** 39
6a 580 **b** 330 **c** 56 000 **d** 3.7 **7a** 600 **b** 300 **c** 60 000
d 4.0 **8a** 56 cm **b** 190 cm^2

Page 4   Exercise 3A

1a 90 **b** 170 **c** 50 **d** 150 **2a** (i) 100 (ii) 101
b (i) 120 (ii) 121 **c** (i) 160 (ii) 163 **d** (i) 200 (ii) 193
e (i) 15 (ii) 15.2 **f** (i) 30 (ii) 28.8 **g** (i) 1.1 (ii) 1.11
3 Last digits: **a** 1 **b** 1 **c** 3 **d** 3 **e** 2 **f** 8 **g** 1
4a (i) 800 **b** (iii) 851 **c** 851 **5a** 190, 185 **b** 18 m, 18.13 m
6a 290, 310 **b** 28 m, 27.88 m **7a** £180, £170.03 **b** 3
8a 50, 49 **b** 400, 374 **c** 130, 136 **d** 120, 118 **e** 1, 0.9
f 11, 10.7 **g** 0.3, 0.37 **h** 200, 198

Page 5   Exercise 3B

1a 2400 **b** 6000 **c** 50 **d** 15 **2a** 2400, 2550 **b** 1800, 1729
c 6000, 6592 **d** 1500, 1300 **e** 56, 54.6 **f** 8, 9.75
g 240, 226.8 **h** 0.32, 0.2997 **3** £27, £23.49 **4a** 20, 17.6
b 40, 45.1 **c** 3, 2.9 **d** 3, 3.8 **e** 4, 3.4 **f** 5, 5.8 **g** 2, 2.2
5 £1, £1.34 **6 a** and **c**

Page 6   Exercise 4A

1a 64 **b** 169 **c** 2.25 **d** 54 756 **e** 0.09 **2a** 289 **b** 25
c 8.5 **d** 24.2 **3a** 5 **b** 14 **c** 1.1 **d** 10 **e** 0.1 **4a** (i) 169
(ii) 13 **b** (i) 625 (ii) 25 **c** (i) 100 (ii) 10 **d** (i) 225
(ii) 15 **5a** 81 **b** 32 **c** 256 **d** 1 000 000 **e** 15 129
f 0.000 32 **6a** 3^5 **b** 3^2 **c** 3^4 **7a** 1225 cm^2 **b** 2916 cm^2
c 5041 cm^2 **8a** 5832 cm^3 **b** 19 683 cm^3 **c** 46 656 cm^3
9a 2 **b** 247 **c** 4 **d** 10 **10a** 15 **b** 17 **c** 30
11 22.86, 30.48, 40.64, 60.96, 91.44, 152.40 cm
12 £4.73, 13.51, 50.68, 101.35, 4581.08 **13** Same as **9**
14a 6.91 cm **b** 5.03 cm **c** 3.14 cm
15a 3.80 cm^2 **b** 2.01 cm^2 **c** 0.785 cm^2

Page 7   Exercise 4B

1a 784 cm^2, 1225 cm^2, 2025 cm^2, 3844 cm^2 **b** 70 cm
2a (i) 2209 m^2 (ii) 8836 m^2 **b** 491
3a Each area is 16 cm^2 **b** (i) 196 cm^2 (ii) 14 cm
4a (i) 4.75 cm^2 (ii) 2.2 cm **b** (i) 210 cm^2 (ii) 14.5 cm
c (i) 22.4 cm^2 (ii) 4.7 cm **5a** 5 **b** 8.22 **c** 0.10 **d** 33.59
6 8.4 cm, 9.2 cm, 15.3 cm, 30.5 cm, 14.6 cm, 4.8 cm
7 £29.38, £37.60, £43.48, £92.83, £99.88, £148.05
8 Cone 5.22 m, nose 13.63 m, fuel 4.08 m, inner 6.38 m,
outer 8.51 m

Page 9   Exercise 5A

1a 4×10^2 **b** 4×10^3 **c** 4×10^4 **d** 4×10^5
2a 8×10^2 **b** 6×10^1 **c** 2×10^3 **d** 5×10^5
3a 3.5×10^1 **b** 2.4×10^2 **c** 1.2×10^3 **d** 7.8×10^4
4a 2.34×10^3 **b** 3.05×10^2 **c** 9.3×10^7
5a 2×10^3 **b** 3.65×10^2 **c** 1.563×10^3 **d** 1.27×10^4
6a 1.69×10^8 **b** 3×10^{10} **c** 5.98×10^{24} **d** 1.49×10^8
e 8.22×10^8 **7a** $6 \times 10^3 = 6000$ **b** $8 \times 10^5 = 800\,000$
c $5 \times 10^2 = 500$ **d** $7 \times 10^4 = 70\,000$
e $9 \times 10^{10} = 90\,000\,000\,000$ **f** $1 \times 10^1 = 10$
8a $2.13 \times 10^4 = 21\,300$ **b** $1.1 \times 10^9 = 1\,100\,000\,000$
c $9.01 \times 10^5 = 901\,000$ **d** $5.808 \times 10^3 = 5808$
e $6.07 \times 10^6 = 6\,070\,000$ **f** $8.3 \times 10^3 = 8300$
9 $£3.33 \times 10^{10} = £33\,300\,000\,000$ **10a** 3.1536×10^{10}

Page 10   Exercise 5B

1a 4×10^{-1} **b** 7×10^{-3} **c** 9×10^{-4} **d** 2×10^{-2}
2a 2.5×10^{-1} **b** 4.6×10^{-2} **c** 1×10^{-1} **d** 3.7×10^{-3}
3a 2×10^{-6} **b** 1.5×10^{-5} **c** 8×10^{-7}
4a 1.13×10^{-1} **b** 8×10^{-7} **c** 9.11×10^{-21}
5a $6 \times 10^{-4} = 0.0006$ **b** $9 \times 10^{-1} = 0.9$ **c** $3.2 \times 10^{-2} = 0.032$
d $4.98 \times 10^{-3} = 0.004\,98$ **e** $8.25 \times 10^{-5} = 0.000\,082\,5$
f $1.414 \times 10^{-10} = 0.000\,000\,000\,141\,4$

Page 11   Check-up on Calculations and Calculators

1a 101 **b** 53 **c** 29p each **d** 229 **e** 189 **2a** 240 min
b 195 min **c** 0.2 h **d** 1.75 h **3a** 3.8 **b** 4.8 **c** 1.1 **d** 12.2
4a 140 **b** 4600 **c** 4.8 **d** 2.0 **5a** 13.56 **b** 5.21 **c** 2.82
6a 700, 690 **b** 500, 471 **c** 1500, 1222 **d** 40, 49
7 4.4 cm^2, 3.78 cm^2 **8a** 33.64 **b** 16 **c** 20 736 **d** 41
e 22.04 **f** 2.5 **9** 1.48, 14.8, 37, 399.6, 811.04, 2812 dollars
10a 900 cm^2, 650.25 cm^2, 249.64 cm^2 **b** 38.7 cm
11 1728 mm^3, 3375 mm^3, 15 625 mm^3 **12a** 1.2×10^3
b 4.06×10^5 **c** 7.5×10^{-1} **d** 3×10^{-4} **13a** 234
b 1 500 000 **c** 0.000 056 **14a** $4.2 \times 10^5 = 420\,000$
b $6.4 \times 10^{-3} = 0.0064$

2 SHAPE AND SPACE

(Degree symbols are not shown in answer diagrams.)

Page 12 Looking Back

1a

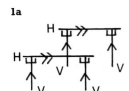

b
c

2a Trapezium **b** (i) 80° (ii) 100° **c** (i) acute (ii) obtuse
3a (i) Equilateral (ii) isosceles **b** kite **c** (i) ∠RQS
(ii) ∠RQP **4** 60°
5a (i) Square (ii)   (iii) quarter-turn

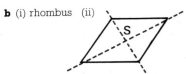
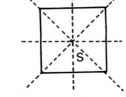

b (i) rhombus (ii)   (iii) half-turn

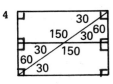

6a A(0, 1), B(3, 1), C(4, 3), D(1, 3) **b** parallelogram **c** (2, 2)
7a Rectangle **b** (i) four (ii) three

Page 13 Exercise 1

1 a = 113, b = 16, c = 130 **2** Obtuse, acute, obtuse
3a

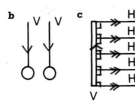

b
c

4

5a ∠CBE **b** ∠CBE **c** ∠BEF **6a** 45° **b** 135° **c** 135°
7 a = 55, b = 60, c = 105, d = 75, e = 40, f = 45
8   **9a** p = 72, q = 72, r = 36, s = 324 **b** s = 324
                                   11a 090° **b** 050° **c** 180° **d** 270°
                                   12

13 045°

Page 15 Exercise 2

1a
b
c

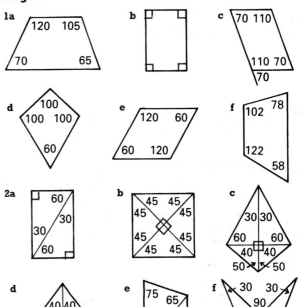

d
e
f

2a
b
c

d
e
f

3 a = 104, b = 76, c = 76 **4** d = 68, e = 112, f = 112
5 g = 106, h = 74, i = 53 **6**

7 Rectangle, parallelogram, kite **8a** Equal, bisect,
perpendicular, bisect the angles, meet corners at 45°
b equal, bisect **c** bisect, perpendicular **d** one is bisected,
and bisects the angles, perpendicular **e** bisect each other

Page 17 Exercise 3

1

2a (i) AB (ii) CD (iii) HG **b** (i) ∠PAN (ii) ∠IHG
(iii) ∠PON **c** (i) APON (ii) AIHGFE
3

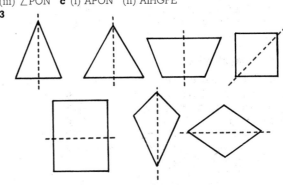

4a P(4, 2), Q(−4, 2) **b** R(−4, −2) **5** S(4, −2)
6b B(3, 5), D(−3, −5) **c** C(3, −5)

7

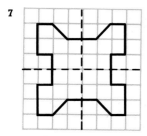

8a 2 **b** 6 **c** 8 **d** any number of ways
9a Equilateral △, 3, 3 **b** square, 4, 4 **c** rhombus, 2, 2
d parallelogram, 0, 2 **e** rectangle, 2, 2 **f** hexagon, 6, 6
g pentagon, 5, 5 **h** kite, 1, 1

Page 19 Exercise 4B

1b All 60° **c** 120° **2a** 45° **b** (i) $67\frac{1}{2}$° (ii) 135°
3a 36° **b** (i) 72° (ii) 144° **4a** $x = 24$ **b** 78° **c** 156°
5a 120° **b** three angles of 120° fit around a point
6 Squares, equilateral triangles
7a 8 **b** (i) (1, 5), (4, 5), (7, 5), (10, 5)
(ii) (1, 5), (4, 5), (1, 8), (4, 8), (1, 11), (4, 11)

Page 21 Exercise 5A

1 A(4, 2), B(2, 4), C(−2, 4), D(−4, 2), E(−4, −2), F(−2, −4),
G(2, −4), H(4, −2) **2b** Hexagon **3a** (7, 6) **b** 25 squares
4a (5, 2) **b** anywhere on line $x = 5$, except at Q and (5, 6)
5b Isosceles △ **c** 9 squares **6a** 24 squares
b P(4, 2), Q(7, 4), R(4, 6), S(1, 4) **c** (i) rhombus
(ii) 12 squares **7a** (i) (0, 0) (ii) 3 cm, 6 cm **b** a square

Page 22 Exercise 5B

1a Square **b** (8, 5) **c** (i) 36 squares (ii) 18 squares
2a (7, 4) **b** 8 squares **3b** (2, 0), (1, 2), (2, 5), (3, 2)
c (−2, 0), (−1, −2), (−2, −5), (−3, −2)
4c (−2, 4) **d** (i) (2, −4) (ii) (−4, −2)
5a,b   **c** No

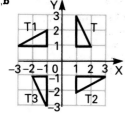

Page 23 Exercise 6A

1a (i) Cylinder (ii) cube (iii) cone (iv) sphere
(v) cuboid (vi) prism (vii) pyramid
2a (i), (iii) **b** (ii), (vii) **c** (v), (vi) **d** (vi), (vii) **3** (i) 3, 0, 2
(ii) 6, 8, 12 (iii) 2, 1, 1 (iv) 1, 0, 0 (v) 6, 8, 12 (vi) 5, 6, 9
(vii) 5, 5, 8 **4a** (i) 9 (ii) 3 (iii) 27 **b** (i) 10 (ii) 4 (iii) 40
5a 512 cm³ **b** 250 cm³ **c** 96 m³ **6a** (i) 4 (ii) 24 **b** (i) 3
(ii) 6 **c** (i) 2 (ii) 4

Page 24 Exercise 6B

1a (i) 18 cm² (ii) 6 cm² (iii) 12 cm² **b** 72 cm² **2b** 160 cm²
3a 486 cm² **b** 61 m²
4a Cube **b** triangular pyramid (tetrahedron)
c cone without a base **d** square pyramid
6

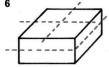

Page 25 Check-up on Shape and Space

1 $a = 21$, $b = 60$, $c = 250$, $x = 30$
2a   **b**

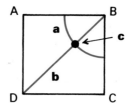

3a (i) Corresponding (ii) alternate **b** (i) 50° (ii) 130°
(iii) 130° **4a** 300° **b** 60° **c** 120° **5a** equilateral
b hexagon **c** parallel, equal **d** 120 **e** 180 **6a** (i) 3
(ii) 6 **b** 2 **7a** 5 **b** 5 **8a** A(−2, −3), B(2, −3) **b** square
c (i) rectangle (ii) parallelogram (iii) trapezium
(iv) kite **d** both 24 sq units **9a** 125 cm³ **b** 150 cm² **c** 24
10

```
     A                 B
        \      a     /
          \        /
            \    /
       a     ●────── c
            /    \
          /        \
        /     b      \
     D                 C
```

REVIEW: NUMBERS 1

Page 26 Numbers

1 £9202.10 **2a** £89.50 **b** £42.57 **3a** £4 **b** £4.25 **c** £7.75
d £26 **4a** 1350 **b** 12 **5a** (i) 100 km (ii) 90 km
(iii) 89 km **b** (i) 700 km (ii) 720 km (iii) 717 km
6a 443.88 **b** 1071.36 **7a** 130 km, 100 km
b 840 km, 800 km **c** 570 km, 600 km **d** 610 km, 600 km
8a 2.2 m **b** 8.8 cm **c** 10.1 seconds **9a** 5.16 km
b 1.02 litres **c** 0.31 m **10a** 55 g, 68 g **b** 13 g
11a (i) 30 cm² (ii) 15 cm² **b** (i) 30.9 cm² (ii) 16.3 cm²
12a 1 kg for 140p **b** 85 ml for £1.65 **13a** 9.21 **b** 1.23
14a (i) 17 (ii) 23 (iii) 15 (iv) 3 (v) 0 (vi) 5
15a 26, 31; add 5 **b** 44, 33; subtract 11
c 512, 2048; multiply by 4 **d** 11, 16; add 1, then 2, then 3, . . .

Page 27 Decimals

1a 1.5 **b** 3 **c** 4.2 **d** 5.7 **e** 7.4 **f** 10,5 **g** 11.7 **h** 12.9
i 0.02 **j** 0.06 **k** 0.09 **2a** 7.8, 8.1, 8.7, 9.1
b 0.29, 0.92, 1.08, 1.23 **3a** 16, 1 **b** 14.73, 1.83 **4a** 4.24
b 0.87 **c** 43.9 **5a** £14 **b** £140 **c** 14p **6** 21.8 cm
7 7 cm, 4 cm, 2 cm, 2 cm, 5 cm, 2 cm **8a** £2.89 **b** £7.07
c £5.33 **d** £0.82 **9a** (i) 72 (ii) 720 **b** (i) 351 (ii) 3510
c (i) 90.3 (ii) 903 **d** (i) 7 (ii) 70 **e** (i) 360 (ii) 3600
10a 0.72 **b** 3.51 **c** 0.903 **d** 0.07 **e** 3.6 **11a** 60, 58.2
b 14, 12.6 **c** 180, 167.4 **d** 160, 151.2 **e** 8, 7.76
12a 8, 7.8 **b** 6, 6.2 **c** 4, 3.8 **d** 15, 14.5 **e** 0.7, 0.71
13a (i) 48p (ii) £1.80 (iii) £6 **b** (i) 47p (ii) £1.88
(iii) £5.64 **c** 851 **14** 9p **15a** 0.9 **b** 7.7 **c** 0.23 **d** 0.03
16a 22.4 **b** 32.4 **17a** $188.40 **b** £19.11

Page 28 Fractions, Decimals and
Percentages

1a $\frac{2}{5}$, 0.4, 40% **b** $\frac{3}{5}$, 0.6, 60% **2a** £2.50 **b** 27 kg
c 0.04 m or 4 cm **d** £7.20 **e** 16.5 g **f** £28 **3a** 861.3 m²
b 126.6 m **4a** £5.60 **b** £50.40 **5a** £6.75 **b** £38.25 **6a** £8
b £60 **c** £3.40 **7a** £250 at 6% **b** £1 more **8a** £30 **b** £15

9a 13p **b** 20% **10a** (i) £600 (ii) 30% **b** £2700
11 New cars £108 000, used cars £72 000, repairs £36 000, car hire £24 000 **12** Fraction $\frac{2}{5}$, $\frac{9}{10}$, $\frac{3}{100}$, $\frac{1}{8}$, $\frac{3}{50}$, $\frac{13}{25}$; decimal 0.4, 0.9, 0.03, 0.125, 0.06, 0.52; percentage 40%, 90%, 3%, 12.5%, 6%, 52%
13a $\frac{3}{5}$ **b** 0.6 **c** 60% **14** £24.10, £9.05, £33.15, £5.80, £38.95
15a 56% **b** 60% **c** 90% **d** 77.5%

Page 29   Time and Temperature

1a 42 **b** 31 **c** 365 **2a** Thursday **b** 10 **3** 37 **4** 33
5a 10 am **b** 7.45 am **c** 5.15 pm **6a** 1000 **b** 07 45
c 17 15 **7a** 9 **b** 8 **c** 8 **8a** 19 20–19 50, 20 30–22 15
b $\frac{3}{4}$ hour **9** Rows: 8 am, 1 pm; 02 00, 21 00
10 1 h 15 min, 1 h 30 min, 4 h 35 min, 7 h 25 min
11a 13 **b** 28 **c** 0.4 **d** 25.2 **12a** 2.6°C, 0.4°C **b** 2.2°C
13a Majorca, by 12°C **b** 27°C
14

15 −7°C, −4°C, −1°C, 0°C, 3°C, 5°C
16a (i) Rome (ii) Oslo **b** 20°C
17a 7°C **b** 2.5°C **c** −2°C **d** −4°C **e** 0°C **f** 2°C

3   MONEY MATTERS - SAVING AND SPENDING

Page 30   Looking Back

1a £1.35 **b** £9.02 **c** £1.60 **d** £12.50 **2a** £84.60 **b** £125
3 0.25, 0.5, 1.23, 0.08, 0.085 **4a** 17 935 **b** 2159
5a £6 **b** 40 km **c** £9.50 **d** £86.25 **6a** £2.40, £21.60
b £6.50, £26 **c** £9.99, £39.96 **d** £10, £70 **7** 4.2% **8a** £8
b 60% **9a** 35% **b** 60% **c** 17.5% **d** 10% **e** 12.5%

Page 31   Exercise 1A

1a (i) 7 or 8 (ii) 35–40 **b** £175–£200 **2a** £15.20 **b** £26.60
3a £800 **b** income tax, pension, national health, etc
4a £530 **b** (i) £7200 (ii) £600
5a 15 **b** £97.50 **c** £117.50 **6a** £280 **b** £60 **c** £48
7a (i) £33.60 (ii) £168 **b** (i) £6.30 (ii) £25.20
8a £310.80 **b** £100.80 **9a** £42 **b** £2700 **c** £1
10a £5 **b** (i) £10 (ii) £25 (iii) £17.50 (iv) £34.45
11a £2 **b** £8.50 **c** £0.62 **d** £10.10
12a (i) £4.80 (ii) £7.20 (iii) 18p **b** to encourage staff to make sales

Page 33   Exercise 1B

1a £63 **b** £531 **2a** £1333.33 **b** (i) £18 000 (ii) £1500
3 Keith, by £10 **4** £10 400 **5a** £820 **b** yes, by £35 a week

Page 34   Exercise 2

2a (i) He paid in £50 (ii) he paid out £25.10 by cheque to Top Ten (iii) the Regional Council paid him £475
b (i) £24.90 (ii) £487.40 (iii) £387.40
3 Balance: **a** 20.00, 12.00, 22.00, 17.00
b 35.00, 18.00, 23.50, 14.00 **4** £13.50 **5a** £6 **b** £15 **c** £21
d £37.50 **e** £1.50 **6** £5 **7a** £10 **b** £15 **c** £35 **d** £50
8a £4.50 **b** £27 **c** £38.25 **d** £41.62 **9** Maeve, by 30p

10 £495 **11a** £3.20, £1.60 **b** £23, £11.50 **c** £4.20, £2.10
d £3.66, £1.83 **12a** £76.80, £6.40, £25.60
b (i) £9 (ii) £4.80 (iii) £5 (iv) £210

Page 36   Exercise 3

1a £5.25 **b** £8.75 **c** £131.25 **d** £28
2a (i) £1.40 (ii) £9.40 **b** £3.50, £23.50 **c** £6.65, £44.65
3 Scot Travel is £1.50 cheaper **4a** £48 **b** £56.40
5 £9.60 + £1.68 = £11.28 **6** Total £98.24
7 Locost better, £27.10 against £27.13
8 Rows: £130, £140.40, £152.75; £215, £232.20, £252.63

Page 38   Exercise 4

1a Cheap **b** daytime **c** daytime **d** cheap
2a 5p **b** 10p **c** 10p **d** 15p **3a** 10p **b** 5p **c** 10p
d 20p **4** £99.41 **5a** A69.82, B12.22, C82.04
6 A97.05, B16.98, C114.03 **7a** £57.09, 9.99, 67.08
b £47.30, 8.28, 55.58 **c** £109.04, 19.08, 128.12

Page 39   Exercise 5

1a 1124 **b** 468 **2a** £76.34 **b** £90.62
3a £98.75 **b** £105.30 **c** £123.73
4 A1122, B84.71, C91.21, D15.96, E107.17 **5a** £150.61
b £161.56 **c** £189.83 **6** A261.30, B272.24, C47.64, D319.88
7 £279.10 **8** A1608, B124.62, C131.37, D22.99, E154.36
9 £344.78 **10** A117, B9.20, C814, D24.83, E41.18, F7.21, G48.39

Page 41   Exercise 6

1a (i) £1000 (ii) £1800 (iii) £2800 **b** £300 **2a** £42 **b** £2
3a £124.80 **b** £7.30 **4a** £85 **b** £3 **5a** £175 **b** £27
6a £156 **b** £6.01 **7a** £5775 **b** £776
8a £35 **b** £390.20 **c** £40.20 **9a** £184, £193.80
b £5, £14.80 **10a** £19.81, £46.63, £79 **b** the first

Page 43   Check-up on Money Matters—Saving and Spending

1 £750 **2** £254.60 **3** £5.12 **4a** £13.20 **b** £66 **c** £96.80
5a £45 **b** £115 **c** £3.76 **6a** £30 **b** £75 **c** £1.50
7 £293.75 **8a** 887 **b** £68.74 **c** £77.99 **d** £91.64
9 £66.14, £11.57, £77.71 **10a** HP by £120 **b** 5%
11 A950, B76.95, C84.15, D14.73, E98.88

4   SCALE DRAWINGS AND SIMILAR SHAPES

Page 44   Looking Back

1a $\frac{2}{5}$ **b** $\frac{1}{2}$ **c** $\frac{3}{1}$ **3a** 10 km **b** 7 m **c** 2.5 cm
4 It is 6 cm by 4 cm **5a** 5 m by 4 m **b** 6 m by 2.5 m
6a 180° **b** 270° **c** 000° **d** 135° **e** 225° **f** 315°
7b 25 km **8a** (i) 4 cm (ii) 3.5 cm (iii) 4.5 cm **b** (i) 40 km
(ii) 35 km (iii) 45 km **c** (i) Lochgilphead (ii) Dalmally
(iii) Inveraray

Page 45   Exercise 1

1a 3 cm, 30 cm **b** 4 cm, 4 m **c** 2 cm, 20 cm **d** 1 cm, 100 cm
2a (i) 50 cm × 50 cm (ii) 100 cm × 75 cm
(iii) 325 cm × 200 cm **b** 150 cm **3a** 60 cm × 45 cm
b 28 cm by 22 cm **c** 20 cm by 15 cm **d** 15 cm by 10 cm

4a 22 m **b** 12 m, 14 m, 8 m
5a 100 m **b** 150 m **c** 175 m **d** 250 m
6a 1 cm to 100 km **b** Belfast 500 km, Cardiff 200 km,
Dublin 450 km, Edinburgh 550 km, Glasgow 550 km,
John O'Groats 800 km, Land's End 450 km, Manchester 250 km

Page 47　Exercise 2

1 Row: 8 cm, 3 cm, 10 cm **2** Outside 8 cm by 3 cm,
panel 6 cm by 1 cm **3** Front 10 cm by 5 cm;
back 10 cm by 1.5 cm; ends 6 cm wide, 1.5 cm and 5 cm high
4b 260° **5** Scale distance is 7 cm
6b 20 km **c** 303°, to the nearest degree

Page 48　Exercise 3

1a $\frac{4}{1}$ **b** 4 **2a** $\frac{1}{3}$ **b** $\frac{1}{3}$ **3a** 2 **b** $\frac{1}{2}$ **8a** (i) $\frac{3}{2}$ (ii) $\frac{2}{3}$

Page 50　Exercise 4A

1a 10 m **b** 6 m **2** 18 cm **3a** 40 cm **b** 27 cm
4a 800 cm **b** 8 cm **5a** 400 cm **b** 4 m
6a 1000 cm **b** 10 m **7a** 50 **b** (i) 300 cm (ii) 3 m **8** 5 km

Page 51　Exercise 4B

1a 100 **b** (i) 300 cm, 3 m (ii) 450 cm, 4.5 m
(iii) 720 cm, 7.2 m **2** 60 cm, 102 cm **3** 20 cm, 34 cm
4a 4 **b** 100 cm by 80 cm **5a** 4 m **b** 4 cm
6a 120 m by 40 m **b** 25 cm

Page 52　Exercise 5A

1 (iv) **2** (i) and (iv) **3a** All 90° **b** (i) $\frac{18}{6}=3$ (ii) $\frac{15}{5}=3$
c (i) 3 (ii) $\frac{1}{3}$ **4a** All 90° **b** (i) $\frac{8}{4}=2$ (ii) $\frac{24}{12}=2$ **c** (i) 2
(ii) $\frac{1}{2}$ **5** Yes. The ratios of corresponding sides are $\frac{60}{54}=\frac{10}{9}$,
and $\frac{100}{90}=\frac{10}{9}$; also, all corner angles are 90°
6a 2 **b** 4 **7a** $\frac{1}{4}$ **b** 30

Page 53　Exercise 5B

1 a, b, d are similar **2a** Yes **b** $\frac{5}{4}$
3 No. Ratios of corresponding sides are not equal
4a $\frac{3}{2}$ **b** 54 **5a** $\frac{3}{4}$ **b** $4\frac{1}{2}$ **6a** 10 **b** 24 cm **7a** 200 **b** 27 mm

Page 56　Exercise 6A

1a Both 40°, 50°, 90°; yes **b** both 30°, 60°, 90°; yes
c both 45°, 45°, 90°; yes **d** both 20°, 70°, 90°; yes
e 35°, 55°, 90°; 25°, 65°, 90°; no **f** both 44°, 46°, 90°; yes **2a** 3
b 15 **3a** $\frac{4}{5}$ **b** 9.6 **4a** Corresponding angles are equal
b 52 cm, 30 cm **5a** Both have angles of 20°, 70°, 90° **b** (i) $\frac{2}{3}$
(ii) $\frac{3}{2}$ **6a** (i) 22° (ii) 68° **b** 12.5 m

Page 57　Exercise 6B

1a, b, d, e, f 2a $\frac{2}{3}$ **b** 8 **3a** $\frac{3}{2}$ **b** 30 cm **4a** $\frac{6}{5}$ **b** 3 m
5a The triangles are equiangular **b** 75
6a They are equiangular **b** (i) XY (ii) YZ (iii) XZ **c** $\frac{5}{3}$
d 40 cm

Page 59　Check-up on Scale Drawings and Similar Shapes

1 Lawn 10 cm by 6 cm, flower bed radius 2 cm **2a** 3 **b** $\frac{1}{3}$
4a 24 cm, 15 cm **b** 40 cm², 360 cm² **5a** 5000 cm **b** 50 m
6a $\frac{1}{2}$ **b** 60 cm, 45 cm **7a** 3.5 m **b** ~~36 cm~~ 3·6cm
8a Both have angles of 65°, 25°, 90° **b** (i) $\frac{5}{2}$ (ii) 5
9a $\frac{3}{8}$ **b** (i) 9 feet (ii) 192 ft², 27 ft²

REVIEW: LETTERS AND NUMBERS 1

Page 60　Using Letters and Numbers 1

1a 10 **b** 7 **c** 6 **d** 8 **2a** 5 **b** 10 **c** 9 **d** 10
3a 3 **b** 9 **c** 4 **d** 16 **e** 7 **f** 8 **4a** $2x$ **b** $6y$ **c** u **d** p
e x **f** 0 **g** $4x+6$ **h** $2y+2$ **i** $t+1$ **j** $2x+y$ **k** y **l** $2x$
5a $2m+5$ **b** $3m+3$ **c** $4m$ **d** $10m$
6a $a=4, b=6, c=15, d=8, e=30$ **b** 7, 12 **7a** $3m$
b $7n$ **c** $5x$ **d** y **e** $6x+5$ **f** $8y+8$ **g** $4a+1$ **h** $3x+7$
8a 1 **b** $2y+1$ **c** $5z$ **d** t **e** 0 **f** 0 **g** $2y+2z$ **h** $2n$
9 $13+4t$ metres **10a** $4x$ **b** $9y$ **c** $10k$ **d** 0 **e** p **f** $3x$
g $4c+2d$ **h** $u+v$

Page 61　Using Letters and Numbers 2

1a 24, 26, $2n$ **b** 100, 105, $5x$ **c** 24, 25, $y+1$
2a (i) 6 (ii) 10 (iii) $2c$ **b** (i) 6 (ii) 30 (iii) $6s$ **c** (i) 60
(ii) $12p$ **d** (i) 125 (ii) $25w$ **e** (i) 12 (ii) $4c$
3a 10 **b** 10 **c** 7 **d** 11 **e** 5 **f** 8 **g** 100 **h** 1
4 Second row: **a** 8, 16, 24, 32 **b** 4, 6, 8, 10 **c** 1, 4, 16, 36
d 11, 17, 23, 29 **5a** $P=2x+2y$ **b** $P=26$
6 Rows ; 3, 4, 5, 6, 7, . . . , $n+2$; 3, 5, 7, 9, 11, . . . , $2n+1$
7a $100+x$ **b** $3T+4R$ **8a** 7 **b** 6 **c** 10 **d** 0 **e** 10 **f** 10
g 5 **h** 6 **i** 9 **j** 4 **k** 30 **l** 24

Page 62　Using Letters and Numbers 3

1a $6a$ **b** $3x$ **c** $2y$ **d** t^2 **e** $2n^2$ **f** $2m+1$
2a $6m$ cm **b** $2x+1$ cm **c** $2t+3$ cm **d** $2u+2$ cm
3a $3y$ **b** $3x$ **c** $m-2$ **d** $t+4$ **4a** $1+n, 2n, 4n$ **b** $n, n^2, 3n^2$
5a 10 **b** 7 **c** 11 **d** 13 **6a** 9 **b** 15 **c** 1 **d** 9 **e** 25
f 12 **g** 30 **h** 18 **7a** $P=4k, A=k^2$ **b** $P=10t, A=4t^2$
c $P=6x, A=2x^2$ **d** $P=8y, A=3y^2$ **8a** $P=12u, A=5u$
b $6x+4y$ cm, $4xy$ cm² **9a** $10m^2$ **b** $3(x+2)$ m² or $3x+6$ m²
10a $2x+2$ **b** $3y+6$ **c** $4z+12$ **d** $5t-5$ **e** $2u-4$
f $3v-12$ **g** $10+2x$ **h** $3+3y$ **i** $16+4t$ **j** $6a+42$
k $8b-16$ **l** $9c-54$ **11a** $L=16y$ **b** $A=10y^2$ **c** $V=2y^3$

Page 63　Positive and Negative Numbers

1a $-2, -1, 0, 1, 2, 3, 4$ **b** $-8, -6, -4, -2, 0, 2, 4$
c $-15, -10, -5, 0, 5, 10, 15$ **2a** (i) Cardiff (ii) Dundee
b $-6°C, -4°C, -3°C, -2°C, -1°C$
3a (i) 1 (ii) -3 **b** (i) $-4, -5$ (ii) 0, 1, 2
4a $-8, -5, -2, 2, 5, 8$ **b** $-5, -3, -2, -1, 3, 4$
5a $-4+4=0$ **b** $-3-2=-5$ **c** $-3-3=-6$
d $-3+1=-2$ **e** $-2+4=2$ **f** $-5+3=-2$
6a 4, 3, 2, 1, 0, -1, . . . , -5, -6
b 4, 3, 2, 1, 0, -1, . . . , -3, -4
7 $4+(-2), 4+(-3), 4+(-4), 4+(-5)$; 6, 5, 4, 3, 2, 1, 0, -1
8a -1 **b** -2 **c** 4 **d** 2 **e** -1 **f** -1 **g** -10 **h** 4
i -6 **j** -1 **k** 2 **l** 2 **m** -8 **n** -14 **o** 0 **9a** 4, 2
b 4, -3 **10a** $x=-1$ **b** $y=-3$ **c** $z=0$ **d** $t=-1$
e $u=-1$ **f** $v=5$ **11c** A kite **d** $(-2, 0)$
12a -3 **b** -5 **c** -4 **d** -6
13a $(1, -1)$ **b** $P(2, 1), Q(0, 1), R(0, -1), S(2, -1)$

5　GOING PLACES

Page 64　Looking Back

1a Distances, directions **b** times **c** directions, distances
d speeds, distances **2a** (i) 60 (ii) 30 (iii) 15 (iv) 90
b (i) $\frac{1}{2}$ (ii) $\frac{3}{4}$ (iii) $\frac{1}{6}$ **3a** (i) 29 km (ii) 66 km **b** Southport

4a 45 min **b** 1 h 45 min **c** 2 h 30 min
5a (i) 20 km (ii) 10 km **b** (i) after 3 hours (ii) 30 km
6a 40 min **b** 1 h 15 min **c** 40 min **d** 30 min
7a 10 s **b** 70 miles **c** $2\frac{1}{4}$ h **d** 125 mph **e** (i) about 8 am
(ii) about 8.40 am

Page 65 Exercise 1A

1a (i) 3 km (ii) 4 km **b** (i) 20 min (ii) 10 min (iii) 10 min
c (i) the first part (ii) yes **2a** 16 00 **b** 16 30
c the bus is stopped **d** 4 km **e** at 16 05 **f** the first part
g . . . , stopped for 5 minutes, then went more slowly for
15 minutes **3a** OA, BC, CD **b** $\frac{1}{2}$ h **c** (i) 6 km (ii) 12 km/h
4a 6 miles **b** 30 min **c** 42 min **d** 12 miles **e** 1 h 30 min
f going home

Page 66 Exercise 1B

1c (i) 3.4 km (ii) 46–48 min **2b** 6 km **c** (i) 2 km (ii) 5 km
d the first part. Her first run was faster. **3b** 20 min and 60 min

Page 67 Exercise 2

1a 30 km **b** 32 km **c** 90 km **d** 70 km
2a 12 miles **b** 24 miles **c** 21 miles **d** 240 miles
3a 15 km **b** 16 km **c** 125 miles **d** 240 miles
4a 150 km **b** 450 km **c** 72 miles **d** 540 m
5a 24 km **b** 200 miles **c** 735 km **d** 240 m **6** 90 miles
7 90 km **8** 12 km **9** 900 miles **10** 8050 km
11a 75 km **b** 76 km **c** 54 km **12** 6800 km
13a N–E 12 km, E–W 15 km, N–W $7\frac{1}{2}$ km **b**

Page 68 Exercise 3A

1a 4 km/h **b** 8 km/h **c** 40 mph **d** 90 mph **2a** 5 km/h
b 5 km/h **c** 2 km/h **d** 1 km/h **e** 11 km/h **f** 10 km/h
3a 215 mph **b** 250 mph **c** 500 mph
4a 20 m/s, 30 m/s, 25 m/s **b** no. 2, no. 3, no. 1 **5a** 1840 km/h
b 83 km/h **6a** 25 km/h **b** 60 mph **c** 10 m/s **d** 5.5 km/h
e 700 km/h **f** 8000 km/h **7** 93.75 miles per day

Page 69 Exercise 3B

1a 1.5 h **b** 2.25 h **c** 0.75 h **2a** (i) 4 km/h (ii) 2.4 km/h
(iii) 4.8 km/h **b** (i) 6.4 km/h (ii) 3.2 km/h (iii) 16 km/h
3 30 km/h **4** 6 km/h **5a** 0.13 h **b** 0.73 h **c** 1.32 h
6a 34 km/h **b** 81 km/h **7a** 20 miles **b** 30 min, 1 hour
c 40 mph, 20 mph **d** the steeper the slope, the faster the
speed **8a** 98 km/h **b** 96 km/h
9a 6450 km **b** 40 500 km **c** 2250 km/h

Page 71 Exercise 4

1a 2 h **b** 4 h **c** 4 h **d** $1\frac{1}{2}$ h **2a** 4 h **b** 4 h **c** 8 h **d** 3 h
3a 2 h **b** 6 h **c** 4 h **d** 50 s **e** 4 s **f** 50 s **g** 3 h **h** $1\frac{1}{4}$ h
i $1\frac{1}{2}$ h **j** $3\frac{1}{2}$ s **4a** Noon **b** 6 pm **c** 2.15 pm **5a** 2 h **b** 4 h
c 3 h **6a** (i) 2 h (ii) $\frac{1}{2}$ h (iii) $1\frac{1}{2}$ h (iv) $1\frac{1}{2}$ h **b** 15 45
7 10 pm **8** $2\frac{3}{4}$ s **9** 500 s, or $8\frac{1}{3}$ min

Page 73 Exercise 5A

1a 6 km/h **b** 120 km **c** 5 h **d** 21 mph **e** 4 h **f** 125 miles
2a Speed = 7 km/h **b** distance = 54 km **c** time = 8 h
d speed = $7\frac{1}{2}$ mph **e** time = 4 h **f** distance = 10 miles
3 250 miles per day **4** 540 km **5** 7770 km
6a Elephant 20 km, kangaroo 30 km, zebra 25 km
b 3 h, 2 h, 2.4 h **7a** 11.30 am **b** 40 km **c** $1\frac{1}{2}$ hours
d Linda 14 km/h, Paul 12.8 km/h

Page 74 Exercise 5B

1a 37.5 km/h **b** 7.5 h **c** 208 miles **d** 8.8 m/s
2a 16 km/h **b** 2 h **c** 85 km **3a** 267 mph **b** 364 mph
c 398 mph **d** 354.5 mph **4** A and C **5** 84 mph
6a 344 km/h **b** 399 km/h **7a** 15 h **b** 100 **c** 225 **d** 300
e 10.83 h = 10 h 50 min **f** 397.9

Page 75 Check-up on Going Places

1a 28 km/h **b** 4 h **c** 3600 km **2a** 8 km/h **b** 6 h
3 270 km **4a** 60 miles **b** 30 mph **c** $\frac{1}{2}$ hour **d** 30 miles
e 60 mph, 0 mph, 52 mph, 8 mph **5** 7.30 pm **6** 12 45
7a (i) 1 h (ii) 3 h **b** (i) 25 km/h (ii) 10 km/h (iii) 15 km/h
8a 140 miles **b** $6\frac{1}{4}$ min **c** (i) 18 km, 75 min (ii) 14.4 km/h
9 96 km/h

6 BRACKETS AND EQUATIONS

Page 76 Looking Back

1a $2x$ **b** $3y$ **c** $5u$ **d** $3v$ **e** y^2 **f** $5t$ **g** $3pq$
2a $2n+2$ **b** $5m+1$ **3a** 45 **b** $6t+3$
4a 4 **b** 10 **c** 7 **d** 6 **5a** $4x$ **b** $8y$ **c** $4k+4$ **d** $4p$
6a x^2 **b** $3y^2$ **c** $k \times (k+2)$ **d** $(p+3) \times (p-3)$ **7a** $x=4$
b $y=12$ **c** $t=7$ **d** $u=5$ **e** $x=4$ **8a** $2x$ **b** $4y$ **9a** 30
b 24 **10a** $2x+6$ **b** $6y-6$ **c** $30+10z$ **11** $x+9=23$, $x=14$

Page 77 Exercise 1A

1a $y+3+y+3 = 2y+6$ **b** $y+1+y+1+y+1 = 3y+3$
c $t+5+t+5 = 2t+10$ **d** $n+2+n+2+n+2+n+2 = 4n+8$
e $x+6+x+6+x+6 = 3x+18$
f $x+1+x+1+x+1+x+1+x+1 = 5x+5$
2a $3x+6$ **b** $4y+4$ **c** $5z+15$ **d** $2t+14$ **e** $6u+6$
f $8x+32$ **g** $7v+21$ **h** $9m+81$ **i** $7n+56$
3a $6+2x$ **b** $6+6y$ **c** $6+3z$ **d** $25+5t$ **e** $28+7u$
f $48+8v$ **g** $32+4w$ **h** $36+6m$ **i** $90+10n$ **j** $2+2p$
k $27+9q$ **l** $16+8k$ **4a** $(x+1) \times 6 = 6(x+1) = 6x+6$
b $(x+4) \times 2 = 2(x+4) = 2x+8$
c $(x+5) \times 3 = 3(x+5) = 3x+15$ **5a** (i) 8 (ii) 8 **b** (i) 12
(ii) 12 **c** (i) 2 (ii) 2 **6a** (i) 45 cm² (ii) 30, 15 cm²
(iii) 45 cm²; $5(6+3) = 5 \times 6 + 5 \times 3$ **b** (i) 36 cm²
(ii) 12, 24 cm² (iii) 36 cm²; $6(2+4) = 6 \times 2 + 6 \times 4$
c (i) 64 cm² (ii) 32, 32 cm²
(iii) 64 cm²; $8(4+4) = 8 \times 4 + 8 \times 4$ **d** (i) 16 cm² (ii) 10, 6 cm²
(iii) 16 cm²; $2(5+3) = 2 \times 5 + 2 \times 3$ **7a** $4(5+x) = 20+4x$
b $10(x+2) = 10x+20$ **c** $5(7+x) = 35+5x$
d $6(8+x) = 48+6x$

Page 78 Exercise 1B

1a $10x+5$ **b** $6a+2$ **c** $15b+6$ **d** $8c+12$ **e** $24u+30$
f $40v+32$ **g** $14y+35$ **h** $24z+6$ **i** $9x+12$ **j** $30+15u$
k $20+24v$ **l** $18+27t$ **2** A–1, B–4, C–3, D–2, E–5
3a $P = 2x+10$, $P = 2(x+5)$ **b** $P = 4m+2$, $P = 2(2m+1)$
c $P = 12+2t$, $P = 2(6+t)$ **d** $P = 6u+4$, $P = 2(3u+2)$
4a x^2+2x **b** $xy+3x$ **c** t^2+t **d** $ab+4a$ **e** b^2+5b
f $cd+c$ **g** u^2+6u **h** $uv+3u$ **i** w^2+8w
5a $A = 2(p+q)$, $A = 2p+2q$ **b** $A = 5(u+v)$, $A = 5u+5v$
c $A = 3(x+y)$, $A = 3x+3y$
6a $5(x+3) = 5x+15$ **b** $9(y+6) = 9y+54$
c $20(2x+12) = 40x+240$ **d** $12(x+10) = 12x+120$

Page 79   Exercise 2A

1a $3x-6$ **b** $2x-8$ **c** $5y-5$ **2a** $4t-12$ **b** $6u-30$
c $8v-8$ **3a** $2a-20$ **b** $5b-35$ **c** $6c-36$ **4a** $7d-49$
b $10e-10$ **c** $4f-32$ **5a** $(x-2)\times 5=5(x-2)=5x-10$
b $(x-5)\times 2=2(x-5)=2x-10$
c $(x-8)\times 7=7(x-8)=7x-56$
6a (i) 3 (ii) 3 **b** (i) 18 (ii) 18 **7a** $10-2x$ **b** $12-3y$
c $24-4z$ **d** $8-8a$ **e** $18-9b$ **f** $21-7c$ **g** $24-6d$
h $45-5t$ **i** $80-10s$ **j** $21-3u$ **k** $48-6v$ **l** $9-9w$
8a (i) $6\times(x-8)=6(x-8)$ (ii) $6x-48$
b (i) $5\times(y-2)=5(y-2)$ (ii) $5y-10$
c (i) $10\times(t-4)=10(t-4)$ (ii) $10t-40$ **9a** $2a+10$
b $2a-10$ **c** $6+3b$ **d** $6-3b$ **e** $4c+4$ **f** $4+4c$ **g** $4c-4$
h $4-4c$ **i** $5d+30$ **j** $6e-42$ **k** $49+7f$ **l** $8g-72$

Page 80   Exercise 2B

1a $2x+10$ **b** $3x+5$ **c** $4y+5$ **d** $2y+5$
2a $3u+10$ **b** $4v+5$ **c** $7w+12$ **d** $2t+9$
3a $3y-5$ **b** $5x-6$ **c** $7t+17$ **d** $8k+6$
4a $2m+11$ **b** $3n+2$ **c** $4k+3$ **d** $5n$
5a You should **b** $(x+2)\times 3=3(x+2)=3x+6$ **6a** $6x-3$
b $12y-8$ **c** $5x-40$ **d** $7y-7$ **e** $10x-6$ **f** $2a+8$
g $6d+3$ **h** $15c-10$ **i** $16+24k$ **j** $4u+4v$ **k** $2a+2b$
l $3x-3y$ **7a** $5x+1$ **b** $7y+3$ **c** $4u$ **d** $7v+5$ **e** $5y$ **f** 15
g $10t$ **h** $k+43$ **8** $2x+2y+14$ cm

Page 80   Exercise 3A

1a $x=3$ **b** $x=12$ **c** $y=2$ **d** $m=1$ **e** $k=10$ **f** $x=13$
g $t=\frac{1}{2}$ **2a** $x=6$ **b** $y=6$ **c** $n=7$ **d** $t=10$ **e** $u=2\frac{1}{2}$
f $v=0$ **3a** $x=2$ **b** $a=4$ **c** $b=1$ **d** $y=3$ **e** $m=3$
f $x=2$ **g** $p=5$ **h** $q=10$ **i** $r=2\frac{1}{2}$
4a $x=1$ **b** $x=3$ **c** $y=3$ **d** $m=7$ **e** $t=1$ **f** $n=1$
5a $x=1$ **b** $y=3\frac{1}{2}$ **c** $p=0$ **d** $k=8$ **e** $w=0$ **f** $t=1$
6a Length $\times$ breadth **b** $x=4$ **c** 6 cm
7a $4(x+1)=24$, $x=5$, 6 cm **b** $3(x+6)=24$, $x=2$, 8 cm
c $2(x+5)=20$, $x=5$, 10 cm **d** $5(x+4)=50$, $x=6$, 10 cm
8a $3(x+2)=12$, $x=2$ **b** $5(y-1)=20$, $y=5$
c $4(t+5)=36$, $t=4$ **9** $x=6$, 6p
10 $y=18$, 18p **11** $w=26$, 26 g

Page 82   Exercise 3B

1a $x=3$ **b** $y=3$ **c** $u=2$ **d** $v=3$ **2a** $x=7$, 15 kg
b $3(3x-1)=10\times 6$, $x=7$, 20 kg **c** $2(x+7)=14$, $x=0$, 7 kg
d $2(y-5)=12$, $y=11$, 6 kg **e** $5(3u+1)=20$, $u=1$, 4 kg
3a $x=2$ **b** $y=1\frac{1}{2}$ **c** $p=3$ **d** $t=1$
4 $6(x+7)=90$, $x=8$ **5a** $6(x+2)+3=21$, $x=1$, £3
b $8(x-1)+7=23$, $x=3$, £2 **c** $10(x+3)+4=44$, $x=1$, £4
d $2(x-4)+6=10$, $x=6$, £2
e $3(2x+1)+10=43$, $x=5$, £11
f $5(2x-1)+12=37$, $x=3$, £5

Page 83   Exercise 4A

1a $1\times 6, 2\times 3$; 1, 2, 3, 6 **b** $1\times 8, 2\times 4$; 1, 2, 4, 8
c $1\times 9, 3\times 3$; 1, 3, 9 **d** $1\times 10, 2\times 5$; 1, 2, 5, 10
2a 2×2 **b** 6×5 **c** 1×9 **d** 4×4 **e** 8×2 **f** 1×16
3a $1\times 2x, 2\times x$; 1, 2, x, $2x$ **b** $1\times 7x, 7\times x$; 1, 7, x, $7x$
c $1\times x^2, x\times x$; 1, x, x^2 **4a** $2\times d$ **b** $3\times 3y$ **c** $3\times 2t$
d $5\times 2n$ **e** $4\times 3k$ **f** $8\times x$ **g** $u\times u$ **h** $v\times v$ **i** $w\times w$
5a 2 **b** 5 **c** 1 **d** $3x$ **e** $2y$ **f** $5t$
6a $3(x+2)$ **b** $2(x+4)$ **c** $5(x-2)$ **d** $6(n+2)$ **e** $2(4-m)$
f $4(2k-3)$ **g** $4(x+y)$ **h** $7(u-3v)$ **7a** $2(x+1)$ **b** $2(x+3)$
c $2(x+4)$ **d** $3(y+1)$ **e** $3(y-1)$ **f** $3(y+2)$ **g** $2(c+2)$
h $3(d-2)$ **i** $4(e+1)$ **j** $5(x-2)$ **k** $7(y+1)$ **l** $6(t-3)$
8a $5(x+y)$ **b** $5(x-y)$ **c** $2(x+2y)$ **d** $3(u+3v)$
e $3(u-2v)$ **f** $3(u+4v)$ **g** $7(m+n)$ **h** $7(m+2n)$

i $7(m-3n)$ **j** $2(a+b)$ **k** $3(c-3d)$ **l** $6(e-2f)$
9a $3(t+6)$ **b** $2(3u+1)$ **c** $2(x-10)$ **d** $3(3m-5)$ **e** $2(5+k)$
f $3(4-p)$ **g** $7(a-2b)$ **h** $10(u+2v)$ **i** $3(5c-6d)$ **j** $6(1+k)$
k $3(3-u)$ **l** $8(1-v)$

Page 84   Exercise 4B

1a 3 **b** 2 **c** 7 **d** 4 **e** 4 **f** 10 **g** 6 **h** 4 **i** 8
2a $4(x+1)$ **b** $4(y+7)$ **c** $6(z+3)$ **d** $3(2u-3)$ **e** $9(v-1)$
f $9(w-2)$ **g** $4(2a+3)$ **h** $10(2b+3)$ **i** $6(2c-3)$
3a $x(x+3)$ **b** $y(y-5)$ **c** $z(z+1)$ **d** $s(s-2)$ **e** $u(u+8)$
f $t(t-1)$ **g** $2x(x+2)$ **h** $3y(y-2)$ **i** $5z(z+2)$ **j** $3p(1-3p)$
k $4n(1+3n)$ **l** $6k(1-3k)$

Page 86   Check-up on Brackets and Equations

1a $2x+6$ **b** $4y-12$ **c** $5n+10$ **2a** $14-7x$ **b** $6x+3$
c $20-12y$ **3** $3(12+x)$ cm^2, $36+3x$ cm^2; $3(12+x)=36+3x$
4 Both 66 **5a** $2x+10$ **b** $4y-6$ **c** $2u+8$ **d** $3v+2$
6a $(x+2)\times 4=4(x+2)=4x+8$
b $(y-3)\times 9=9(y-3)=9y-27$ **7a** $x=7$ **b** $y=9$
c $z=0$ **d** $d=5\frac{1}{2}$ **e** $e=5$ **f** $t=5$ **8a** $x=1$ **b** $y=4\frac{1}{2}$
c $w=6$ **d** $k=8$ **9a** $6(u+4)=30$, $u=1$
b $3(v-7)=12$, $v=11$ **10a** $2(x+4)=18$, $x=5$ **b** 9 kg
11a $4(3x-1)+16=48$, $x=3$ **b** £8 **12a** 1, 2, 4, 8 **b** 1, 11
c 1, 2, 3, 4, 6, 12 **13a** $6\times x$ **b** $2x\times 3$ **c** $y\times y$ **d** $3p\times p$
14a $3(x+5)$ **b** $2(y-7)$ **c** $7(a-b)$ **d** $6(m-5n)$ **e** $x(x-2)$
f $y(y-1)$

REVIEW: STATISTICS AND PROBABILITY

Page 87   Statistics 1

1a 15 **b** Cola **c** 65 **2a** Number of holes: 1, 8, 8, 7, 8, 3, 1
b 17 **3** Height of bars: 3, 8, 4, 9, 13, 10, 3
4b 2 am **c** (i) 100.5°F (ii) 99–100°F **5a** 1950
b 30 hundred million **c** 14 hundred million
d it has been increasing fairly rapidly for some years
6a Vegetables, flowers, shrubs = lawn **b** (i) $\frac{1}{2}$ (ii) $\frac{1}{4}$ (iii) $\frac{1}{4}$
7 The angles are: toys 120°, sweets 60°, book 90°, raffle 50°,
white elephant 40° **8a** Number: 1, 5, 9, 9, 4

Page 88   Statistics 2

1a $23\frac{1}{3}$ **b** Wednesday **c** there is a weekly dip, and an
overall increase, in absence
2a 45, 30, 30, 136 (median or mode)
b 23, 16, 14, 51 (median) **c** 20, 19, 16, 11 (mean)
3a (i) Week 1: 14, 14, 12 and 16, 6
(ii) Week 2: 15, 15, none, 6 **b** 14.5, 14.5, 12, and 16, 7
4b Both graphs peak on day 4, and dip on days 6 and 7
5 8.8 minutes **6a** 0, 2, 2, 5, 7, 8, 5, 1 **b** 24 **c** 26–30
7a 185 **b** (i) 26% (ii) 34%
c

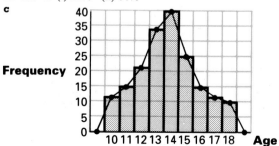

8a 20 **b** (i) 2.06 cm (ii) 60 min **c** 2.2 cm

Page 89   Probability 1

1a Certain **b** impossible **c** likely **d** unlikely
e even chance **2a** $\frac{1}{4}$ **b** $\frac{1}{2}$ **3a** 0.6 **b** 0.4 **4a** 0.26 **b** 0.28
c 0.7 **5a** $\frac{1}{6}$ **b** $\frac{3}{8}$ **c** $\frac{1}{2}$ **6a** $\frac{2}{9}$ **b** $\frac{1}{9}$ **c** $\frac{4}{9}$ **d** $\frac{4}{9}$
7a $\frac{1}{300}$ **b** $\frac{1}{100}$ **c** $\frac{1}{5}$ **8a**, because $P(W) = \frac{4}{7}$ in **a** and
$P(W) = \frac{5}{9}$ in **b**, and $\frac{4}{7} > \frac{5}{9}$ **9a** Carry out a survey of a suitable
sample **b** check weather records over the past few years

Page 90   Probability 2

1a (i) $\frac{3}{7}$ (ii) $\frac{4}{7}$ **b** $\frac{1}{2}, \frac{1}{2}$ **2**

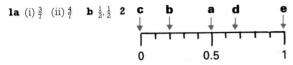

3a 94% **b** 0.94 **4a** $\frac{3}{5}$ **b** $\frac{1}{20}$ **c** $\frac{7}{20}$ **d** $\frac{2}{5}$ **5** 1000
6a 17 **b** 14 **7a** 0.3 **b** 0.4 **c** 0.6 **8** $\frac{2}{3}$ **9a** $\frac{1}{28}$ **b** $\frac{1}{4}$ **c** $\frac{3}{28}$

7   HANDLING DATA

Page 91   Looking Back

1a 8 cm **b** £14 **2a** (i) 19°C (ii) 2 pm **b** (i) 8 am
(ii) 2 pm **c** 8 am–10 am
3a (i) $\frac{1}{4}$ (ii) $\frac{1}{8}$ **b** Comedy 10, romance 5, thriller 25
4a (i) 130 min, 60 min (ii) 70 min **b** 80 min **c** (i) 595 min
(ii) 85 min **5a** (i) 15° (ii) angles, sleep 150°, school 105°,
homework 30°, leisure 45°, other 30°

Page 92   Exercise 1A

1a 0°C **b** 25°C **c** 60°C **d** 100°C
2a 45 m **b** 125 m **c** 320 m

3

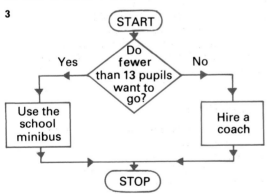

4

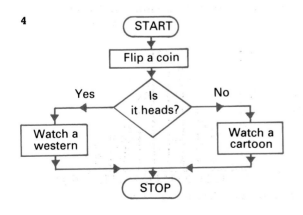

5

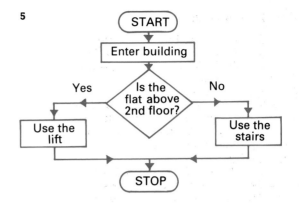

Page 94   Exercise 1B

1   Marking the register

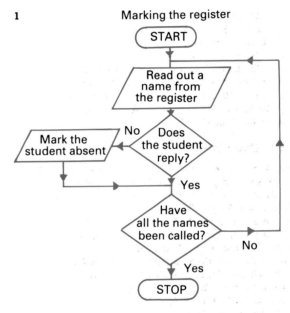

2a 1, 3, 5, 7, 9, 11, 13, 15, 17, 19 **b** Making odd numbers

3   A game at the fair

4 BE GOOD **5a** (i) small (ii) medium (iii) none
b more than 140 cm, up to 152 cm

Page 96   Exercise 2

1a £125 000   **b** £30 000   **2a** Daily News, Daily Chat
b the scales are not given in detail. No
c 1 200 000 or 1 300 000   **3b** (i) Escalator   (ii) same
(iii) Escalator
4a Few people using it   **b** (i) 09 00, 17 00 hours
(ii) meal times, people putting on lights, heaters, etc
5a No speed, no stopping distance   **b** 25 ft, 80 ft
c more distance is needed for higher speeds
d 15, 40, 75, 120, 175 ft
6a (i) 80 cm, 90 cm   (ii) 100 cm, 100 cm   (iii) 162 cm, 170 cm
b (i) 1 year, 8 months   (ii) 9 years, 9 years
(iii) 14 years, 14 years   **c** (i) 16   (ii) 17   (iii) 0–2 years
7a (i) 8000   (ii) 14 000   (iii) 30 000   **b** 2.30 pm   **c** 3.15 pm
d it dips steeply after 4.45 pm, to zero
8a Record Co, retailer, VAT, artist, publisher, manufacturer
b £12.99   **c** (i) 41%   (ii) 8%
9a (i) Petroleum, gas, electricity   (ii) solid fuel
b it has been greatly reduced

Page 99   Exercise 3A

1a 5, 8   **b** 5, 4   **c** Janice was more consistent
2a 16   **b** 30 and 45   **c** 0   **3a** 6   **b** 3 cm   **c** £2.40   **d** 4.5 g
4 3, 2, 2   **5a** To avoid extremes which might be too far out
b 8.57, 1.3   **6b** 17.25, 17, 15   **c** 10   **7a** 42.5   **b** 44
c Mean and range   **8** Blue team: 62.5, 62, 62 kg;
Red team: 63.3, 54, 47 kg
9a 1st firm: 83.125 t, 21 t, 82.5 t; 2nd firm: 92 t, 98 t, 120 t
b chains made by the first firm are more reliable

Page 101   Exercise 3B

1a 5, 6, 30; 8, 3, 24; 10, 1, 10; 10, 64   **b** 6.4, 5, 5
2a 5, 2, 10; 8, 5, 40; 10, 3, 30; 10, 80   **b** 8, 8, 8   **c** Tony
3a Numbers × frequencies: 66, 230, 216, 150, 156, 162;
Totals 40, 980   **b** (i) 23   (ii) 24   (iii) 24.5   **c** median
4a Lengths × frequencies: 174, 236, 120, 122, 496, 63;
Totals 20, 1211   **b** 60.55 mm, 61 mm, 62 mm   **c** yes
5a Windproof: (i) 6   (ii) 6   (iii) 6   (iv) 5.4 days
Clearglass: (i) 2   (ii) 5   (iii) 5   (iv) 5.3 days
b Clearglass is more reliable
6a Mid-values × frequencies: 114, 230, 224, 66, 42;
Totals 140, 676   **b** 1–3   **c** 4.8
7a Mid-values × frequencies: 2, 12, 30, 70, 144, 22;
Totals 20, 280   **b** 16–20 m   **c** 14 m

Page 103   Exercise 4A

1a It fell   **b** no   **c** the more sunshine, the higher the
temperature   **2a** (iv)   **b** (iii)   **c** (ii)   **d** (i)

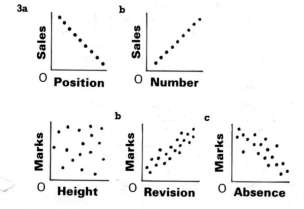

Page 104   Exercise 4B

1a,b

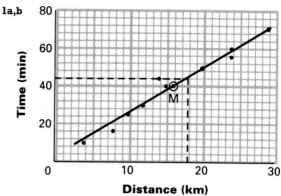

c 44 min

2a (i) 34.3 min   (ii) 42.8
b,c

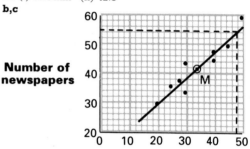

d 48 min

3a 17.5 and 13.2   **b**
c more goals
against, then
fewer points
d 11 goals against

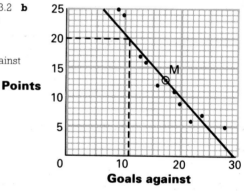

Page 105   Spreadsheets and Questionnaires

1c (i) David   (ii) Vanita

Page 106   A Day Trip

1 W.A., S.E., W.R., C.T., and J.F., T.R., S.T., P.Y.

2a
Preference	Seaside	London	Zoo	Concert	Funfair
1	11	7	0	8	0
2	1	7	12	0	6
3	1	0	6	9	10
4	3	5	1	7	10
5	10	7	7	2	0

b (i) seaside   (ii) seaside
4 For example, use a points system—1st choice, 5 points;
2nd choice, 4 points; 3rd choice, 3 points and so on
5 a (i) No   (ii) yes
b London and the zoo
London: W.A., R.B., S.E., I.H., J.M., P.M., S.N., A.P.,
J.R., W.R., N.S., C.T., G.T., T.Y.
Zoo: J.A., T.C., J.F., T.F., R.M., T.R., K.S., S.T.,
A.W., K.W., P.Y., R.Y.

Page 107 Check-up on Handling Data

1 £102.37 **2a** Ladies' **b** 1993 **c** Ladies' sales rose fairly steadily; men's fell, faster in 1993 and 1994 **d** £10 million
3a 70 cm **b** 50 cm **c** 60 cm **d** 60 cm
4a Goals × frequencies: 0, 8, 20, 18, 16, 10, 6 **b** 2.2 **c** 2, 2
5a Mid-values × frequencies: 65, 144, 299, 168; Totals 32, 676
b 21 **c** 21–25
6a

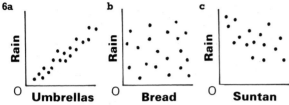

8 PYTHAGORAS

Page 108 Looking Back

1a 49 **b** 361 **c** 3.24 **d** 0.81 **e** 0.09
2a 25 cm² **b** 100 cm² **c** 6.25 cm² **d** 2500 cm² **3a** 3 **b** 6
c 1.4 **d** 0.6 **e** 17 **4a** 8 cm **b** 11 cm **c** 35 cm **d** 2.3 cm
5a A(1, 1), B(5, 1), C(5, 5), D(1, 5) **b** 4 cm each **c** 16 cm²
6a A(−2, −1), B(1, −1), C(1, 2), D(−2, 2) **b** 3 cm each
c 9 cm² **7a** 36 **b** 225 **8a** 4 **b** 12
9a 41 **b** 8.5 **c** 33 **10a** 3.5 **b** 2.9 **c** 0.6 **d** 11.2
11a   **b**   **c**

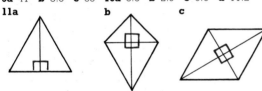

Page 109 Class Discussion/Exercise 1

1a (i) About 11 m (10.8) (ii) 27 m (26.9) (iii) 5 m (5) **b** scale drawing **2** 25, 16, 9, 25 **3a** 8, 4, 4, 8 **b** 32, 16, 16, 32
4a 100, 36, 64, 100 **b** Area A = area B + C
5a 2 cm **b** 5 cm **c** 10 cm **d** 4 cm **e** 3.2 cm **f** 8.2 cm
6a 10 **b** 13 **c** 17 **d** 6.5 **7** (i) 10.8 (ii) 26.9 (iii) 5

Page 111 Exercise 2A

1a 15 **b** 25 **c** 26 **d** 41 **2a** 25 **b** 8.7 **c** 2.5 **d** 20
3 $a = 7.8$, $b = 12.8$, $c = 27.7$, $d = 20.5$
4a 2 m **b** 12 m **c** 7.5 cm **d** 0.5 mm **5** 4 m **6** 13 m
7 18.5 m **8** 4.5 m **9** 25 cm **10** 137 m **11** 75 m

Page 112 Exercise 2B

1a ABD, CBD **b** KOL, LOM, MON, NOK
c PTQ, QTR, RTS, PTS **d** IFG, FGH, GHI, HIF
2 $a = 61$, $b = 52$, $c = 2.5$, $d = 4$, $e = 9.9$ **3** 2.6 m
4 17.0 inches **5** 7.4 m **6a** 52 cm **b** 208 cm
7 56.5 mm, 56.5 mm, 12.5 mm, 12.5 mm **8** 89 cm, 100 cm

Page 114 Exercise 3

1a (i) AC = 6, BC = 5 (ii) AB = 7.8 **b** (i) DF = 4, EF = 7
(ii) DE = 8.1 **c** (i) GI = 5, IH = 2 (ii) GH = 5.4
d (i) JL = 5, KL = 5 (ii) JK = 7.1 **2** AB = 3.6 m **3** 3.2 m
4 OA = 3 m, OB = 6.1 m, OC = 4.5 m, OD = 2.8 m

5a No, it is only 3.6 km shorter **b** 1.6 km
6b PQ = 4.1, QR = 4.1 **c** isosceles **7a** (ii) AB = 5
b (ii) DE = 6.7 (iii) GH = 5.7 **8a** 8.1 km **b** 23.5 km
c 15.4 km

Page 116 Exercise 4A

1a 8 **b** 20 **c** 12 **d** 3.2
2 $a = 3.6$, $b = 11.4$, $c = 15.8$, $d = 9.8$ **3a** 5 cm **b** (i) 24
(ii) 26 **4** 20 m **5** 40 mm **6** 0.8 m **7a** 1 m **b** 2.4 m

Page 117 Exercise 4B

1 $x = 48$, $y = 60$ **2a** 15 **b** 6 **c** 21 cm **3** 18 cm
4a 6000 m, 4123 m **b** 1877 m **5a** 6.5 **b** 9.6 **c** 16.1 m

Page 118 Exercise 5

1a 12 cm **b** 20 cm **2a** 1.5 m **b** 2.5 m **3** 3.16 m
4a (i) 5 m (ii) 2 m **b** 5.39 m **5b** (i) 4.5 cm (ii) 27 cm²
6b 42 m

Page 119 Exercise 6A

1 $a = 33$, $b = 61$, $c = 60$, $d = 11.6$
2 $e = 350$, $f = 77$, $g = 10.4$, $h = 6$
3 2.1 m **4** 50 cm **5** 3 m **6** 3150 mm **7** 520 km **8** 12 m

Page 120 Exercise 6B

1a 31 m **b** 18 m **2a** 22 km **b** 50 km **c** 45 km **3a** 70
b 25 **4** 14 cm **5a** 2.5 **b** 16 cm **6** 34 cm **7a** 6 m **b** 10 m
8a 30 yards **b** 70 yards

Page 121 Check-up on Pythagoras

1a 30 **b** 48 **c** 101 **d** 40
2 The triangle may not be right-angled **3a** 12 **b** 68
4 45 cm **5** 4.8 cm, 14 cm **6a** 10 **b** 13
7a 8 m **b** 5 m **c** 6.4 m **8** 2.4 m **9** 19.5 cm
10a 20 m **b** 24 m **11a** 50 cm **b** 260 cm

REVIEW: NUMBERS 2

Page 122 Length and Area

1a OA = 25 mm, OB = 63 mm, AB = 38 mm
b 2.5 cm, 6.3 cm, 3.8 cm **2b** 10.5 cm **c** 29 cm
3a (i) 17 mm (ii) 1.7 cm **b** (i) 94 mm (ii) 9.4 cm
c (i) 70 mm (ii) 7 cm **4a** 375 km **b** 58
5a 0.28 m or 28 cm, 6.02 m **b** 0.98 m or 98 cm **6** 3.7 cm
7a 12 sq. units **b** (i) 4 sq. units (ii) 8 sq. units **8** 600
9a 150 cm² **b** 72 cm² **c** 4000 cm² **d** 3 m² **e** 17 600 cm²
10a 36 cm² **b** 49.5 cm² **c** 3.5 m² **d** 6.48 m² **11a** 11 cm
b 4.5 cm **12a** 66 m² **b** 128 cm² **c** 84 m² **d** 48 cm²

Page 123 Circles

1a 35 cm **b** 28 cm **2** 105 cm, 168 cm **3a** (i) 6 cm
(ii) 3 cm² **b** (i) 45 cm (ii) 168.75 cm² **c** (i) 72 cm
(ii) 432 cm² **4a** 31.4 m **b** 78.5 m² **5** Banjo 81.7 cm, 531 cm²;
tambourine 88.0 cm, 616 cm²; drum 94.2 cm, 707 cm²
6a 1.8 m **b** 18 m **c** 1800 m or 1.8 km **d** 0.9 m
7a 94.2 cm **b** 314 cm² **8a** 8.80 m **b** 6.16 m²
9 4420 mm² **10a** 116 cm **b** 28.3 cm **c** 10.1 m
11a 580 000 000 miles **b** 5.8×10^8

Page 124   Volume

1a 6 cm³ **b** 12 cm³ **c** 18 cm³ **d** 24 cm³ **e** 45 cm³
2a 2000 cm³ **b** 360 000 cm³ **c** 32 768 mm³ **d** 1 008 000 cm³
3a 1 008 000 ml **b** 1008 litres **4a** 2000 **b** 40
5a Coolcon, by 44 litres **b** Coolcon **6a** 5 **b** 25 **c** 125
7a 28 m **b** 14 000 m³ **8a** 35 cm **b** 37.5 cm² **c** 15.625 cm³
9a 60 **b** 20 cm

Page 125   Ratio and Proportion

1a 1:4 **b** 4:5 **c** 5:1 **2a** 4, 4, 6 **b** (i) 1:1 (ii) 2:3
(iii) 3:2 **3a** 40p, 40p **b** 64p, 16p **c** 32p, 48p **4a** 1:10
b 1:2 **c** 1:5 **d** 1:20 **5a** 18 **b** 12 **6a** 8 **b** 12 **c** 4
7a £4.80 **b** £14.40 **c** £19.20 **8** 235 km **9a** 100 cm
10a 56 **b** 300 g **11a** 360 km **b** 4½ hours **12a** (ii) **b** (i)
13a 3, 6, 9, 12, 15, 18, 21 **c, d** earnings and hours are in
direct proportion

9   AREAS AND VOLUMES

Page 126   Looking Back

1a 25 sq. **b** 50 sq. **c** 18 sq. **d** 28 sq.
3a 9 cm² **b** 16 cm² **c** 30 cm² **d** 13 cm² **4a** 12 cm
b 20 cm **c** 30 cm **d** 13 cm **5a** (i) 6 (ii) 6.2 **b** (i) 2
(ii) 1.8 **c** (i) 19 (ii) 19.5 **6a** 27 **b** 24 **7a** 64 cm³
b 60 cm³ **8a** 2000 cm² **b** 900 cm² **c** 707 cm²
9a 14 000 cm³ **b** 3375 cm³

Page 127   Exercise 1A

1 216 cm², 120 cm², 500 cm² **2a** 4.5 m² **b** 8.6 m **3a** 72 ft²
b (i) 18 ft² (ii) ¼ **4a** 180 mm² **b** 144 cm² **c** 30 m²
d 5.7 m² **5a** A 3000 m², B 2250 m², C 2400 m², D 1800 m²
b 9450 m² **6** Radius: 10 mm, 13 mm, 9 mm, 12 mm;
Diameter: 20 mm, 26 mm, 18 mm, 24 mm;
Circumference: 62.8 mm, 81.7 mm, 56.5 mm, 75.4 mm;
Area: 314 mm², 531 mm², 254 mm², 452 mm²
7a 707 m² **b** 30 m **c** 94.2 m

Page 128   Exercise 1B

1a 36 cm² **b** 63 cm² **2a** 64 m² **b** 4 m **c** 50.3 m²
d 13.7 m² **3a** 4 m² **b** 1 m **c** 1.57 m² **d** 5.57 m²
4a 126 m **b** 326 m
5a 4000 m² **b** 20 m **c** 1260 m² **d** 5260 m²
6a 3200 cm² **b** 70 cm, 30 cm **c** 2100 cm² **d** 1100 cm²
7a 227 cm² **b** 7.07 cm² **c** 220 cm² **8a** 3.75 m² **b** 38 m²

Page 129   Exercise 2

1a 20 sq. **b** 30 sq. **c** 40 sq. **d** 35 sq. **2a** 54 cm²
b 14 cm² **c** 90 cm² **d** 24 cm² **3** 486 cm² **4a** 360 cm²
b 180 cm² **5a** 250 m, 100 m **b** (i) 12 500 m² (ii) 37 500 m²

Page 130   Exercise 3

1a 120 cm² **b** 162 cm² **c** 154 cm² **d** 176 cm² **2a** 880 mm²
b 7920 mm² **3** Area = 40 m², so cost = £2000. £1800 is not
enough, by £200 **4a** 300 cm² **b** 160 cm² **c** 630 cm²
d 144 cm²

Page 131   Exercise 4

1a 72 cm² **b** 66 cm² **c** 30 cm² **d** 190 cm²
2 22 m², 30 m², 140 m² **3a** 6.25 m² **b** 108 mm² **c** 4 m²
d 60 m² **e** 216 cm² **f** 49 m² **4a** 48 cm² **b** 250 cm²
c 45 cm² **d** 672 cm²

Page 132   Exercise 5

1a 27 cm³ **b** 330 cm³ **c** 504 cm³ **d** 336 cm³ **e** 273 cm³
f 252 cm³ **2a** (i) 1200 cm³ (ii) 1.2 litres **b** (i) 750 cm³
(ii) 0.75 litre **3a** 42 **b** 378 km **4a** 27 **b** (i) 8 cm³
(ii) 216 cm³ **5a** 4410 cm³ **b** 735 cm³ **c** 3675 cm³
6a Dining 180 m³, kitchen 60 m³, lounge 225 m³ **b** (i) ⅓
(ii) ⅘ **7a** (i) 7406 mm³ (ii) 207 368 mm³ **b** 28 **c** in 4 layers,
with 7 dominoes in each layer, and the 46 mm edges matching

Page 134   Exercise 6

1a 30 cm³ **b** 28 cm³ **c** 30 cm³ **d** 30 cm³
2a 12 cm³ **b** 240 cm³ **c** 0.6 m³ **d** 30 m³
3a 96 cm² **b** 9600 cm³ **4a** 18 cm² **b** 54 cm³ **c** 145.8 g
5a 3 m² **b** 12 m³ **6a** 12 m² **b** 144 m³

Page 135   Exercise 7

1a (i) 6 cm (ii) 452 cm³ **b** (i) 3 cm (ii) 283 cm³ **c** (i) 5 cm
(ii) 628 cm³ **d** (i) 4 cm (ii) 603 cm³ **2 a**, by 16 cm³
3a 1.77 m² **b** 4.43 m³
4a 314 mm³ **b** 724 mm³ **c** 1140 mm³
5a 236 cm³ **b** (i) 59 cm³ (ii) 118 cm³ (iii) 177 cm³
6a 314 cm² **b** 11 300 cm³
7a 1260 cm² **b** 630 000 (628 000) cm³

Page 136   Exercise 8A

1a (i) 16 cm² (ii) 96 cm² **b** 96 cm² **2a** 6 cm² **b** 216 cm²
3a 6 cm² **b** 12 cm² **c** 3 cm² **d** 6 cm² **e** 2 cm² **f** 4 cm²
g 22 cm² **4**(i)**a** 25 cm² **b** 50 cm² **c** 60 cm² **d** 120 cm²
e 60 cm² **f** 120 cm² **g** 290 cm² (ii)**a** 32 cm² **b** 64 cm²
c 48 cm² **d** 96 cm² **e** 96 cm² **f** 192 cm² **g** 352 cm²
5a 500 cm² **b** 480 cm² **6a** 6 m² **b** 6200 cm²

Page 137   Exercise 8B

1a 60 cm², 72 cm², 60 cm² **b** 12 cm² **c** 216 cm²
2a 32 cm², 24 cm², 40 cm² **b** 6 cm² **c** 108 cm² **3** 38 m²
4a Two rectangles, each 1200 cm²; three right-angled
triangles, each 288 cm² **b** 3264 cm² **5a** 44 cm² **b** 608 cm²

Page 138   Exercise 9B

1a 120 cm² **b** 360 cm² **c** 72 cm² **d** 7.5 m² **2a** 25.1 cm
b 126 cm² **3a** 3140 cm² **b** 942 cm² **4** 17 000 cm²
5a 28.3 cm² **b** 188 cm² **6** 1880 cm² **7a** (i) 113 cm²
(ii) 603 cm² (iii) 829 cm² **b** (i) 50.3 cm² (ii) 226 cm²
(iii) 327 cm² **c** (i) 28.3 cm² (ii) 188 cm² (iii) 245 cm²
d (i) 78.5 cm² (ii) 251 cm² (iii) 408 cm²

Page 140   Check-up on Areas and Volumes

1a 36 cm² **b** 54 cm² **c** 30 cm² **d** 113 cm² **2a** 24 cm
b 30 cm **c** 30 cm **d** 37.7 cm **3a** 216 cm² **b** 640 cm²
4a 26 cm **b** (i) 104 cm (ii) 480 cm² **5** 3186 cm², 8910 cm³
6a 729 cm³ **b** 105 cm³ **7a** 486 cm² **b** 142 cm² **8a** 11.4 m²
b 3 m³ **9a** 396 cm³ **b** 960 cm³ **10a** 3140 cm² **b** 4240 cm²
11 320 cm³, 348 cm²

10 MONEY MATTERS - PERSONAL FINANCE

Page 141 Looking Back

1a £361 **b** £253 **c** £450 **2a** £5 **b** £890 **c** £44.50
3a £12.50 **b** £33.81 **4a** £7.80 **b** £15.28
5a £251.60 **b** (i) £10.20 (ii) £323 **6a** £175 **b** £230
7 £17.41 **8a** (i) £58.50 (ii) £13.50 **b** £126

Page 142 Exercise 1A

1 £276 **2** £255.50 **3** £68 **4** £102.10 **5** £175.30
6 £132.50 **7** £277, £212 **8a** £278.50 **b** £63.54 **c** £214.96
9a £321.75 **b** £97.77 **c** £223.98

Page 143 Exercise 1B

1 £9 **2** £92.40 **3a** £13.22 **b** £158.40 **4a** £1422.65
b £405.07 **c** £1017.58 **5b** £1498, £430.48, £1067.52

Page 145 Exercise 2

1a £3500 **b** £5000 **2a** £13 500 **b** £12 100 **c** £16 100
d £13 865 **3** £2100 **4a** £5000 **b** £13 650
5a £3720 **b** £5740 **6a** None **b** £875 **c** £520 **d** none

Page 146 Exercise 3

1a £8500 **b** £600, £5500 at 25% = £1375, £1975
2a £13 200 **b** £600, £10 200 at 25% = £2550, £3150
3a £2500, £500, —, £500 **b** £6000, £600, £750, £1350
c £11 000, £600, £2000, £2600 **4a** £5740 **b** £1285
5a £2205 **b** £441 **6a** £11 100 **b** £2625 **7a** £1317.50
b £25.34 **8a** £11 440 **b** £6440 **c** £1460, £28.08
d £191.92

Page 149 Exercise 4

1a (i) £1.90 (ii) £2.95 **b** (i) £11.29 (ii) £4.58 **2a** More risk
to the insurance company of the client dying or being unable
to pay the premiums due to ill health **b** life expectancy of
females is longer than that of males **c** life expectancy of a
smoker is shorter, and there is a greater risk of ill health
3a £2.10 **b** (i) £4.20 (ii) £6.30 (iii) £10.50 (iv) £21
4 £27 **5** £19 **6a** £19 **b** £27.48 **c** £56.45 **d** £52.50
7a £5.36 **b** (i) £10.72 (ii) £21.44 (iii) £26.80 (iv) £64.32
8a £446.40 **b** £244.80 **9a** £3387 **b** £492

Page 150 Exercise 5A

1 7.25 dollars, 42.25 francs, 12.2 marks, 970 pesetas,
1250 escudos, 12 500 lire, 1750 drachmas, 10.85 Swiss francs
2a (i) 183 (ii) 187.88 (iii) 3050 **b** (i) 97 000 (ii) 29 488
(iii) 16 490 **c** (i) 125 000 (ii) 22 500 (iii) 3 750 000
3 1267.5, 1521, 1183, 1394.25 **4a** (i) 3500 (ii) 4900
b (i) £6 (ii) £4 (iii) £3 (iv) £13 (v) £14 (vi) £17

Page 151 Exercise 5B

1a £7 **b** £11.83 **c** £34.48
2a Britain, France, USA, Spain, Germany
b Pierre £175.15, Karl £157.79, Manuel £144.33,
Andrew £142.50, Wilbur £134.48 **3a** 1845 **b** £17.61
4a For £40 you get $56 **b** $10, 14, 35, 45; £5, 14, 32, 47

Page 152 Check-up on Money Matters— Personal Finance

1a £250.50 **b** £223.00 **2** £182.00, £64.97, £117.03
3 £10.68 **4** £3700 **5a** £13 450 **b** £3212.50
6a £15 000 **b** £11 500 **c** £2725 **d** £12 275
7a £13.30 **b** £16.10 **c** £352.80 **8a** 976 **b** 36

REVIEW: LETTERS AND NUMBERS 2

Page 153 Equations 1

1a $x = 4$ **b** $x = 6$ **c** $x = 9$ **d** $y = 3$ **e** $y = 9$ **f** $y = 20$
g $t = 7$ **h** $u = 14$ **i** $t = 0$ **2a** $v + 1 = 10, v = 9$
b $v + 3 = 8, v = 5$ **c** $2w + 1 = 11, w = 5$ **d** $3w = 36, w = 12$
3a $x + 3 = 9, x = 6$ **b** $y - 2 = 5, y = 7$ **c** $t + 6 = 14, t = 8$
d $u - 10 = 2, u = 12$ **4a** $m + 8 = 15, m = 7$
b $n - 6 = 3, n = 9$ **5** $a + 1 = 8, a = 7; b - 3 = 7, b = 10;$
$c + 7 = 11, c = 4; d - 8 = 14, d = 22$ **6a** $x = 7$ **b** $y = 5$
c $m = 1$ **d** $n = 2$ **e** $x = 2$ **f** $y = 5$ **g** $d = 4$ **h** $e = 8$
7a $2p + 4 = 18, p = 7$ **b** $3t + 3 = 15, t = 4$
c $x + 3 = 7, x = 4$ **d** $2t = 8, t = 4$ **e** $t + 4 = 10, t = 6$
f $2t = 10, t = 5$ **8a** $28x$ cm **b** $28x = 28, x = 1$
c 4 cm, 2 cm, 1 cm **9a** $p = 3$ **b** $t = 1$ **c** $u = 2$ **d** $v = 1$
e $x = 3$ **f** $y = 5$ **10a** $x = 1$ **b** $y = 2$ **c** $u = 3$ **d** $v = 5$

Page 154 Equations 2

1a $x = 5$ **b** $x = 9$ **c** $x = 2$ **d** $y = 5$ **e** $y = 6$ **f** $y = 6$
2a (i) x (ii) 0 **b** (i) $2a$ (ii) a **c** (i) $3n$ (ii) $4n$ **d** (i) $2t + 1$
(ii) 1 **3a** $2x + 1$ **b** $2y - 1$ **c** $n + 3$ **d** 1 **4a** $x = 6$
b $y = 5$ **c** $t = 3$ **d** $y = 2$ **e** $x = 1$ **f** $n = 5$ **g** $p = 1$
h $t = 2$ **i** $u = 2$ **5a** $3x = x + 8, x = 4; 12$ cm
b $4t = 24, t = 6; 24$ cm **c** $2y = y + 20, y = 20; 40$ cm
6a $3t = 2t + 1, t = 1$ **b** $2k = k + 3, k = 3$
7 $3n + 1 = n + 39, n = 19$
8a $2x = x + 5, x = 5$ **b** $3n = n + 8, n = 4$
9a $3x = x + 32, x = 16; 48$ cm **b** $5t = 2t + 30, t = 10; 50$ cm
10a $x = 2$ **b** $x = 3$ **c** $u = 2$ **d** $v = 2$ **e** $d = 2$ **f** $t = 5$

Page 155 Formulae and Sequences

1a $d = 3x + 5y$ **b** 300 m **2a** $N = 20 + x - y$ **b** $A = 40 - 3x$
c $T = x + y + z$ **d** $L = m - n$
3a (i) $P = 2x + y$ (ii) $P = 2x + 2y$ (iii) $P = 2y + \pi x$
b (i) 40 cm (ii) 50 cm (iii) 51 cm **4a** Add 4 **b** subtract 2
c multiply by 3 **d** subtract 1 **5a** 3, 5, 7 **b** 0, 5, 10
6a $2n$ **b** $n + 1$ **c** $3n - 2$ **d** $8n - 1$
7a 4, 4, 4, . . . ; 21, 25, 29 **b** 2, 3, 4, . . . ; 17, 23, 30
c $-4, -4, -4, . . . ; 24, 20, 16$ **d** 3, 5, 7, . . . ; 25, 36, 49 **8** 20
9a (i) $P = 4a + 2b, A = 2ac$ (ii) $P = 4x + 2\pi x, A = 4x^2 + \pi x^2$
b (i) 22 m, 24 m² (ii) 411 m, 11 427 m²

Page 156 Equations and Inequations

1a $x = 3$ **b** $y = 1$ **c** $t = 12$ **d** $x = 6$ **e** $y = 1$ **f** $t = 0$
2a $2x + 3 = 7, x = 2$ **b** $5y - 2 = 13, y = 3$
3a $y = 3$ **b** $t = 2$ **c** $u = 3$ **d** $x = 3$ **e** $n = 7$ **f** $v = 1$
g $x = 1$ **h** $x = 5$ **i** $x = 0$ **4a** $x = 4$ **b** $y = 2$ **c** $t = 5$
5a $2x + 5 = 3x, x = 5$ **b** $3x = x + 12, x = 6$
6a $2(x - 1) = 4, x = 3$ **b** $2(x + 2) = 18, x = 7$
c $3(x - 5) = 2(x - 3), x = 9$
7a F **b** T **c** T **d** T **e** F **f** T **8a** $n < 5$ **b** $k < 4$
9a $x > 5$ **b** $y < 2.5$ **c** $d < 18$ **d** $k > 5$
10a (i) $2n - 1$ (ii) $n + 19$ **b** $2n - 1 = n + 19, n = 20$
11a (i) $3(x + 2)$ cm² (ii) $3(x + 2) = 12, x = 2$ **b** (i) $2x + 10$ cm
(ii) $2x + 10 = 16, x = 3$
12a 4, 5 **b** $-2, -1, 0$ **c** $-2, -1, 0, 1, 2$

FORMULAE AND SEQUENCES

Page 157 Looking Back

1a $p = 500$ **b** $p = 2000$ **2a** $u = 200$ **b** $u = 625$
3a $C = 80$ **b** $C = 170$ **4a** $W = 2x$ **b** $W = 3y$
c $W = x+y$ **d** $W = 3x$ **5a** 9, 10, 11 **b** 10, 12, 14
c 25, 24, 23 **d** 25, 30, 35 **6a** 12 **b** 16 **c** 22 **d** 40
7a 4, 5 **b** 9, 11 **8** 25, 36 **9a** $5t$ **b** $y-3$ **c** $2n+5$
10a 10, 20, 30, 40, 50 **b** 1, 4, 9, 16, 25, 36 **11** 5, 9, 13, 17, 21
12a $P = 4m$ **b** $P = 2x+2y$ **c** $P = 3t$ **13a** 60 **b** $n = p-q$

Page 158 Exercise 1A

1 353 **2** 1240 **3** 42 **4** 7 **5** 125 **6** 960 **7** 15 **8** 32 **9** 46
10 6.25 **11** 55 **12** 50 **13** 80 **14** 125 **15** 50 **16** 50
17 226 **18** 40 **19** 1.75 **20** 50%

Page 159 Exercise 1B

1a 2000 **b** 750 **2a** 60 **b** 54 **3a** 36 **b** 25.7
4a 60 **b** 50.3 **5a** 1000 **b** 1350 **6a** 13 **b** 10.8
7a 124 pounds **b** 132 pounds **8a** 5.6 **b** 14 **9a** 4 **b** 1
c 0.04 **10** 8

Page 161 Exercise 2A

1a $P = x+y+z$ **b** $P = 3m$ **c** $P = n+2k$ **d** $P = u+v+2t$
e $P = 4x$ **f** $P = 2y+2z$ **2a** $W = 2w$ **b** $W = 3w+x$
3a $W = 4x+y$ **b** $W = 2s+2t+u$ **4a** $S = 3d$ **b** $S = p+2q$
c $S = 2a+2b$ **5a** $N = 6p$ **b** $N = px$ **6a** $N = 3u$ **b** $N = tu$
7a $A = xy$ **b** 750 **c** $V = xyz$ **8a** $V = ab^2$ **b** 2000
9a $C = 2N$ **b** $D = 20T$ **c** $M = \frac{1}{100}C$ **10a** $x^2 = y^2 + z^2$
b (i) 15 (ii) 6.5

Page 163 Exercise 2B

1a $P = 5x+1$ **b** $Q = (y+2) \times 3$ **2a** $M = 2x-3$
b $N = (y-4) \times 6$ **3a** $4\frac{1}{2}$ hours **b** $T = p+q+r$
4a £26 **b** $m = p-3t$ **5a** $S = x+y$ **b** $D = x-y$
c $A = \dfrac{x+y}{2}$ **6a** $M = \dfrac{A}{S}$ **b** (i) 3 (ii) 4.5 **7** $A = d^2 - \pi r^2$
8a $A = 12r^2$ **b** 2700

Page 164 Exercise 3A

1 2 2 2; $N = 2n+1$; 11, 13; 11, $2 \times 6 + 1$, 13
3a $N = 3n-2$ **b** $N = 2n+2$ **c** $N = 4n-1$ **d** $N = 3n+4$
4a $N = 2n$ **b** 30 **5a** Rows: 4, 7, 10, 13, 16; 4, 6, 8, 10, 12
b (i) $G = 3n+1$ (ii) $P = 2n+2$ **6a** 3, 5, 7, 9, 11; 3, 4, 5, 6, 7
b (i) $G = 2n+1$ (ii) $P = n+2$ **7a** 6, 11, 16, 21, 26;
6, 10, 14, 18, 22 **b** (i) $G = 5n+1$ (ii) $P = 4n+2$

Page 165 Exercise 3B

1a $N = 7n+2$ **b** $N = 5n-1$ **c** $N = 5n$ **d** $N = 6n-5$
2a $N = 2n-1$ **b** 199 **3a** Row: 5, 8, 11 **b** $F = 3n+2$ **c** 62
4a Rows: 6, 9, 12; 7, 12, 17 **b** (i) $J = 3n+3$ (ii) $P = 5n+2$
c (i) 21, 32 (ii) 81, 117 **5a** Rows: 2, 4, 6; 3, 6, 9; 4, 8, 12
b (i) $P = 2n$ (ii) $C = 3n$ (iii) $A = 4n$

Page 166 Check-up on Formulae and Sequences

1 110 **2** 8 **3** 30 **4a** £3 **b** £7.50 **c** £28.35 **5a** 8 km
b 32 km **c** 160 km **6a** 18 **b** 14 **7** 0°C **8a** (i) $P = 8x$

(ii) $A = 4x^2$ **b** (i) $P = 2u+2v+6$ (ii) $A = u(v+3)$
9a (i) 80 (ii) 400 **b** (i) 26 (ii) 40 **10** $p = s-c$
11 $P = 2x+y$ **12a** $P = 3x+7$ **b** $Q = (y-1) \times 2$
13a $N = 3n+5$ **b** $N = 5n-4$ **14a** Rows: 4, 6, 8; 5, 8, 11
b $H = 2n+2$, $T = 3n+2$ **c** (i) 42 (ii) 62

 PROBABILITY

Page 167 Looking Back

1a $\frac{1}{2}$ **b** 1 **c** $\frac{1}{6}$ **d** 0 **e** $\frac{1}{2}$ **f** $\frac{1}{4}$ **g** $\frac{3}{5}$
2

```
    d      c     f          a e   g              b
    |------|-----|----------|↓↑---|--------------|
    0   0.1  0.2  0.3  0.4  0.5  0.6  0.7  0.8  0.9  1
```

3a $\frac{1}{8}$ **b** $\frac{1}{2}$ **c** $\frac{1}{4}$ **d** $\frac{1}{2}$ **e** 0 **f** 1
4a

$P(R) = \frac{2}{3}$ → R
$P(W) = \frac{1}{3}$ → W

b

$P(R) = \frac{1}{2}$ → R
$P(W) = \frac{1}{2}$ → W

c

$P(R) = \frac{1}{4}$ → R
$P(W) = \frac{3}{4}$ → W

5a 18 **b** 13 or 14
6a It will not snow **b** there is an even chance of snow
c it is certain to snow **7a** Survey **b** past data **c** survey
d experiment, or equally likely calculation

Page 168 Exercise 1A

1a 1, 2, 3, 4, 5, 6 **b** $\frac{1}{6}, \frac{1}{6}, \frac{1}{6}, \frac{1}{6}, \frac{1}{6}, \frac{1}{6}$, 1 **2a** $\frac{1}{4}$ **b** $\frac{3}{4}$ **c** 1
3a 4 **b** (i) $\frac{1}{4}$ (ii) $\frac{1}{4}$ (iii) $\frac{1}{4}$ (iv) $\frac{1}{4}$ **c** 1
4a $\frac{2}{9}$ **b** $\frac{4}{9}$ **c** $\frac{1}{3}$ **d** 1 **5a** $\frac{2}{8}$ **b** $\frac{3}{8}$ **6** 80% **7** 0.8 **8** $\frac{4}{5}$
9

$P(\text{rain}) = 20\%$ — Rain
$P(\text{no rain}) = 80\%$ — No rain

$P(\text{jam}) = 0.2$ — Jam
$P(\text{no jam}) = 0.8$ — No jam

$P(\text{flu}) = \frac{1}{5}$ — Flu
$P(\text{no flu}) = \frac{4}{5}$ — No flu

Page 169 Exercise 1B

1a $\frac{1}{6}$ **b** $\frac{5}{6}$ **2a** $\frac{1}{3}$ **b** $\frac{2}{3}$ **3** $\frac{1}{2}$ **4a** $\frac{99}{100}$ **b** 99% **5a** $\frac{2}{7}$ **b** $\frac{1}{7}$
6 There are 3 possible outcomes: Win, Lose, Draw, so
$P(\text{Win}) + P(\text{Lose}) + P(\text{Draw}) = 1$ **7a** $\frac{1}{20}$ **b** $\frac{1}{10}$ **c** $\frac{17}{20}$

Page 170 Exercise 2A

1a 1st row (S, S) (S, R); 2nd row (R, S) (R, R) **b** 4 **2a** (i) $\frac{1}{4}$
(ii) $\frac{1}{4}$ (iii) $\frac{1}{2}$ **b** S, (S, S); R, (S, R); S, (R, S); R, (R, R)
3a 1st row (W, 5) (W, 10); 2nd row (L, 5) (L, 10) **b** 4
4a (i) $\frac{1}{4}$ (ii) $\frac{1}{4}$ (iii) $\frac{3}{4}$ **b** £5, (W, £5); £10, (W, £10); £5, (L, £5);
£10, (L, £10) **5a** 1st row G(am), E(am); G(am), E(pm);
2nd row G(pm), E(am); G(pm), E(pm) **b** $\frac{1}{4}$
6a 16 **b** (i) $\frac{1}{16}$ (ii) $\frac{1}{16}$ (iii) $\frac{1}{4}$ (iv) $\frac{3}{8}$

7a 1st row (R, B)(R, W); 2nd row (Y, B)(Y, W);
3rd row (G, B)(G, W) **b** 6 **c** (i) $\frac{1}{6}$ (ii) $\frac{1}{3}$ (iii) 0 (iv) 1
8a 1, (H, 1); 2, (H, 2); 3, (H, 3): 1, (T, 1); 2, (T, 2); 3, (T, 3) **b** 6
c (i) $\frac{1}{6}$ (ii) $\frac{1}{6}$ (iii) $\frac{1}{2}$

Page 172   Exercise 2B

1a 1, (1, 1); 2, (1, 2); 3, (1, 3); 1, (2, 1); 2, (2, 2); 3, (2, 3); 1, (3, 1);
2, (3, 2); 3, (3, 3) **b** (i) $\frac{1}{9}$ (ii) $\frac{2}{9}$ (iii) $\frac{1}{3}$ (iv) $\frac{1}{3}$
2a 1st row (H, W)(H, D)(H, L); 2nd row (A, W)(A, D)(A, L)
b (i) $\frac{1}{6}$ (ii) $\frac{1}{3}$ (iii) $\frac{1}{3}$ **c** W, (H, W); D, (H, D); L, (H, L);
W, (A, W); D, (A, D); L, (A, L) **3a** Rows: (1, 1), . . ., (1, 6);
(2, 1), . . ., (2, 6); (3, 1), . . ., (3, 6); (4, 1), . . ., (4, 6);
(5, 1), . . ., (5, 6); (6, 1), . . ., (6, 6) **b** (i) $\frac{1}{36}$ (ii) $\frac{11}{36}$ (iii) $\frac{1}{6}$
4a Rows: 2, . . ., 7; 3, . . ., 8; 4, . . ., 9; 5, . . ., 10; 6, . . ., 11;
7, . . ., 12 **b** $\frac{1}{36}, \frac{1}{18}, \frac{1}{12}, \frac{1}{9}, \frac{5}{36}, \frac{1}{6}, \frac{5}{36}, \frac{1}{9}, \frac{1}{12}, \frac{1}{18}, \frac{1}{36}$ **c** 7
5a Rows 1, 2, 3, . . ., 6; 2, 4, 6, . . ., 12; 3, 6, 9, . . ., 18;
4, 8, 12, . . ., 24; 5, 10, 15, . . ., 30; 6, 12, 18, . . ., 36 **b** (i) $\frac{1}{4}$
(ii) $\frac{3}{4}$ (iii) $\frac{1}{9}$ (iv) $\frac{2}{9}$ (v) $\frac{5}{9}$

Page 173   Exercise 3

1a $\frac{1}{2}$ **b** $\frac{1}{2}$ **c** 1 **2a** $\frac{1}{6}$ **b** $\frac{1}{6}$ **c** $\frac{1}{3}$ **3a** $\frac{1}{4}$ **b** $\frac{1}{2}$ **c** $\frac{3}{4}$
4a 40% **b** 60% **5a** $\frac{3}{13}$ **b** $\frac{1}{13}$ **c** $\frac{4}{13}$ **d** $\frac{3}{13}$ **e** $\frac{3}{13}$ **f** $\frac{6}{13}$ **g** $\frac{5}{13}$
h $\frac{8}{13}$ **i** 1 **6a** 0.7 **b** 0.3 **7a** $\frac{1}{4}$ **b** $\frac{2}{5}$ **c** $\frac{13}{20}$ **d** $\frac{7}{20}$ **e** $\frac{3}{5}$ **f** 1
8a $\frac{1}{3}$ **b** $\frac{2}{3}$ **c** 1 **9** $\frac{5}{12}$ **10a** $\frac{2}{15}$ **b** $\frac{2}{15}$ **c** $\frac{4}{15}$ **11a** $\frac{3}{5}$ **b** $\frac{2}{5}$ **c** 1
12a $\frac{1}{7}$ **b** $\frac{2}{7}$ **c** $\frac{3}{7}$ **d** 1

Page 175   Class Discussion/Exercise 4

1b (i) 0.2 (ii) 0.18 (iii) 0.16
2d 0.45, 0.4, 0.36, 0.32, 0.32 **e** 0.32

Page 176   Exercise 5A

1a $\frac{1}{2}$ **b** 50 **2a** $\frac{1}{6}$ **b** 16 or 17 **3** About 840
4a 0.3 **b** 20, 8, 12 **5a** $\frac{1}{4}$ **b** 5 **c** £1.50 **d** 90p loss
6a $\frac{1}{13}$ **b** about 8 **7a** $\frac{1}{7}$ **b** 5 **8** 30 **9a** $\frac{4}{9}$ **b** 55 or 56

Page 177   Exercise 5B

1a 0.0375 **b** 180 **2a** (i) $\frac{1}{3}$ (ii) $\frac{2}{3}$ **b** (i) 20 (ii) 40
3a H, (H, H); T, (H, T); H, (T, H); T, (T, T) **b** $\frac{1}{2}$ **c** 50
4 Tea 90, Cola 330, Milk 150, Orange 180 **5** £1500 **6** £50

Page 178   Check-up on Probability

1a $\frac{1}{4}$ **b** $\frac{3}{4}$ **2** $\frac{3}{10}$ or 0.3 **3** 0.25 **4a** $\frac{7}{25}$ **b** $\frac{2}{5}$ **c** $\frac{17}{25}$ **d** $\frac{8}{25}$ **e** $\frac{8}{25}$
5a $\frac{4}{11}$ **b** 36 or 37 **6a** 2 **b** 30
7a (i) 1st row (V, C)(V, L)(V, O); 2nd row (R, C)(R, L)(R, O)
(ii) C, (V, C); L, (V, L); O, (V, O); C, (R, C); L, (R, L); O, (R, O)
b (i) $\frac{1}{3}$ (ii) $\frac{1}{2}$
8a 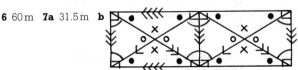 **b** $\frac{1}{4}$

9a Rows: 1, 2, 3, 4, 5, 6; 2, 4, 6, 8, 10, 12 **b** (i) 0 (ii) $\frac{1}{6}$ (iii) $\frac{1}{4}$
10 3 or 4

REVIEW: SHAPE AND SPACE

Page 179   Angles 1

1a Acute **b** right **c** obtuse **d** reflex **e** straight
2a Obtuse **b** obtuse **c** right **d** acute **e** straight

3 ∠AOB = 65°, ∠COD = 10°, ∠AOC = 170°, ∠BOC = 105°,
∠DOB = 115° **4** ∠PQR = 150°, ∠XYZ = 40°
6a ∠ABC = 135° **b** ∠HFG = 26° **c** ∠JKH = 136°
7a 45° **b** 90° **c** 90° **d** 135° **8a** 72° **b** 144° **c** 288°
d 216° **9a** AB, DC **b** AD, BC **c** ∠s ACD, BAC
10a 7.2 cm **b** 5.9 cm **c** 75°
11a SU, RP **b** SU and TQ; TQ and RP **12** 170°

Page 180   Angles 2

1a **b** **c**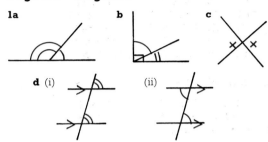
d (i) (ii)

2a (i) ∠DBA (ii) ∠DBE **b** (i) 55° (ii) 145° **3a** ∠FMG
b ∠JNI **c** ∠MNH **4a** 156° **b** 24° **c** 24° **d** 24° **5a** 60
b 18 **c** 50 **d** 108 **6** $a = 64, b = 64, c = 71$

7 **8a** **b**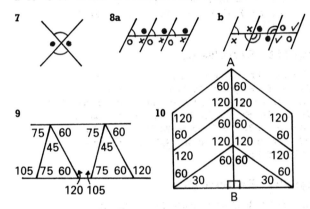

9 **10**

11 $10x = 360, x = 36$; 36, 72, 108, 144

Page 181   Rectangles and Squares

1b (i) 7.1 cm (ii) 7.2 cm
2b (i) All equal (ii) bisect the angles; cross at 90°
(iii) four lines of symmetry, $\frac{1}{4}$ turn symmetry
3a (i) MN, QP; MQ, NP (ii) MON, NOP, POQ, QOM;
MNP, NPQ, PQM, QMN **b** (i) M(−5, 5), Q(−5, −5), P(5, −5)
(ii) 100 square units

4 **5a** **b** 9 cm²
(Lengths in cm) (Lengths in cm)

6 60 m **7a** 31.5 m **b**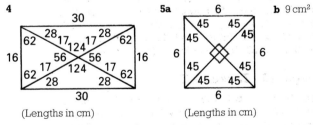

8b (i) D(4, 6) (ii) (4, 3) **9** (1, −3), (4, −6), (7, −3), (4, 0)
10 UVT, RVS; UVR, TVS; UTS, TSR, SRU, RUT

Page 182 Triangles

1 a and **c** **2a** Equilateral **b** right-angled **c** isosceles
d obtuse-angled **3** $a = 35$, $b = 62$, $c = 56$, $d = 10$, $e = 39$,
$f = 39$, $g = 43$ **4a** 40 cm² **b** 54 cm² **c** 6 cm² **d** 49.5 cm²
5a Yes **b** no **c** no

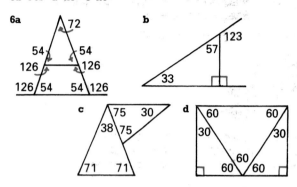

7a 8 m **b** (i) 48 m² (ii) 12 m² (iii) 36 m² **8a** 2400 cm²
b 180 cm² **c** 2040 cm² **9b** 10 square units

Page 183 Tiling and Symmetry

2a A(6, −6), B(0, −2), C(−6, −6), D(−6, 6) **b** H(−2, 2),
I(−8, 0), J(−2, −2), K(0, −8), L(2, −2) **3a** 2 **b** 4

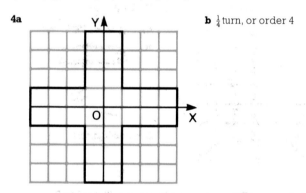

4a
b ¼ turn, or order 4

5a (i) 6 (ii) $\frac{1}{6}$ turn **b** (i) 2 (ii) $\frac{1}{2}$ turn **c** (i) 4 (ii) $\frac{1}{4}$ turn
d (i) 0 (ii) $\frac{1}{3}$ turn

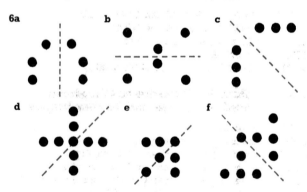

7a (i) Yes, one line (ii) no **b** (i) yes, two lines
(ii) yes, $\frac{1}{2}$ turn **c** (i) yes, five lines (ii) yes, $\frac{1}{5}$ turn
d (i) yes, four lines (ii) yes, $\frac{1}{4}$ turn
8c (3, −1), (1, −3), (−3, 1), (−1, 3)

Page 184 Quadrilaterals

1 (i) **a** **b** **c**

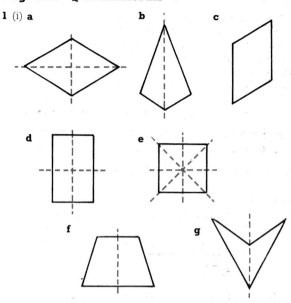

(ii)**a** rhombus **b** kite **c** parallelogram **d** rectangle
e square **f** trapezium **g** V-kite
2a A parallelogram **b** (5, 2)

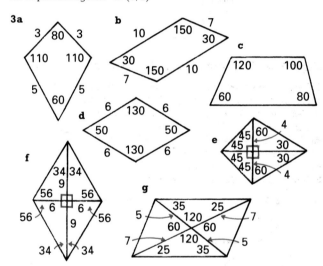

4 340 cm **5** 240 cm

6a
b 240 cm

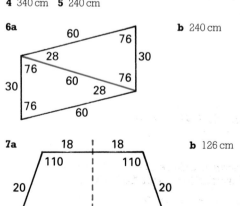

7a
b 126 cm

Page 185   Three Dimensions

1a (i) Cube   (ii) six squares   **b** (i) cuboid
(ii) six rectangles   **c** (i) square-based pyramid
(ii) four triangles, one square   **d** (i) triangular prism
(ii) two triangles, three rectangles
2a Sphere   **b** cone   **c** triangular-based pyramid
d cylinder   **3a** 68 cm   **b** 60 cm
4a 5   **b** 22

c (i)    (ii)   (iii)

5a 720 cm³   **b** (i) 90 cm²   (ii) 144 cm²   (iii) 40 cm²
c 548 cm²
d Example:

8 cm   18 cm   5 cm

6a AE, BF, CG, DH   **b** ABFIE, BCGF, CGJHD, DHEA
c FG, EH, IJ, AD   **d** JHG   **e** FB, BC, AD, AE

7a Example: **b** (i) 24 cm²   (ii) 8 cm³

Page 186   Distances and Directions

1 Rectangle 8 cm by 5 cm has quarter-circles of radii 2 cm
removed at the corners   **2** PQ = 7 cm, QR = 6 cm
3a AB = 10 cm, AD = 7 cm, BC = 9 cm   **b** 10.2 cm; 204 cm
c ∠BCD = 79°, ∠ADC = 101°   **4a** 270°   **b** 105°   **c** 230°
5a (i) S   (ii) NW   (iii) NE   **b** (i) telephone box
(ii) bus station   (iii) windmill
6a (i) 030°   (ii) 290°   (iii) 260°
b Buxsea 45 km, Cowton 30 km, Dipmouth 20 km

7a   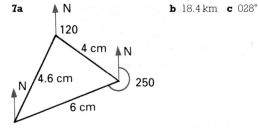   **b** 18.4 km   **c** 028°

120   4 cm   4.6 cm   6 cm   250   N

REVISION EXERCISES

Page 192   Revision Exercise on Chapter 1:
Calculations and Calculators

1a 3.1   **b** 8.2   **c** 10.1   **d** 0.5   **2a** 20   **b** 200   **c** 700
d 3000   **3a** (ii) 400   **b** 444   **c** 444   **4a** 800, 798
b 5000, 5568   **c** 2000, 1968.3   **d** 4000, 4505.28   **5** £16.66
6 38.9, 48.3, 54.6, 60.3, 65.5, 71.6 kg
7a 36 000 mm³   **b** 120 cm³   **8a** (iv) 324   **b** 324

9a 201.06 cm², 314.16 cm², 530.93 cm²   **b** 13.82 cm
10a 2.4×10^3 **b** 3×10^8 **c** 6.6×10^{21} **d** 8.5×10^{-2}
e 7×10^{-4} **11a** $1.6 \times 10^3 = 1600$ **b** $2 \times 10^5 = 200\,000$
c $7 \times 10^{-2} = 0.07$ **12** No

Page 193   Revision Exercise on Chapter 2:
Shape and Space

1a x = 20   **b** x = 90   **2a** 5 cm   **b** 17°
3

48   132   132   48   132   48   132   48

4a x = 51   **b** x = 95   **5a** (i) GF   (ii) PA   (iii) DC
b (i) ∠BAP   (ii) ∠HJK   (iii) ∠NDC   **c** GFEH
6a rectangle   **b** kite   **c** parallelogram

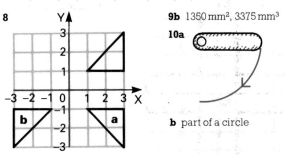

7a C(3, −4), D(−3, −4)   **b** E(3, −3), F(−3, −3)

8

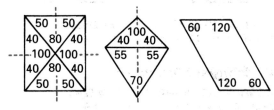

9b 1350 mm², 3375 mm³
10a

b part of a circle

Page 194   Revision Exercise on Chapter 3:
Money Matters—Saving and
Spending

1a £3.75   **b** £138.75   **c** £832.50   **2a** £9.25   **b** £33.30
c £103.60   **3** £22 000   **4a** £29.90   **b** £22.42
5 £23.50, £14.10, £9.40, £3.53, £1.76, £0.71
6 £35.74, £6.25, £41.99
7 A1208, B91.20, C97.70, D17.10, E114.80   **8** £8.21

Page 195   Revision Exercise on Chapter 4:
Scale Drawings and Similar Shapes

1b (i) 130 km   (ii) 293°
2 Enlargements 2, 3, $\frac{3}{2}$; reductions $\frac{1}{3}$, $\frac{1}{2}$, $\frac{2}{3}$
3a 10 000   **b** (i) 50 000 cm   (ii) 500 m   **4** 6 mm, 4 mm
5a 100 000 cm   **b** 1000 m   **c** 1 km   **6a** 12 cm   **b** 1.5 cm
7a $\frac{1}{3}$ **b** 8 cm   **8a** (i) $\frac{2}{3}$ (ii) 3   **b** (i) $\frac{3}{2}$ (ii) 2.7   **9a** Both have
angles of 30°, 60°, 90°   **b** $\frac{3}{2}$ **c** 8.7 cm   **d** 17.4 cm

Page 196   Revision Exercise on Chapter 5:
Going Places

1a 275 km   **b** 5 h   **2** 60 miles   **3a** 44 mph   **b** 4 hours
4 296 km   **5a** 5 h   **b** 2 h   **c** $1\frac{1}{2}$ h   **6a** 90 km   **b** 4 h
c 40 km   **d** 1 h   **e** 20 km/h, 40 km/h, 0 km/h, 30 km/h
7 125 km   **8** 3 h   **9a** 104 km   **b** (i) 1 h   (ii) 1 h 45 min
10 5.2 km   **11** Car 95 km/h; van 57 km/h; coach 76 km/h

Page 197   Revision Exercise on Chapter 6: Brackets and Equations

1a $4x+8$ **b** $5y-5$ **c** $6-2t$ **d** $8-8n$ **e** $6x+15$ **f** $4-12y$
2a $18(30+2x)$, $540+36x$ **b** $972\,cm^2$ **3a** $5(x+2)=5x+10$
b $2(y-3)=2y-6$ **4a** $3x+5$ **b** $5x+1$ **c** $2p+10$
d $3q+1$ **5a** $x=6$ **b** $y=12$ **c** $x=8$ **d** $u=16$ **e** $v=5$
f $t=2$ **6a** $y=10$ **b** $s=1$ **c** $k=7$ **d** $m=2$
7a $3(x+4)=15$, $x=1$ **b** $5(y-6)=30$, $y=12$
8 $5(x+3)=55$, $x=8$, $11\,cm$ **9** $3(x+7)=45$, $x=8$, $15\,kg$
10a $x=0$ **b** $y=4$ **c** $a=5$ **d** $c=2$
11 $6(45+x)=318$, $x=8$, 8p **12a** $1\times6, 2\times3$ **b** $1\times3t, 3\times t$
c $1\times y^2, y\times y$ **13a** $2(x+2)$ **b** $3(y-2)$ **c** $4(z+1)$
d $3(3+t)$ **e** $5(3-u)$ **f** $7(3-2v)$ **14a** 3 **b** 10 **c** 6
15a $2(3x+4)$ **b** $6(x+2)$ **c** $x(6+x)$ **d** $3(3y-5)$ **e** $4(t+2)$
f $2u(u-4)$

Page 198   Revision Exercise on Chapter 7: Handling Data

1a (i) 24 mm (ii) 28 cm **b** The perimeter of a rectangle
2a Some months, cars and percentages of the market
b about 31% **c** October **d** C **3a** (i) 3.5 kg
(ii) 7 kg, 7 kg **b** 6 kg **4a** Totals: 30 and 772 **b** 25.7 g
c 25 g, 25.5 g **5a** Totals: 30 and 774 **b** 25.8 g
6a TV 10.8 h, homework 9.7 h

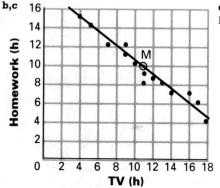

b,c

d the more TV, the less homework

Page 199   Revision Exercise on Chapter 8: Pythagoras

1a $1521\,mm^2$ **b** 15 mm, 36 mm, 39 mm
2 $a=9.4, b=7.8, c=21.3, d=45.8$
3a 5.8 cm **b** 2.8 cm **4** 250 cm **5** 7 m 14 cm

6b OA 10, OB 10.3, OC 10, OD 9.9, OE 10, OF 9.8, OG 10
c A, C, E, G **7a** 24 cm **b** 25 cm **8** 1.58 m **9** 50 m

Page 200   Revision Exercise on Chapter 9: Areas and Volumes

1a 1100 m **b** (i) 60 000 m² (ii) 6 ha
2 White 10 m², blue 20 m² **3** 420 m² **4a** 17 m **b** 90 m
5 796 cm² **6a** (i) 125 cm³ (ii) 12 000 cm³ **b** 96 **7** 232 cm²
8a 2450 cm³ **b** 1500 cm³ **c** 1875 cm³ **9a** 1.8 m² **b** 9 m³
10a 314 cm² **b** (i) 2510 cm³ (ii) 2.51 litres
11a 452 cm³ **b** 276 cm²

Page 201   Revision Exercise on Chapter 10: Money Matters—Personal finance

1 £180.00, £51.00, £129.00 **2** £1369, £478.73, £890.27
3 £77.40 **4** Allowances £3500 + £1500 = £5000;
Taxable income = £15 800 − £5000 = £10 800;
Tax due = £600 + 25% of £7800 = £2550 **5** Allowance £3500;
Taxable income £9300; Tax due £2175 **6** £31.50, £378
7 £145.50 **8** 4225 francs, 1240 marks **9** £2395.83

Page 202   Revision Exercise on Chapter 11: Formulae and Sequences

1a 1620 cm³ **b** 25.1 cm **c** 34 cm **d** 71 250 m²
2a (i) $P=14x$ (ii) $A=12x^2$ **b** 168, 1728
3a $C=(F-32)\div2$ **b** (i) 9 (ii) 0 **4a** 7, 12, 17 **b** 1, 3, 5
c 1, 5, 11 **5a** 17 **b** 7.5 **c** 200 **d** 25 **e** 60 **f** 25 **6** 100
7 $P=(8x+6)\times2$ **8** $D=3x+2y$ **9a** $N=3n+4$
b $N=6n-4$ **10a** Rows: 2, 6, 10; 4, 7, 10; 5, 12, 19
b $T=4n-2, J=3n+1, R=7n-2$ **c** (i) 25, 54 (ii) 116, 236

Page 203   Revision Exercise on Chapter 12: Probability

1a $\frac{1}{8}$ **b** $\frac{1}{4}$ **c** $\frac{3}{8}$ **2** 10% **3a** $\frac{1}{6}$ **b** $\frac{1}{3}$ **c** $\frac{1}{2}$ **d** $\frac{1}{2}$
4a $\frac{2}{15}$ **b** $\frac{1}{3}$ **c** $\frac{1}{2}$ **5a** $\frac{4}{5}$ **b** 24 times **6a** Rows: 2 2 3 4 5 6,
2 2 3 4 5 6, 3 3 4 5 6 7, 4 4 5 6 7 8, 5 5 6 7 8 9, 6 6 7 8 9 10
b (i) $\frac{1}{9}$ (ii) $\frac{1}{18}$ (iii) $\frac{1}{6}$ (iv) $\frac{17}{36}$ **7** 1, (1, 1); 2, (1, 2); 3, (1, 3):
1, (2, 1); 2, (2, 2); 3, (2, 3): 1, (3, 1); 2, (3, 2); 3, (3, 3):
1, (4, 1); 2, (4, 2); 3, (4, 3): 1, (5, 1); 2, (5, 2); 3, (5, 3)
8a 0.35 **b** 11 **9a** 15% **b** 5 or 6
10a 1st row (C, C) (C, D) (C, H) (C, S);
2nd row (D, C) (D, D) (D, H) (D, S);
3rd row (H, C) (H, D) (H, H) (H, S);
4th row (S, C) (S, D) (S, H) (S, S) **b** (i) $\frac{1}{16}$ (ii) $\frac{1}{4}$